ELEMENTARY

Algebra

FOR
COLLEGE
STUDENTS

By the same authors:

Programmed Beginning Algebra, Wiley, 1963

A Programmed Introduction to Number Systems
Irving Drooyan and Walter Hadel, Wiley, 1964

Elementary Algebra: Structure and Skills
Irving Drooyan, Walter Hadel, and Frank Fleming, Wiley, 1966

ELEMENTARY

Algebra

FOR
COLLEGE
STUDENTS

SECOND EDITION

77577

IRVING DROOYAN
Los Angeles Pierce College

WILLIAM WOOTON
Los Angeles Pierce College

JOHN WILEY & SONS, INC.

New York · London · Sydney

PREFACE

This second edition retains the basic point of view of the original edition, regarding both subject matter and pedagogy. The functional use of a second color in this edition makes it possible to provide increased emphasis on certain of the routine procedures employed to simplify fractions, evaluate expressions, and transform equations. Color is also used to highlight the introduction of a new procedure and to set off formal statements of standardized processes. In addition to improving the clarity of the exercise sets by means of a revised format, certain sets also have been improved by the alteration of some of the original problems and by the addition of some new problems. Answers are again provided for all odd-numbered problems, and this edition includes answers involving graphs, as well as answers for the ten final cumulative reviews. One new section has been added, dealing with the graphing of linear equations by the use of the intercept method.

We are indebted to our colleagues in the mathematics department at Pierce College for advice on improving the first edition. We also gratefully acknowledge the contributions of Gertrude Drooyan and Doris Wooton in preparing the manuscript for this edition.

Excerpts from the preface of the original edition that are still applicable to this new edition are printed below.

This textbook has been written for students who are beginning their study of algebra at the college level and who are scheduled to complete two semesters of high-school work in one semester. The general organization of the material is traditional. Algebra is developed as a generalized arithmetic, and the assumptions underlying the operations of both arithmetic and algebra are stressed. No notion of a mathematical proof has been introduced in this book since experience dictates that students at this level profit more from an intuitive approach.

The textual material is brief. A large number of sample problems are included, however, and are placed directly before exercises of a similar type. Word problems are introduced carefully, with emphasis on methods

v

of solution. The line graph is used frequently in the early chapters as a basis for the concept of order and as a valuable background for the treatment of graphing equations in two variables in Chapter 6. Graphing an equation is accomplished directly from ordered pairs which satisfy the equation. We have found that our students use this procedure quite successfully and, furthermore, that this approach provides a stronger background for future work in mathematics.

Subject matter is continually reviewed through the use of both chapter and cumulative reviews at the end of each chapter. At the end of the book there are ten cumulative reviews.

A glossary and a table of squares, square roots, and prime factors are placed at the end of the book for the convenience of the student. Answers are provided for the odd-numbered exercises in Chapters 1 through 9 and for all the exercises in Chapter 10, in the chapter reviews, and in the cumulative reviews.

Irving Drooyan
William Wooton

Woodland Hills,
California, 1968

Contents

4. PRODUCTS AND FACTORS

5. FRACTIONS

6. FIRST-DEGREE EQUATIONS IN TWO VARIABLES

7. QUADRATIC EQUATIONS

8. RADICAL EXPRESSIONS

9. SOLUTION OF QUADRATIC EQUATIONS BY OTHER METHODS

10.   NUMBER SYSTEMS

ELEMENTARY

Algebra

FOR
COLLEGE
STUDENTS

CHAPTER 1

NATURAL NUMBERS AND THEIR REPRESENTATION

In this book, the things upon which we intend to focus our attention are numbers. We shall use the same procedures and symbols that we used in arithmetic, together with certain new symbols. The vocabulary used in arithmetic will apply in algebra, but we shall also need a number of new words. In short, we shall be studying arithmetic, but from a different and more general point of view.

1.1 NUMBERS AND THEIR GRAPHICAL REPRESENTATION

The numbers that we use to count things are called **natural numbers.** 1, 2, 3, 4, 5, . . . etc., are natural numbers, whereas $\frac{2}{3}$, 3.141, $\sqrt{2}$, etc., are not.

A **prime number** is a natural number that is exactly divisible by itself and 1 only, that is, a multiple of no natural number other than itself and 1. For example, 2, 3, 5, 7, 11, and 13 are prime numbers. We exclude 1 from the set of prime numbers for reasons that will be noted on page 6.

Statements about numbers such as $4 = 2 \times 2$, $7 - 2 = 5$, and $6 + 5 = 1$ are called **equality statements,** and are interpreted to mean that the symbols on the left-hand side of the **equals** symbol, $=$, name the same number as the symbols on the right-hand side. Thus, "4" and "2×2" name the same natural number, as do "$7 - 2$" and "5."

The natural numbers are ordered; that is, it is always possible to say that one natural number is greater than, equal to, or less than another. Because of this property, we can use a **line graph** or **number line** to represent the relative order of a set of natural numbers. To do this we proceed as follows:

1. Draw a straight line.
2. Decide on a convenient unit of scale and mark off units of this length on the line, beginning on the left.

3. Label, on the bottom side of the line, enough of these units to establish the scale, usually two or three points.
4. Label, on the top side of the line, those points which represent the numbers to be graphed, and represent these points by heavy dots.

As an example, the graph of the prime numbers less than 8 appears as in Figure 1.1.

Figure 1.1

When representing the natural numbers on a line graph, we place a small arrow on the right to indicate that the numbers continue indefinitely to the right but no further to the left. The point representing 0 is called the **origin.**

The line graph tells us immediately whether one number is less than or greater than another. Of any two numbers, the number whose graph is to the left is less than the number whose graph is to the right.

EXERCISES 1.1

Which of the following are natural numbers?

1. *a.* 23   *b.* 2×3 *c.* $\dfrac{24}{3}$ *d.* $\dfrac{15}{2}$ *e.* $6 + 1$ *f.* 2.34

2. *a.* $\dfrac{15}{3}$ *b.* $5 - 2$ *c.* $\dfrac{31}{2}$ *d.* $\dfrac{4}{28}$ *e.* $8 \div 2$ *f.* 4.5

Which of the following are prime numbers?

3. *a.* 2   *b.* 3   *c.* 8   *d.* 9   *e.* 11   *f.* 17
4. *a.* 5   *b.* 13   *c.* 29   *d.* 63   *e.* 27   *f.* 19

List all prime numbers between the given numbers.

5. *a.* 1 and 6   *b.* 7 and 18   *c.* 19 and 26
   d. 27 and 35   *e.* 36 and 45   *f.* 46 and 50
6. *a.* 51 and 58   *b.* 59 and 65   *c.* 66 and 72
   d. 73 and 80   *e.* 81 and 90   *f.* 91 and 100

Write a simpler representation for each of the following.

7. *a.* $\dfrac{6}{2}$ *b.* $18 - 14$ *c.* $18 + 7$ *d.* $\dfrac{48}{24}$ *e.* $4 + 6 + 2$ *f.* $\dfrac{100}{4}$

8. *a.* $24 - 13$ *b.* $16 + 15$ *c.* $\dfrac{28}{4}$ *d.* $2 + 3 + 8$ *e.* $\dfrac{20}{4}$ *f.* $\dfrac{51}{17}$

Graph the following numbers on a line graph (use a separate line graph for each set).

Sample problem: The first four natural numbers divisible by 2.

9. The natural numbers greater than 1 and less than 17.

10. The even natural numbers less than 19.

11. The natural numbers exactly divisible by 3 and less than 27.

12. All prime numbers less than 30.

13. The first four prime numbers.

14. The first five even natural numbers.

15. The first five odd natural numbers.

16. The natural numbers from 9 to 14, inclusive.

17. The first three natural numbers exactly divisible by 3.

18. The first ten natural numbers not exactly divisible by 3.

Sample problems: *a.* The prime numbers between 50 and 60.

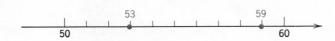

b. The odd natural numbers.

19. The prime numbers between 60 and 70.

20. The prime numbers between 70 and 80.

21. All natural numbers exactly divisible by 3.

22. All natural numbers exactly divisible by 4.

1.2 VARIABLES

It has been said that mathematics is a language. As such, it has a number of things in common with any other language. In mathematics, we find such things as verbs, nouns, pronouns, phrases, sentences, and many other concepts which are normally associated with a language. There are different names for these things in mathematics, but the ideas are very comparable.

In a language, we use pronouns such as *he, she,* or *it* to stand in the place of nouns. In mathematics, we use symbols such as x, y, z, a, b, c, etc., to stand in the place of numbers. Thus, if we are asked to indicate the sum of a certain unspecified number and 5, we might use $x + 5$, $y + 5$, $n + 5$, etc., where the letters x, y, or n used in this way are called **variables.** These symbols are sometimes also called literal numbers or unknowns.

In a language, the verbs are action words, expressing what happens to nouns. In mathematics, operations such as addition or multiplication express an action involving numbers. The symbols we use for these operations are the same in algebra as in arithmetic. However, since we use the symbol x so frequently in algebra as a variable, multiplication is indicated by using either a dot between the numbers, as $2 \cdot 3$, or by enclosing one or both of the numbers in parentheses, as $2(3)$ or $(2)(3)$. Multiplication of variables may be indicated in the same way or may be indicated by writing the symbols side by side. For example, ab means the number a times the number b; $3x$ means the number 3 times the number x; abc means the number a times the number b times the number c; etc.

In a language, we use punctuation marks such as commas, periods, and semicolons to group words. In mathematics, we use symbols such as parentheses ( ) or brackets [ ] to group numbers. If we are asked to represent symbolically the phrase "divide the sum of x and y by 7," we may write

$$(x + y) \div 7,$$

which shows that 7 is to be divided into the sum of x and y and not merely into one or the other. In algebra, however, we prefer to represent division by the use of the fraction, and in this case we have

$$\frac{x + y}{7},$$

where the line beneath the $x + y$ indicates grouping in the same sense as parentheses.

In a language, we can express ideas by using phrases; in mathematics, we can express ideas by using **algebraic expressions.** Thus, in the example just cited, $\dfrac{x + y}{7}$ is an algebraic expression.

EXERCISES 1.2

1. Each of the following phrases indicates the performance of a mathematical operation. Separate the phrases into four groups so that those in one group indicate addition, those in another subtraction, in another multiplication, and in another division.

     Take away, increased by, less than, divide, times, add, difference, decreased by, multiply, more than, product, diminished by, exceeded by, sum, quotient, subtract.

2. Each of the following expressions indicates the performance of a mathematical operation. Separate them into four groups as in Exercise 1.

$(3)(4), \qquad 4 \div 3, \qquad 4 - 3, \qquad 3\overline{)4}, \qquad 3 \cdot 4, \qquad 4 + 3, \qquad \tfrac{4}{3},$

$a \cdot b, \qquad a \div b, \qquad a - b, \qquad \dfrac{a}{b}, \qquad ab, \qquad b\overline{)a}, \qquad a + b$

Express the following word phrases by using algebraic expressions.

Sample problems: *Answers:*

a. The product of three and four. $3 \cdot 4, 4 \cdot 3, 3(4),$ or $4(3)$

b. Three divided by four. $\dfrac{3}{4}$

c. The sum of x and two. $x + 2$ or $2 + x$

d. The product of x and the quantity y plus three. $x(y + 3)$ or $(y + 3)x$

3. Add three and five.   4. Seven diminished by six.

5. Sum of four and six.   6. Two times seven.

7. Nine divided by four.   8. Product of four and five.

9. x divided by y.   10. c multiplied by a.

11. Subtract a from b.   12. Product of g and h.

13. x less y.   14. r diminished by t.

15. x increased by seven.   16. Add four to y.

17. r less three.   18. Product of two and x.

19. Twice x.   20. From g subtract four.

21. Principal (P) times rate (r).   22. Distance (d) divided by time (t).

23. Sum of length (l) and width (w).   **24.** Cost (c) less five.

25. Five more than the cost (c).   **26.** Five times the cost (c).

27. Three times the sum of two and x.

28. Twenty divided by the sum of y and three.

29. Two plus the product of x and y.

30. Ten less the quotient of a divided by three.

31. x less the sum of four and y.

32. x diminished by the product of six and y.

33. Product of a and the sum of b and c.

34. Divide the sum of a and b by three.

35. Sum of p and q less the product of 3 and r.

36. Product of 3 and x added to the sum of 4 and y.

37. Sum of r and s divided by the product of 2 and y.

38. Subtract the sum of x and y from the quotient of x divided by 2.

1.3 PRODUCTS AND FACTORS

If we multiply 3 by 4, we obtain 12. We call 12 the **product** of the **factors** 3 and 4. A product is the result of multiplying two or more numbers together, whereas the numbers multiplied together are factors of the product. We might also obtain 12 by multiplying the natural numbers 2 and 6, or 12 and 1, or 2, 2, and 3. If we permit the use of fractions, we can also obtain 12 by multiplying 9 by $\frac{4}{3}$, or 24 by $\frac{1}{2}$, etc. We shall agree to use only natural numbers as factors of natural numbers. In this book we are going to be interested primarily in the **prime factors** of a number, that is, factors which are themselves prime numbers. If we now ask for the prime factors of 12, we are restricted to the single set 2, 2, and 3. This is the reason we do not include 1 in the set of prime numbers. If 1 were included, another set of prime factors of 12 would be 1, 2, 2, and 3.

Many times, as in the factors of 12, the same factor occurs more than once in a product. We have a shorthand way of writing such products by using **exponents**. An exponent is a number written to the right and a little above a factor to indicate the number of times this factor occurs in a product, and the product is referred to as a **power** of the factor. Thus,

5^2 means $(5)(5)$; read "five squared."

x^3 means xxx; read "x cubed" or "x to the third power."

2^4 means $(2)(2)(2)(2)$; read "two to the fourth power."

The number to which an exponent is attached is called the **base.** In the foregoing examples, 5^2, x^3, and 2^4, the bases are 5, x, and 2, respectively. It is to be understood that the exponent is attached only to the base and not to some other factor in the product. Thus,

$3x^2$ means $3xx$; read "three x squared."
$5x^2y^3$ means $5xxyyy$; read "five x squared y cubed."
$(2x)^3$ means $(2x)(2x)(2x)$; read "the quantity $2x$ cubed."

In the event that we write a variable such as x with no exponent indicated, it is to be understood that the exponent 1 is intended; that is,

$$x = x^1.$$

EXERCISES 1.3

Write in exponential form and read answers orally.

Sample problems:

   a. $2 \cdot 2 \cdot 2xxy$ *b.* *abbccc*   *c.* $(x + 1)(x + 1)(x + 1)$

   Ans. 2^3x^2y *Ans.* ab^2c^3 *Ans.* $(x + 1)^3$

1. $2 \cdot 2$ **2.** $3 \cdot 3$ **3.** $3 \cdot 3 \cdot 3 \cdot 3$ **4.** *xxxxx*

5. *yyy*   **6.** *aaaaa*   **7.** *aabbb*   **8.** *xyyzz*

9. *aabbcc*   **10.** $2 \cdot 2 \cdot 3aa$ **11.** $5 \cdot 5xxx$ **12.** $3aaaab$

13. $2 \cdot 3 \cdot 3yyz$ **14.** $5abbc$ **15.** $6xyzz$ **16.** *aaacc*

17. $(x + 2)(x + 2)$ **18.** $(x - y)(x - y)$ **19.** $(2x)(2x)(2x)$ **20.** $(3y)(3y)(2x)(2x)$

Write in completely factored form without exponents.*

Sample problems:

   a. $12a^2b^4$ *b.* $9r^3t$ *c.* $(4x)^2$

   Ans. $2 \cdot 2 \cdot 3aabbbb$ *Ans.* $3 \cdot 3rrrt$ *Ans.* $(4x)(4x)$

21. 8   **22.** 24   **23.** $2^3 \cdot 3^2$ **24.** $3^3 \cdot 5^2$

25. 100   **26.** 125   **27.** x^3 **28.** x^5

29. xy^2 **30.** x^3y^2 **31.** ab^2c **32.** a^3b^2c

33. $3x^3$ **34.** 5^2xy^2z **35.** $6x$ **36.** $12k^3m$

37. $(3z)^3$ **38.** $(5z)^2$ **39.** $3(x + 2)^3$ **40.** $(3x)^2(x + y)^3$

* A table of the prime factors of the natural numbers from 2 to 100 appears on page 246.

1.4 ORDER OF OPERATIONS

The expression $4 + 6 \div 2$ could be interpreted in more than one way. We might look at it as meaning either

$$(4 + 6) \div 2 \qquad \text{or} \qquad 4 + (6 \div 2)$$

$$\frac{4 + 6}{2} = \frac{10}{2} = 5 \qquad 4 + 3 = 7.$$

This is clearly an undesirable situation. To avoid such ambiguities, we shall make some agreements relative to the use of parentheses and fraction bars and with respect to the order of performing mathematical operations. Let us agree to accomplish any sequence of mathematical operations in the following order:

1. Perform any operations inside parentheses, or above or below a fraction bar.
2. Compute all indicated powers.
3. Perform all other multiplication operations and any division operations in the order in which they occur from left to right.
4. Perform additions and subtractions in any order.

EXERCISES 1.4

Simplify.

Sample problem:

$$3^2 + 4(6 + 3)$$

Simplify quantity in the parentheses.

$$3^2 + 4(9)$$

Compute power.

$$9 + 4(9)$$

Multiply.

$$9 + 36$$

Add.

Ans. 45

1. $(3)(2) - 5$	**2.** $(3)(2) + 16$	**3.** $7 + (2)(6)$
4. $(21)(4) + 3$	**5.** $6(0) + 12$	**6.** $4 + 6(0)$
7. $6 + 2(4) + 2^3$	**8.** $25(25) + 5^3$	**9.** $3^2(2^2) + 3(2^2)$
10. $25(6) + 30(2^2)$	**11.** $2(3 + 4)$	**12.** $3(2 + 1)$
13. $(3 - 2)(3)$	**14.** $(3^2 + 2)(3)$	**15.** $(8 - 4)(8 + 4)$

16. $(2 + 3)(3 + 2)$ **17.** $(2 + 3) + (3 + 2)$ **18.** $2 + (3)(2) + 3$

19. $0(2 + 1) + 2^3$ **20.** $3(4 - 1)^2$

Sample problem:

$$\frac{8 + 7}{5 - 2} - \frac{2^2 + 2^2}{2}$$

Simplify the numerators and denominators.

$$\frac{15}{3} - \frac{8}{2}$$

Divide as indicated.

$$5 - 4$$

Subtract.

Ans. 1

21. $\dfrac{6(3)}{9} + 5$

22. $\dfrac{3 + 5}{4} - 1$

23. $\dfrac{24(3)}{9} - 6$

24. $6 + \dfrac{12 + 3}{5}$

25. $\dfrac{3(8)}{12} + \dfrac{9 + 3}{6}$

26. $\dfrac{8(6)}{2(4)} - \dfrac{4(6)}{8(3)}$

27. $\dfrac{5^2 + 3}{2} + \dfrac{3^2 + 1}{5}$

28. $\dfrac{3^3}{9} + \dfrac{6 + 4^2}{2}$

29. $\dfrac{3^2 + 4^2}{7 - 2} + \dfrac{8^2 - 6^2}{5 + 2}$

30. $\dfrac{2(6)}{3(2)} + \dfrac{8(3)}{6(2)} - \dfrac{3(0)}{2(1)}$

31. $\dfrac{2(3) + 4}{6 - 1} - \dfrac{8(3)}{3(4)}$

32. $\dfrac{3^3 + 3}{5(2)} + \dfrac{2 + 2^3}{5(2)} - \dfrac{8^2}{16}$

33. $\dfrac{4^2 - 3^2}{7} + \dfrac{2(3^2) + 2}{2(5)} - \dfrac{26}{3(5) - 2}$

34. $\dfrac{26 - 2(3)^2}{4^2 - 3(4)} + \dfrac{4 + 6^2}{3(5) - 7} - \dfrac{5 + 5^2}{6 + 3^2}$

35. $3\left(\dfrac{5^3 - 100}{3 + 2}\right)\left(\dfrac{2^5 + 4}{15 - 3^2}\right)$

36. $4\left(\dfrac{8^2 - 2(3)^2}{5^2 - 2}\right)\left(\dfrac{6^3 - 4(5^2)}{5^2 + 4}\right)$

37. $\left(\dfrac{4^4 + 2^6}{2^5}\right)^3$

38. $\left(\dfrac{9^2 + 8^2}{3^3 + 2}\right)^3$

39. $\left(\dfrac{7^2(7^2 + 1)}{6^2 - 1}\right)^2 - \left(\dfrac{12^3 - 108}{7^2 + 5}\right)^2$

40. $\left(\dfrac{8(5^3) - 2(10^2)}{11^2 - 3(7)}\right)^3 - \left(\dfrac{5^2(5^2) + 95}{7^2 - 13}\right)^2$

1.5 NUMERICAL EVALUATION

Any meaningful collection of numbers, variables, and signs of operation such as $2xy + y$ is called an **algebraic expression** or, simply, an **expression**.

In the algebraic expression $x + 3$, the letter x represents some number. Suppose now, that we are supplied with the information that x represents the number 7. We may remove the letter and substitute in its place 7, which gives us $7 + 3$ or 10. We have made a **numerical evaluation** of $x + 3$ when x is 7.

EXERCISES 1.5

If $x = 3$, find the value of each expression.

Sample problem:

$$6 + x^2$$

Substitute 3 for x.

$$6 + 3^2$$

Simplify.

$$6 + 9$$

Ans. 15

1. $2x$ **2.** x^2 **3.** $2x + 1$ **4.** $1 + 2x$

5. $3(2 + x)$ **6.** $2(3 + x)$ **7.** x^3 **8.** $2x^3$

9. $3x^2 - 1$ **10.** $2x^2 + 1$ **11.** $2x^2 + x$ **12.** $3x^2 + 2x$

13. $x^2 + 3x + 1$ **14.** $2(x^2 - 1)$ **15.** $\dfrac{(3 + x^2)}{3}$ **16.** $\dfrac{3(x^2 + 1)}{5}$

17. $\dfrac{4x + 8}{5}$ **18.** $\dfrac{2x + 3}{3}$ **19.** $\dfrac{(2x - 4)^2}{2}$ **20.** $\dfrac{(3x - 1)^2}{4}$

If $x = 2$ and $y = 3$, find the value of each expression.

Sample problem:

$$x(y - 1) + 2$$

Substitute values.

$$2(3 - 1) + 2$$

Simplify.

$$2(2) + 2$$

Ans. 6

21. xy **22.** xy^2 **23.** $3(y - x)$ **24.** $2(x + y)$

25. $2x - y$ **26.** $3x + y$ **27.** $\dfrac{x^2y}{6}$ **28.** $\dfrac{x^3 - y}{5}$

29. $\dfrac{(x + y)^2}{5}$ **30.** $\dfrac{2y^2}{6}$ **31.** $\dfrac{(2)^2}{x^2}$ **32.** $\dfrac{(3x)^2 + y^2}{y}$

If $a = 1$, $b = 3$, $c = 2$, find the value of each of the following.

33. abc **34.** abc^2 **35.** ab^2c **36.** a^2bc

37. a^2b^2c **38.** $a(bc)^2$ **39.** $(abc)^2$ **40.** $ab + c$

41. $a(b + c)$ **42.** $a + (b - c)$ **43.** $(a + b)^2 + c$ **44.** $a + (b - c)^2$

45. $(a + b + c)^2$ **46.** $a(b - c)^2$ **47.** $a^2(b + c)$ **48.** $\dfrac{a + b}{c}$

49. $\dfrac{(b - a)^2}{c} + \dfrac{(b + a)^2}{c}$ **50.** $\left(\dfrac{b^2 - c^3}{a}\right) + \left(\dfrac{b^2 + c^3}{a}\right)$

51. $\left(\dfrac{bc + b^2}{5a}\right)^2 + \left(\dfrac{c^3 + 4b}{c^2}\right)^2$ **52.** $\left(\dfrac{a^2 + b^2 + c^2}{b^2 - 2a}\right)^3 + \left(\dfrac{b^2 - c^2 - a^2}{c^2 - 2a}\right)^3$

1.6 FORMULAS

It is often useful to express relationships between physical quantities symbolically. We may express such relationships by means of a **formula**. Thus, in geometry, we find that the area of a rectangle is equal to the product of its length and its width. This relationship can be stated concisely by means of the formula $A = lw$, where it is understood that the symbols A, l, and w represent numbers. This is a handy tool because if we are required to find the area of any rectangle, we can evaluate the formula by substituting numbers for l and w.

The following formulas, which should be familiar to you from your studies in arithmetic, are stated here for reference.

1. Square

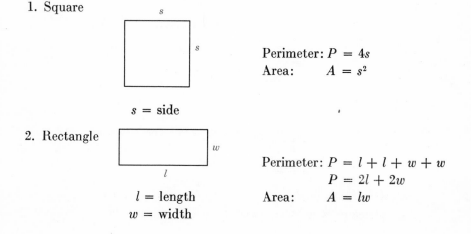

Perimeter: $P = 4s$

Area: $A = s^2$

s = side

2. Rectangle

Perimeter: $P = l + l + w + w$

  $P = 2l + 2w$

Area: $A = lw$

l = length

w = width

3. Triangle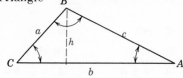

Perimeter: $P = a + b + c$
Area: $A = \frac{1}{2}hb$
Sum of interior angles:
$\angle A + \angle B + \angle C = 180°$

b = base
h = height or altitude

(*a*) Isosceles triangle

2 equal sides: $a = b$
2 equal angles: $\angle A = \angle B$

(*b*) Equilateral triangle

3 equal sides: $a = b = c$
3 equal angles: $\angle A = \angle B = \angle C$

(*c*) Right triangle

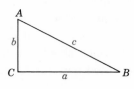

a = leg, b = leg,
c = hypotenuse; angle $C = 90°$

4. Angles

Acute angle: less than 90°

Right angle: equals 90°

Obtuse angle: greater than 90° and less than 180°

Straight angle: equals 180°

Supplementary angles: two angles whose sum is 180°
Complementary angles: two angles whose sum is 90°

5. Circle

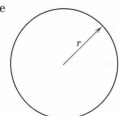

Diameter: $d = 2r$
Circumference: $C = 2\pi r$ or πd
Area: $A = \pi r^2$

EXERCISES 1.6

Perform the indicated evaluations, using the approximation 3.14 for π.

Sample problems:

a. $A = \pi r^2$; $r = 2$
     $A = 3.14(2)^2$
     $A = 3.14(4)$

 Ans. $A = 12.56$

b. $P = 2(l + w)$; $l = 4$, $w = 6$
     $P = 2(4 + 6)$
     $P = 2(10)$

 Ans. $P = 20$

1. $A = lw$; $l = 6$, $w = 4$

2. $P = 4s$; $s = 6$

3. $C = \pi d$; $d = 5$

4. $A = \pi r^2$; $r = 3$

5. $P = 2(l + w)$; $l = 4$, $w = 3$

6. $A = \frac{1}{2} hb$; $h = 4$, $b = 3$

7. $A = \frac{1}{2} h(a + b)$; $h = 4$, $a = 4$, $b = 8$

8. $C = 2\pi r$; $r = 4$

9. $A = 180° - (B + C)$; $B = 30°$, $C = 60°$

10. $B = 180° - (A + C)$; $A = 50°$, $C = 60°$

11. $P = a + b + c$; $a = 2$, $b = 3$, $c = 5$

12. $A = \frac{1}{2} hb$; $h = 6$, $b = 8$

13. What is the area of a triangle with a height of 6 inches and a base of 3 inches?

14. What is the area of a circle with a radius of length 5 inches (use $\pi = 3.14$)?

15. What is the area of a rectangle with a length of 12 feet and a width of 10 feet?

16. What is the perimeter of a triangle if the sides are of length 3, 4, and 5 inches?

Find the area of the shaded portion of the figure shown on page 14. All curves shown are parts of circles, and all horizontal and vertical lines meet at right angles.

17.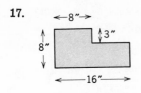

18.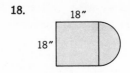

19.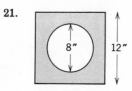

20.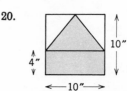

21.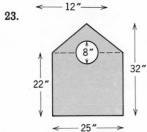

22.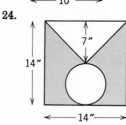

23.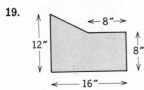

24.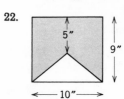

1.7 ALGEBRAIC EXPRESSIONS

Any single collection of factors such as xyz, 2, or $2x^2y$ is called a **term**. An expression containing one term, such as

$$x, \quad y^2z, \quad 3x^2y^3, \quad \text{or} \quad x^2y$$

is called a **monomial**. An expression containing two terms, such as

$$2x + y, \quad 2a - 3b, \quad \text{or} \quad x^2 + y^2$$

is called a **binomial**. An expression containing three terms, such as

$$x + y + z, \quad 2a + 3b + 5c, \quad \text{or} \quad x^2 - 3x + 4$$

is called a **trinomial**. Any term or sum of terms is called a **polynomial**.

Any collection of factors in a term is called the **coefficient** of the remaining factors in the term. Thus, in the term $3xy$, 3 is the coefficient of xy, x is the coefficient of $3y$, y is the coefficient of $3x$, and $3x$ is the coefficient of y.

In the event that we wish to refer to the numerical part of the term only, we speak of the **numerical coefficient**. For example, in $3xy$, 3 is the numerical coefficient. In a term such as xy, the numerical coefficient is understood to be 1.

EXERCISES 1.7

    a. Identify each expression as a monomial, binomial, or trinomial.

    b. Write each term separately and state the numerical coefficient of the term.

Sample problem : $2x^3 + x^2 + 4x$

      Ans. a. trinomial

          b. $2x^3$ x^2 $4x$

               coefficient: 2   coefficient: 1   coefficient: 4

1. $2x^3 + 3y^2$	**2.** $x^2 + 3y$	**3.** $x^3 + z$
4. $2x + 3y + 4z$	**5.** $3x^2 + 6x$	**6.** $2x^4 + 3$
7. $3x^4$	**8.** $3x$	**9.** $4y^3$
10. y^5	**11.** $6x^5 + 2y^4$	**12.** $x^7 + y^7 + 2y^3$
13. $2x^4 + 2$	**14.** $4t^3 + 4$	**15.** $3x^2 + 3y + 4z$
16. $3y + 6xy$	**17.** $x^3 + x^2 + 4x$	**18.** $x^2 + x^3y$
19. $3xy^2 + y$	**20.** $x^2y + yx^2$	**21.** 3
22. 7	**23.** $7xyz + 3x$	**24.** $7z + 4xy^2z$

1.8 SUMS INVOLVING VARIABLES

In adding natural numbers, a counting procedure can be used to arrive at a sum. If we wish to add 3 to 5, we can first count out five units, then, starting with the next unit, count out three more, yielding the number 8 as the sum. Suppose now, we wish to add three 2's to five 2's, that is, $5(2) + 3(2)$. These like quantities can be added by counting out five 2's, arriving at the number 10, and then counting out three more 2's, to make a total of eight 2's or 16. This addition is demonstrated on a line graph in Figure 1.2.

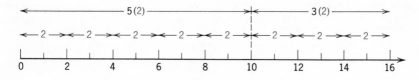

Figure 1.2

In algebra, where terms are usually made up of both numerals and variables, we have to decide what constitutes like quantities in order that we may apply the idea of addition just developed. We could add 2's as we did because they represented a common unit in each number. For variables, we may be sure that $x = x$ or that $ab = ab$ regardless of the numbers that these letters represent. It is also apparent that, in general, $x \neq x^2$ (the symbol $\neq$ is read "is not equal to"), $a^3 \neq a^2$, $x \neq xy$, etc. We therefore define **like terms** to be any terms which are exactly alike in their variable factors. Like terms may differ only in numerical coefficients. Thus, $2x$ and $3x$ are like terms; $2x$ and $3x^2$ are unlike terms. With this definition for like terms and in view of the discussion above, we state the rule:

| *To add like terms, add their numerical coefficients.*

For example,

$$5(2) + 3(2) = 8(2), \quad 2x + 4x = 6x,$$
$$3ay^2 + 2ay^2 + 5ay^2 = 10ay^2, \quad \text{and} \quad xy + xy = 2xy.$$

We can illustrate the addition of like terms on a line graph by considering the unit of distance to be equal to the variable part of each term. Thus, $2x + 3x = 5x$ is represented as in Figure 1.3.

Algebraic expressions having identical values for all substitutions for any variable or variables they contain are called **equivalent expressions**. Thus,

$$2x + 3x \quad \text{and} \quad 5x$$

are equivalent expressions since their values are the same for every number substituted for x.

If we have an algebraic expression containing unlike terms, we cannot

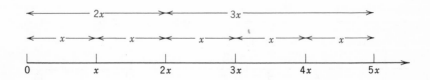

Figure 1.3

combine the numerical coefficients of the terms. In the event that we have both like and unlike terms in the same expression, we can add the like terms and leave the unlike terms in the same form in which they originally appear. Thus, $2x + 3y + 4x$ can be simplified to $6x + 3y$ or $3y + 6x$, but the x and y terms cannot be combined. The expressions $6x + 3y$ and $3y + 6x$ are equivalent.

The fact that $2x + 3y + 4x$ can be simplified to either $6x + 3y$ or $3y + 6x$ reflects a general property of sums called the **commutative law of addition**. This law asserts that the order in which the addends of a sum are considered does not change the sum. Thus, it is always true that

$$a + b = b + a.$$

There is another useful property of sums called the **associative law of addition**. This law asserts that

$$(a + b) + c = a + (b + c).$$

In other words, when adding three terms we may add the first two and then add the third term to the sum, or we may add the last two and then add the first term to the sum. By virtue of both the commutative and associative laws of addition, we may add the terms in any expression in any order that we wish. As an example, consider the sum of $3 + 4 + 5$. Application of the two laws leads to the following twelve possibilities:

$$(3 + 4) + 5 = 12, \quad (3 + 5) + 4 = 12, \quad (4 + 5) + 3 = 12,$$

$$(4 + 3) + 5 = 12, \quad (5 + 3) + 4 = 12, \quad (5 + 4) + 3 = 12,$$

$$5 + (4 + 3) = 12, \quad 4 + (5 + 3) = 12, \quad 3 + (4 + 5) = 12,$$

$$5 + (3 + 4) = 12, \quad 4 + (3 + 5) = 12, \quad 3 + (5 + 4) = 12.$$

EXERCISES 1.8

Simplify.

Sample problem:

$$2y^2 + 3y + 4y^2 + y$$

, Add the coefficients of like terms.

Ans. $6y^2 + 4y$

1. $2a + 5a$

2. $3c + 5c$

3. $2x + 4x$

4. $2y^2 + 3y^2$

5. $2x^2 + 3x^2 + 3x$

6. $2d + d^2 + d^2$

7. $3a + a^2 + 2a^2$

8. $b + b^3 + 2b$

9. $b^4 + b^4 + 2b^3 + b^2$

10. $5t^2 + t^3 + t^2 + 3t^3$

11. $3r^4 + 2r^4 + r^3 + 4r^3$

12. $r^2 + r^2 + 3r^2 + r$

13. $a^3 + 2a^2 + a^2 + a^3$

14. $2xy^3 + 2xy^3 + xy^3$

15. $xy^2 + 3x^2y + 2x^2y$

16. $2xy + 3xy + x^2$

17. $3x + 4y + 2xy + xy$

18. $2x^2y^2 + x^2y + 4x^2y^2$

19. $3xy^2 + 4x^2y + xy^2$

20. $5xy^2 + 6xy + xy$

21. $x + 2y + z + 2x + 2y + z$

22. $2a^2 + 3a + 1 + a^2 + a + 1$

23. $x^2y + xy + xy^2 + xy^2 + xy$

24. $3x^2y + 4x + 2z + 7x^2y + 5x$

25. $2x + 3x + 4x^2 + x^3 + 2x^3$

26. $x + 2x^2 + x^3 + 4 + 2x + x^2$

27. $5x + 7y + 3z^2 + 2z + 3x$

28. $x + y + z + y + x + z$

29. $5x^2y + 2xy + 3x + 2y + x^2$

30. $a^2b + 3ab + 2b^2 + ab + 2a^2b$

31. $3ax + 2x + 3y + 2ax + x$

32. $4xy + 3yz + 2xz + xz + yz$

33. $s^2 + 2t^2 + r^2 + 7s^2 + 2st$

34. $a^2 + b^2 + c^2 + ac + c^2$

35. $2a + 2b + 2c + 3ab + 3b$

36. $4y^2 + 2y + 3z^2 + 6y + 4z + z^2 + 4$

37. $x^2yz + xy^2z + 2xyz^2 + 3xy^2z + xyz^2 + x^2yz$

38. $abc + a^3bc + 2a^2bc + a^3bc + 5abc + 7a^2bc$

39. $10x^2yz + 3xyz + 8x^3yz + xyz + 5x^3yz + 3x^2yz$

40. $15xyz + 3wxy + 4wxz + 3wxy + 7wxz + 6xyz$

1.9 DIFFERENCES INVOLVING VARIABLES

In subtracting one number from another, say in finding the **difference** $5 - 3$, we are seeking a number, 2, which, when added to 3, equals 5. More generally,

$a - b$ is the number which, when added to b, equals a.

In the same way in which we add like terms, we may subtract like terms by subtracting the numerical coefficients of the terms. For example, $7x - 3x$ is equivalent to $4x$, and $3x^2 - x^2$ is equivalent to $2x^2$. In the case of $7x - 3y$, we can only indicate the subtraction since these are unlike terms.

EXERCISES 1.9

Simplify the following expressions.

Sample problem:

$$4x^2 - x^2 + 3x^2$$

Add or subtract coefficients of like terms.

Ans. $6x^2$

1. $4x^2 - 2x^2$ 2. $6x^3 - x^3$ 3. $7y^3 - 2y^3$

4. $8r^2 - 3r^2$ 5. $7b^2 - b^2 - 2b^2$ 6. $8x^2 + 4x^2 - x^2$

7. $2r^2 + 3r^2 - r^2$ 8. $6y^3 - y^3 - 2y^3$ 9. $4x^2 - 3x^2 + 2x^2$

10. $2x^2y + 3x^2y - x^2y$ 11. $8xy^2 - 4xy^2 - 4xy^2$ 12. $6x^2y + 2x^2y - x^2y$

13. $5ab - 3ab + 2a$ 14. $3a^2 + a - a^2$ 15. $6b^2 - 3b^2 + b$

16. $a^2b + 2a^2b - ab^2$ 17. $4r^3 + 8s^2 - 5s^2$ 18. $7t^2 + 11u^3 - 10u^3$

19. $9x^2 + 4y - 3x^2 - 2y$ 20. $6y^2 + 7y - 3y - y^2$

21. $7g^2 + 5h - 7g^2 + 2h$ 22. $8t + 5r^2s - 5t - 5r^2s$

23. $8x^2y + 3xy^2 - 2xy^2 - x^2y$ 24. $5x^2yz + 2xy^2z - 3xyz^2 - 2xy^2z$

25. $11x^3yz + 5x^2yz - 3x^3yz + 2xyz - 5x^2yz$

26. $15ab^2c + 6a^2bc - 3ab^2c + 5abc^2 - 11ab^2c$

27. $25xz^2 + 17x^2z - 8xz^2 + 5xz - 4x^2z - 3xz$

28. $23ab + 35ac - 17ab + 18bc - 27ac - 18bc$

1.10 PRODUCTS INVOLVING VARIABLES

We have adopted the use of exponents to indicate the number of times a given factor occurs in a product, e.g., $x^3 = (x)(x)(x)$. This notation not only has the advantage of brevity, but it also provides us with a simple means of multiplying expressions that contain identical factors. Consider the product $(x^2)(x^3)$, which in completely factored form appears as $(x)(x)(x)(x)(x)$. This, in turn, may be written x^5, since it contains x as a factor five times. Again, $(y^5)(y^2)$ is equivalent to $(y)(y)(y)(y)(y)(y)(y)$, which may be written as y^7. In both examples, the product of two expressions having the same base is obtained by adding the exponents of the numbers to be multiplied. We can make a more general approach to this by considering the product $(x^m)(x^n)$. If this is written in completely factored form, it appears as

$$\overset{m \text{ factors}}{[(x)(x)(x) \ \cdots \ (x)]} \overset{n \text{ factors}}{[(x)(x)(x) \ \cdots \ (x)]} = \overset{m + n \text{ factors}}{[(x)(x)(x) \ \cdots \ (x)]},$$

which contains $m + n$ factors, and in exponent notation is written as x^{m+n}. That is,

$$x^m \cdot x^n = x^{m+n}.$$

As in the case of addition, the commutative and associative properties of multiplication are important. The product $(3)(5)$ is identical to the product $(5)(3)$. That is, the order in which factors are multiplied has no effect on the product. This property is called the **commutative law of multiplication** and may be expressed symbolically as

$$ab = ba.$$

The product $(2)(3)(5)$ may be obtained by first multiplying 2 and 3 and then multiplying the result by 5, or by first multiplying 3 and 5 and then multiplying the result by 2. The fact that we can group factors in any way that we wish is formalized in the **associative law of multiplication**, which may be expressed symbolically as

$$(ab)c = a(bc).$$

By applying both the commutative and associative laws, we may arrange the factors in a product in any order that we wish. For example, the product $(2x^2y)(5xy^2)$ can be written directly in completely factored form as $(2)(x)(x)(y)(5)(x)(y)(y)$, and by applying the associative and commutative laws, can be written as $(2)(5)(x)(x)(x)(y)(y)(y)$, which is equivalent to $10x^3y^3$. Wherever possible, as in the numerical coefficients, we perform the multiplication. Wherever it is not possible to multiply, as in the variable factors, we indicate the multiplication.

EXERCISES 1.10

Find each of the following products by first expressing in a rearranged, completely factored form, then simplifying.

Sample problems:

a. x^2x^4	b. $(2x^2y)(3x^3y)$	c. $(2xy)(5x^2y)(xy^2)$
$xxxxxx$	$2 \cdot 3xxxxxyy$	$2 \cdot 5xxxxyyyy$
Ans. x^6	*Ans.* $6x^5y^2$	*Ans.* $10x^4y^4$

1. $x^2 \cdot x^3$ **2.** $x \cdot x^2$ **3.** $a \cdot a^3$ **4.** $y^2 \cdot y^4$

5. $(y^2)(3y^3)$ **6.** $(b^4)(2b^2)$ **7.** $(5b^2)(3b^5)$ **8.** $(3x^2y)(x^3)$

9. $(4ab^2)(b^3)$ **10.** $(2y)(5x^2y^3)$ **11.** $(4r^2)(6)$ **12.** $(3r^3t)(5)$

Find the products directly by multiplying the numerical coefficients and indicating the product of the factors represented by variables.

Sample problems:

a. $(2x^2)(3x^3)$	b. $(3xy^2)(4x^2y)$	c. $(2x^2y^2)(3xy)(x^3y)$
Ans. $6x^5$	*Ans.* $12x^3y^3$	*Ans.* $6x^6y^4$

13. $(4x)(3x)(2x)$ **14.** $(2y^2)(3y)(4y^3)$ **15.** $(3x^2)(4x^2)(x^3)$

16. $(xy^2)(x^2y)(3xy)$ **17.** $(4x^2y^3)(xy^2)(3xy^2)$ **18.** $(3x^3)(2y^2)(x^2y^2)$

19. $(xy)(xy)(xy)$ **20.** $(a^2b^2)(ac)(bc)$ **21.** $(3a^3)(ab^2)(b^2c^2)$

22. $(4c)(a^3)(2a^2bc)$ **23.** $(2b^2)(ab)(3b)$ **24.** $(2ac)(3ab)(4bc)$

Simplify.

Sample problems:

   a. $a^3 + 3a^2(a)$ *b.* $(3x)(xy^3) - xy + 4x^2y^3$

                                              Multiply.

    $a^3 + 3a^3$ $3x^2y^3 - xy + 4x^2y^3$

                                    Combine like terms.

   Ans. $4a^3$ *Ans.* $7x^2y^3 - xy$

25. $4x^3 - x(3x^2)$ **26.** $3x^2(4x) - 2x^3$

27. $x^5 + 2x(x^4)$ **28.** $3b(a^2) + 3a^2(b) - a^2b$

29. $(x)(x^2) + (y^2)(2y) - x^3$ **30.** $x + x(xy) + x^2y$

31. $3a^2(b^2) - b^2$ **32.** $a^2 + 2a^2(3b)$

33. $2y(y^3) - 2y^4(3y)$ **34.** $6t^2(2t) + 4t^3(3)$

1.11   QUOTIENTS INVOLVING VARIABLES

In arithmetic, when we divide one number (the dividend) by another (the divisor), we obtain a third number (the quotient). The quotient is defined as the number which, when multiplied by the divisor, gives the dividend. For example, $12/4 = 3$, because 3 is the number such that $(3)(4) = 12$. The same definition holds in algebra. In general,

$$\frac{a}{b} \text{ is the number } q, \text{ such that } (b)(q) = a.$$

The one exception is the case where the divisor is 0. A symbol such as $5/0$ is meaningless since there is no number which, when multiplied by 0, gives 5. Neither do we use the symbol $0/0$ to represent a number because the product of 0 and any number is 0.

| *Division by 0 is meaningless.*

Any quotient of the form $a/0$ is said to be undefined.

   Thus, assuming that the denominator does not equal zero, *as we shall in the remainder of this book,* $\dfrac{x^5}{x^2} = x^3$ because x^3 is a number such that

$(x^3)(x^2) = x^5$. The expressions

$$\frac{x^5}{x^2} \quad \text{and} \quad x^3$$

are equivalent. We may simplify quotients involving variable factors by expressing the dividend and divisor in completely factored form, and dividing out common factors. Using the previous example,

$$\frac{x^5}{x^2} = \frac{\overset{1}{\cancel{x}} \cdot \overset{1}{\cancel{x}} \cdot x \cdot x \cdot x}{\underset{1}{\cancel{x}} \cdot \underset{1}{\cancel{x}}} = x^3.$$

More generally, consider the quotient $\dfrac{x^m}{x^n}$. If n is less than m, we have

$$\frac{x^m}{x^n} = \frac{\overset{1\ \ 1\ \ 1}{(\cancel{x})(\cancel{x})(\cancel{x})} \ \cdots \ \overset{1}{(\cancel{x})}(x)(x) \ \cdots \ (x)}{\underset{1\ \ 1\ \ 1}{(\cancel{x})(\cancel{x})(\cancel{x})} \ \cdots \ \underset{1}{(\cancel{x})}},$$

$$\overset{m \text{ factors}}{} \qquad \underset{n \text{ factors}}{}$$

from which

$$\frac{x^m}{x^n} = x^{m-n},$$

and the exponent of the quotient is simply the result of subtracting the exponent in the divisor from the exponent in the dividend. Thus,

$$\frac{x^5}{x^2} = x^{5-2} = x^3.$$

In the case where the dividend and divisor contain more than one variable and numerical coefficients as well, we have, for example,

$$\frac{12x^3y^4}{4x^2y} = 3x^{3-2}y^{4-1} = 3xy^3.$$

EXERCISES 1.11

Find each of the following quotients by first writing the expression in completely factored form, then simplify (if the expression is meaningless, so state).

Sample problems:

$a. \dfrac{24}{18}$

$$\dfrac{\overset{1}{\cancel{2}} \cdot 2 \cdot 2 \cdot \overset{1}{\cancel{3}}}{\underset{1}{\cancel{2}} \cdot 3 \cdot \underset{1}{\cancel{3}}}$$

Ans. $\dfrac{4}{3}$

$b. \dfrac{12x^3}{4x}$

$$\dfrac{\overset{1}{\cancel{2}} \cdot \overset{1}{\cancel{2}} \cdot 3\overset{1}{\cancel{x}}xx}{\underset{1}{\cancel{2}} \cdot \underset{1}{\cancel{2}}\underset{1}{\cancel{x}}}$$

Ans. $3x^2$

$c. \ 5a^3b^2c^3 \div bc^2$

$$\dfrac{5aaab\overset{1}{\cancel{b}}\overset{1}{\cancel{c}}\overset{1}{\cancel{c}}c}{\underset{1}{\cancel{b}}\underset{1}{\cancel{c}}\underset{1}{\cancel{c}}}$$

Ans. $5a^3bc$

1. $\dfrac{6}{2}$ 2. $\dfrac{35}{5}$ 3. $\dfrac{72}{24}$ 4. $\dfrac{96}{4}$ 5. $\dfrac{48}{0}$ 6. $\dfrac{21}{0}$ 7. $\dfrac{x^3}{x}$ 8. $\dfrac{x^3}{x^2}$

9. $x^7 \div x^2$ 10. $6x^2 \div 2x^2$ 11. $5x^6 \div x^2$ 12. $24y^5 \div 12y^5$

13. $8x^2y^3 \div 2xy$ 14. $xyz \div xy$ 15. $\dfrac{x^3y^2}{x^2y}$ 16. $\dfrac{6xy^3z^2}{3y^2z^2}$

17. $2x^2 \div 2x^2$ 18. $21a^2b^2c^2 \div 7ab^2c$ 19. $\dfrac{x^4y^7}{x^4y^7}$ 20. $\dfrac{xyz^3}{xyz}$

Find the quotients directly by finding the quotient of the numerical coefficients, and the quotient of the variable factors.

Sample problems:

$a. \dfrac{\overset{2x\ y^2}{\cancel{4x^2y^3}}}{\underset{111}{\cancel{2xy}}}$

Ans. $2xy^2$

$b. \dfrac{\overset{1a}{\cancel{5a^3b}}}{\underset{11}{\cancel{5a^2}}}$

Ans. ab

$c. \dfrac{\overset{3\ 1\ y\ z}{\cancel{12x^2y^2z^2}}}{\underset{11\ 11}{\cancel{4x^2yz}}}$

Ans. $3yz$

21. $\dfrac{a^3b^6}{b^2}$ 22. $\dfrac{4b^2}{b^2}$ 23. $\dfrac{6a^5b^4}{3a^5b}$ 24. $\dfrac{3x^2y}{3x^2y}$

25. $\dfrac{0}{3x^2}$ 26. $\dfrac{0}{x^2y}$ 27. $\dfrac{a^2b^2c^2}{abc^2}$ 28. $\dfrac{4abc^3}{2ac}$

29. $\dfrac{12a^7bc}{4a}$ 30. $\dfrac{125x^3y^2z}{5x^3y^2z}$ 31. $\dfrac{12a^2c^2}{0}$ 32. $\dfrac{abc}{0}$

Simplify.

Sample problem:

$$\frac{2y^2 + y^2}{y} + 3y$$

Combine like terms above fraction bar; divide.

$$\frac{3\overset{y}{\cancel{y^2}}}{\underset{1}{\cancel{y}}} + 3y$$

$$3y + 3y$$

Ans. 6y

Combine like terms.

33. $\dfrac{4x^2 + 2x^2}{x}$

34. $4x^2 + \dfrac{2x^2}{x}$

35. $\dfrac{3x^3}{x^2} - x$

36. $8x^4 + \dfrac{x^4}{x}$

37. $\dfrac{8x^4 + x^4}{x}$

38. $\dfrac{3x^2 + x^2}{x + 3x}$

39. $2x^2y + \dfrac{x^3y^2}{xy}$

40. $x^3y + \dfrac{2x^3y}{xy}$

41. $b^2 + \dfrac{b^2 + 5b^2}{2}$

42. $\dfrac{c^2 + 2c^2}{c} + 3c$

43. $\dfrac{0}{2} + c$

44. $\dfrac{0}{c} + c$

45. $\dfrac{x^2 + 2x^2}{x} + \dfrac{x^3}{x^2}$

46. $\dfrac{x + 5x}{3} + \dfrac{x^2 + 3x^2}{x}$

47. $\dfrac{y + 4y}{y} + \dfrac{6y^2 + 2y^2}{y}$

48. $\dfrac{2y^3 - y^3}{y} + \dfrac{3y^3 - y^3}{y^2}$

49. $\dfrac{2a^2 + a^2}{a - a} - 3a$

50. $4a^3 + \dfrac{3a^5 - a^5}{2a - 2a}$

CHAPTER REVIEW

1. List all prime numbers between 10 and 25.

2. Graph the first six natural numbers exactly divisible by four.

3. Express each word phrase in symbols.

    a. The product of 6 and x.

    b. Divide the sum of 4 and y by 6.

    c. The product of y and the sum of 3 and x.

4. Write in exponential form.

    a. 4aabbb   *b.* xyyzzz   *c.* $3 \cdot 3ccd$

5. Write in completely factored form without exponents.

　　a. $6xy^2$　　　　　　　*b.* a^3b^2　　　　　　*c.* $27cd^2$

6. Simplify.

　　a. $3 + 2(5)$　　　　　　*b.* $8 + 0(4)$　　　*c.* $\dfrac{3^2 - 1}{4} + \dfrac{2^3 + 1}{3}$

7. If $a = 1$, $b = 0$, $c = 2$, find the value of each expression.

　　a. $a^2 + c$　　　　　　*b.* $4a + 3b + c^2$　　*c.* $\dfrac{c^2 - b}{2a}$

8. What is the area of a circle with a radius of length 4 inches? (Use 3.14 for π.)

In Exercises 9–13, simplify the given expression.

9. *a.* $3xy + 2y + 2xy + xy$　*b.* $6a^2 - a^2 - 3a$　*c.* $3r + 5s - r - s$

10. *a.* $(xy^2)(x^2y)$　　　*b.* $(3b^3)(2a)(2b)$　*c.* $(r^3)(s^2)(rs)$

11. *a.* $3x^2 - x^2(2x) + x^2$　*b.* $ab(b^2) - b^2$　*c.* $2r(rs^2) - r^2s^2$

12. *a.* $\dfrac{4a^2b}{2a}$　　　　*b.* $\dfrac{3a^3b}{3a^3b}$　　*c.* $\dfrac{12xy^3}{4y^2}$

13. *a.* $\dfrac{2x^2 + x^2}{x^2} - 2$　　*b.* $\dfrac{4y - y}{3} + 6y$　*c.* $8a + \dfrac{6a^2 - a^2}{a}$

14. If x and y represent two numbers:

　　a. What is their sum?　　　*b.* What is their product?
　　c. What is the quotient of x divided by y?

15. What are the parts of an algebraic expression separated by plus and minus signs called?

16. What is an algebraic expression consisting of two terms called?

17. In the expression $4x^3$, the number 4 is called the __?__ of x^3.

18. What is the numerical coefficient in the expression x^2?

19. For what value of x would the expression $\dfrac{4}{3x}$ be meaningless?

20. For what value of y would the expression $\dfrac{2}{y - 3}$ be meaningless?

CHAPTER 2

THE INTEGERS— SIGNED NUMBERS

2.1 SIGNED NUMBERS AND THEIR GRAPHICAL REPRESENTATION

On occasion, we use natural numbers to represent physical quantities such as money (5 dollars), temperature (20 degrees), and distance (10 miles). Since this representation does not differentiate between gains and losses, degrees above or below zero, or distances in opposite directions from a starting point, mathematicians have found it convenient to represent these ideas symbolically by the use of plus (+) or minus (−) signs. For example, we may represent:

A loss of five dollars as −$5.
A gain of five dollars as +$5.
Ten degrees below zero as −10°.
Ten degrees above zero as +10°.
Ten miles to the west of a starting point as −10 miles.
Ten miles to the east of a starting point as +10 miles.

Nonzero numbers whose numerals are preceded by a minus sign are called **negative numbers,** nonzero numbers whose numerals are preceded by a plus sign are called **positive numbers,** and together these kinds of numbers are called **signed numbers.** The signed whole numbers, together with the number 0 are called **integers.** When a numeral is written without a sign (e.g., 3, 5, 9), it is to be understood that a plus sign is intended.

The line graph used to represent natural numbers can be extended to the left of the origin to include the graphs of negative numbers as shown in Figure 2.1. As before, the line graph is particularly useful in visualizing the relative order of two numbers; the number whose graph lies on the left is less than the number whose graph lies on the right. Thus, −4 is less than −2, −3 is less than 3, and −1 is less than 0. This notion is consistent

Figure 2.1

with our physical experiences. A temperature of $-4°$ is lower or less than one of $-2°$, $-3°$ is less than $3°$, and $-1°$ is less than $0°$.

The **absolute value** of a signed number is the value of the number without regard to its sign and is designated symbolically by the use of two vertical bars.* Thus,

$$|-3| = 3, \quad |2| = 2, \quad |-5| = 5, \quad |0| = 0, \text{ etc.}$$

When we write $|-5| = 5$, we say we have *simplified the expression* $|-5|$.

EXERCISES 2.1

Locate the graphs of the numbers a to f on a line graph. Use a separate line graph for each exercise.

Sample problem: *a.* -8 *b.* -6 *c.* -2 *d.* 1   *e.* 5   *f.* 9

1.	*a.* 0	*b.* -3	*c.* 5	*d.* -5	*e.* 2	*f.* -1
2.	*a.* -4	*b.* 3	*c.* -2	*d.* -1	*e.* 6	*f.* 9

Which number in each pair is the smaller? (Think of the number line.)

3. 2, 3	**4.** $-2, -3$	**5.** 1, 0	**6.** $-1, 0$
7. 3, -2	**8.** $-5, -4$	**9.** $-1, -80$	**10.** 3, 7
11. $-3, -7$	**12.** 5, 0	**13.** $-5, 0$	**14.** 7, -8
15. $-15, -10$	**16.** $-2, -8$	**17.** 0, -4	**18.** $-5, 2$

In Problems 19 to 24, locate the graphs of the sets of points (Use a separate graph for each exercise.)

* Technically, absolute value is defined by

$$|x| = \begin{array}{l} x, \text{ if } x \text{ is greater than or equal to } 0 \\ -x, \text{ if } x \text{ is less than } 0. \end{array}$$

19. The natural numbers less than 10.

20. The integers between -3 and 7.

21. The even integers between -3 and 11.

22. The odd integers between -5 and 5.

23. The odd integers between -5 and -1.

24. The odd integers between -15 and 0.

State whether each number is an integer.

25. 5   **26.** $\dfrac{5}{2}$ **27.** -4 **28.** $-\dfrac{6}{2}$

29. $\dfrac{7}{2}$ **30.** $\dfrac{27}{4}$ **31.** $-\dfrac{30}{6}$ **32.** $\dfrac{30}{5}$

Simplify.

33. $|3|$ **34.** $|-3|$ **35.** $|-8|$ **36.** $|-1|$

37. $|-2|^3$ **38.** $|-1|^3$ **39.** $|-4|$ **40.** $|-4|^3$

2.2 SUMS OF SIGNED NUMBERS

To illustrate the meaning of the sum of two signed numbers, we may consider such numbers as representing gains and losses, $(+)$ numbers denoting gains and $(-)$ numbers denoting losses.

	$+5$ gain	-5 loss	$+5$ gain	-5 loss
	$+3$ gain	-3 loss	-3 loss	$+3$ gain
Sum:	$+8$ gain	-8 loss	$+2$ gain	-2 loss

These examples suggest a rule for the addition of signed numbers.

> *To add two numbers with*
> > *like signs: Add the absolute values of the numbers and prefix the common sign of the numbers to the sum.*
> > *unlike signs: Find the difference of the absolute values of the numbers and prefix the sign of the number with the larger absolute value to the difference.*

We recall from Chapter 1 that like algebraic terms may be combined by adding the numerical coefficients. Thus:

$$(+5x) + (+3x) = +8x, \qquad (+5x) + (-3x) = +2x,$$
$$(-5x) + (-3x) = -8x, \quad \text{and} \quad (-5x) + (+3x) = -2x.$$

In these examples, we observe two uses for the plus sign $(+)$. It may be used as a sign of operation indicating the addition of two numbers, or it may be used as a sign of quality differentiating between a number and its negative. It is convenient to omit the addition (+) sign of operation and express $(+3) + (-4)$ as $3 - 4$ and $(-2) + (3)$ as $-2 + 3$, etc., where all the signs are signs of quality. The operation is understood to be addition. That is:

> *In expressions involving only addition, parentheses which are preceded by a (+) sign may be dropped; each term within the parentheses retains its original sign.*

We assume that the commutative and associative laws of addition hold with respect to signed numbers.

EXERCISES 2.2

Add.

1. $+2$ $+4$	2. $+3$ $+5$	3. -3 -1	4. -3 $+2$
5. $+4$ -1	6. $+3$ 0	7. -6 -2	8. $+4$ $+1$
9. $+10$ -5	10. -5 $+5$	11. 0 -6	12. -10 -5

Simplify.

Sample problems:

a. $(-3) + (-2)$ *b.* $-3 + 6$ *c.* $(4x) + (-5x)$ *d.* $4y - 7y$

Ans. -5 *Ans.* $+3$ *Ans.* $-x$ *Ans.* $-3y$

13. $(+4) + (+2)$	14. $(+3) + (+1)$	15. $(-2) + (-5)$
16. $(+4) + (-6)$	17. $(+2) + (-1)$	18. $(-6) + (+3)$
19. $(-6) + (-4)$	20. $(+5) + (0)$	21. $(0) + (-3)$
22. $(-8) + (+2)$	23. $(-5) + (0)$	24. $(+4) + (0)$
25. $(+4) + (+3)$	26. $(-4) + (-3)$	27. $(-2) + (0)$
28. $(-2) + (+4)$	29. $(+6) + (-3)$	30. $(-6) + (-3)$
31. $(-7) + (+9)$	32. $(+8) + (-8)$	33. $6 + 5$
34. $5 - 3$	35. $-3 + 5$	36. $2 - 5$
37. $-4 - 3$	38. $3 - 6$	39. $6 - 2 + 1$
40. $6 - 2 - 3$	41. $8 - 1 + 3$	42. $6 + 3 - 8$

43. $8 + 0 - 9$ **44.** $-2 - 3 - 4$ **45.** $3 + 4 - 2 - 1$

46. $3 + 2 - 6 - 1$ **47.** $8 - 6 + 2 - 3$ **48.** $-5 - 4 - 3 + 12$

49. $(2x) + (-3x)$ **50.** $(x) + (7x)$ **51.** $(-6y) + (4y)$

52. $(-3a) + (-4a)$ **53.** $(3x) + (-3x)$ **54.** $(-5a) + (-5a)$

55. $(6hk) + (-7hk)$ **56.** $(0) + (-3xz)$ **57.** $(-5cd) + (0)$

58. $(2x^2) + (5x^2)$ **59.** $(6xy) + (-5xy)$ **60.** $(-8abc + (8abc)$

61. $3x + 2x$ **62.** $4y - 8y$ **63.** $-3a - 5a$

64. $2z - 7z$ **65.** $8b - 3b$ **66.** $6k + k$

Simplify.

Sample problems:

a. $2x^2 - x + x^2 + 2x$ *b.* $(3x^3 - 2x^2 + x) + (x + 2x^2)$

$$\text{Remove ( ).}$$
$$3x^3 - 2x^2 + x + x + 2x^2$$
$$\text{Combine like terms.}$$

Ans. $3x^2 + x$ *Ans.* $3x^3 + 2x$

67. $3x^2 + 2x^2 - x$ **68.** $4y - 2y^2 - 6y$

69. $3a^2 - 4a - a$ **70.** $2x^2 - 9x^2 - 2x^2$

71. $x - x^2 + 4x$ **72.** $6y^2 - 3y - y$

73. $2x - x^2 - x^3 + 4x^2$ **74.** $y^3 - 2y^2 + y^2 - y$

75. $a^2 - 2a^3 + 4a^2 + 1$ **76.** $(3a - 2b) + (c - b)$

77. $(3x - y) + (3x - z)$ **78.** $2x^2 - 3y^2 + 2x^2 + y^2$

79. $3xy^2 - 2x^2y + xy^2 + 2x^2y$ **80.** $3ab - 4c + 3c - 2ab$

81. $(6x^2y - 5z) + (3 - 2z)$ **82.** $(6x^3 - 7xy) + (x^3 + xy)$

83. $5rs + 7t - 5rs - 6t$ **84.** $6pg - 7p^2g^2 + 7pg + 6p^2g^2$

85. $7m^2 - 2m + 3 + 2m^2 - 3m$ **86.** $5h - 3k^2 + 2hk - 5h + 3k^2$

87. $3a^2 - 2ab + b^2 - 4b^2 + 2ab$ **88.** $(a^2 + 2a - 3) + (a^2 - 3)$

89. $(-2x^2 - 4x + 2) + (x^2 - 2)$ **90.** $3x^2y^2 - 2xy + x^2y^2 - 3xy$

91. $ab^2 - 3a^2bt + abt^2 - a^2bt$ **92.** $3x^2 + 4ax - a^2 - ax - 3ax$

93. $3g^2 - 8ag + 6ag - 7g^2 + g^2 - 2g^2 + ag - 5ag$

94. $3 - a - a - 3 - 2 + a - a + 2 - 3 + 7 - 2a + 5$

95. $a^2bc - ab^2c - 3a^2bc + 2ab^2c + 3ab^2c - a^2bc$

96. $a + 2b + 3c - 3a - 2b - c + 4c - 2a - b$

97. $10ab - 14c + 21d - 3ab + 15c - 20d + 3c - 4d$

98. $-5x^2y + 3xy^2 + 4x^2y - 3xy^2 + x^2y - 2xy^2 + 6x^2y$

2.3 DIFFERENCES OF SIGNED NUMBERS

When discussing the difference of two natural numbers (Section 1.9), we observed that $5 - 3$ is a number, 2, which, when added to 3, gives 5; in general, $a - b$ is a number which, when added to b, gives a. The same idea holds for the difference of two signed numbers. The following examples illustrate the process of subtraction:

<table>
<tr><td></td><td>+5</td><td></td><td>-5</td><td></td><td>+2</td></tr>
<tr><td>Subt.</td><td>+2</td><td>Subt.</td><td>-2</td><td>Subt.</td><td>+5</td></tr>
</table>

What number added to +2 gives +5?	What number added to -2 gives -5?	What number added to +5 gives +2?
Ans. +3	*Ans.* -3	*Ans.* -3

<table>
<tr><td></td><td>-2</td><td></td><td>-5</td><td></td><td>+2</td></tr>
<tr><td>Subt.</td><td>-5</td><td>Subt.</td><td>+2</td><td>Subt.</td><td>-5</td></tr>
</table>

What number added to -5 gives -2?	What number added to +2 gives -5?	What number added to -5 gives +2?
Ans. +3	*Ans.* -7	*Ans.* +7

These examples suggest a rule for the subtraction of signed numbers:

> *To subtract a signed number b from a signed number a, change the sign of b and add the two algebraically.*

Using this rule for subtraction, we may simplify the above differences systematically as follows:

a.
$$\begin{array}{rr} +5 & +5 \\ \text{Subt. } +2 \quad \text{Change to} & -2 \\ \text{and add} & +3 \end{array}$$

b.
$$\begin{array}{rr} -5 & -5 \\ \text{Subt. } -2 \quad \text{Change to} & +2 \\ \text{and add} & -3 \end{array}$$

c.
$$\begin{array}{rr} +2 & +2 \\ \text{Subt. } +5 \quad \text{Change to} & -5 \\ \text{and add} & -3 \end{array}$$

d.
$$\begin{array}{rr} -2 & -2 \\ \text{Subt. } -5 \quad \text{Change to} & +5 \\ \text{and add} & +3 \end{array}$$

e.
$$\begin{array}{rr} -5 & -5 \\ \text{Subt. } +2 \quad \text{Change to} & -2 \\ \text{and add} & -7 \end{array}$$

f.
$$\begin{array}{rr} +2 & +2 \\ \text{Subt. } -5 \quad \text{Change to} & +5 \\ \text{and add} & +7 \end{array}$$

The same examples represented in horizontal form appear as:

a. $(+5) - (+2) =$　　*b.* $(-5) - (-2) =$　　*c.* $(+2) - (+5) =$

　$(+5) + (-2) =$　　　$(-5) + (+2) =$　　　$(+2) + (-5) =$

　　$5 - 2 = +3$　　　$-5 + 2 = -3$　　　$2 - 5 = -3$

d. $(-2) - (-5) =$　　*e.* $(-5) - (+2) =$　　*f.* $(+2) - (-5) =$

　$(-2) + (+5) =$　　　$(-5) + (-2) =$　　　$(+2) + (+5) =$

　　$-2 + 5 = +3$　　　$-5 - 2 = -7$　　　$+2 + 5 = +7$

From the foregoing examples we observe that:

> *In expressions involving only addition and subtraction, parentheses preceded by a $(-)$ sign may be dropped, provided the sign of each term inside the parentheses is changed.*

EXERCISES 2.3

Subtract the bottom number from the top number.

Sample problems:

　　a. $+6$　　　　　$+6$　　　　*b.* -5　　　　　　-5

　　　$+8$　　Change to -8　　　　-8　　Change to $+8$

　　　　　　and add -2　　　　　　　　and add $+3$

　　Ans. -2　　　　　　　　　Ans. $+3$

1. $+7$	**2.** $+5$	**3.** $+3$	**4.** -5
$+7$	-8	$+4$	$+2$
5. -6	**6.** -7	**7.** $+3$	**8.** $+2$
$+3$	0	$+8$	-5
9. $+1$	**10.** $\;\;0$	**11.** -3	**12.** -1
-7	-8	-9	$+9$

Simplify.

Sample problems:

　　　a. $(+8) - (+6)$　　*b.* $(-5) - (-3)$

　　　　$(+8) + (-6)$　　　$(-5) + (+3)$

　　　　　　　　　　　　　　　　　Remove ( ).

　　　　$+8 - 6$　　　　　$-5 + 3$

　　　　　　　　　　　　　　　　　Simplify.

　　Ans. 2　　　　　Ans. -2

13. $(+8) - (+3)$ **14.** $(+8) - (+4)$ **15.** $(+3) - (-4)$

16. $(-4) - (3)$ **17.** $(-6) - (-2)$ **18.** $(7) - (4)$

19. $(x) - (2x)$ **20.** $(3x) - (2x)$ **21.** $(-4x) - (-x)$

22. $(6z) - (5z)$ **23.** $(3y) - (-3y)$ **24.** $(-2z) - (-2z)$

25. $(3xy) - (2xy)$ **26.** $(2ab) - (-ab)$ **27.** $(-2x^2y) - (3x^2y)$

28. $(-3xz) - (-2xz)$ **29.** $(3r^2) - (-r^2)$ **30.** $(-5p^2) - (p^2)$

Sample problems:

a. $(-4) + (-2) - (-3)$ *b.* $(6x) - (-2x) + (-3x)$

Remove ( ).

$-4 - 2 + 3$ $6x + 2x - 3x$

Add.

Ans. -3 *Ans.* $5x$

31. $(-6) + (-4) - (3)$ **32.** $(-3) - (-2) + (-2)$

33. $(-5) + (2) + (-4)$ **34.** $(-6) + (-3) - (-2)$

35. $(3x) + (2x) - (-x)$ **36.** $(2y) - (-7y) - (+3y)$

37. $(-6g) + (-3g) - (-7g)$ **38.** $(3rx) - (-2rx) + (-3rx)$

39. $(2ab^2) - (-ab^2) + (-3ab^2)$ **40.** $(6a) - (a) - (-2a)$

Subtract the bottom polynomial from the top polynomial.

Sample problem:

$$3x + 2y + z$$
$$\underline{x - 2y + z}$$

Change to
and add

$$3x + 2y + z$$
$$\underline{-x + 2y - z}$$
$$2x + 4y$$

Ans. $2x + 4y$

41. $\begin{array}{l} 7a - 3b \\ \underline{2a - 4b} \end{array}$ **42.** $\begin{array}{l} 3xy - 2x + y \\ \underline{xy - 2x - y} \end{array}$ **43.** $\begin{array}{l} x^2 - 4x + 3 \\ \underline{2x^2 - 3x + 4} \end{array}$

44. $\begin{array}{l} 3a^2b \qquad - 2 \\ \underline{-2a^2b + 2ab - 2} \end{array}$ **45.** $\begin{array}{l} 2x - 3y + 2z \\ \underline{4x + 5y} \end{array}$ **46.** $\begin{array}{l} -2x + 4 \\ \underline{2x^2 + 3x + 1} \end{array}$

Simplify.

Sample problem:

$$(3x^2 - 2y + z) - (-2x^2 + 3y - z)$$

Remove ( ).

$$3x^2 - 2y + z + 2x^2 - 3y + z$$

Simplify.

Ans. $5x^2 - 5y + 2z$

47. $(3x^2 + 2x - 1) - (4x^2 - 2x + 3)$ **48.** $(7x^2 + 2x - 3) - (x^2 + 2x + 1)$

49. $(2y^2 - y + 1) - (3y^2 + 2y + 1)$ **50.** $(4x^2 - 2x - 1) - (3x^2 + x - 1)$

51. $(z^2 - 3z + 1) - (2z^2 + z + 1)$ **52.** $(y^2 - 3y + 4) - (y^2 + 2y - 3)$

53. $(2p^2 - 3p + 1) - (2p^2 - 3p + 1)$ **54.** $(y^2 - 3y + 1) - (2y^2 - 6y + 2)$

55. $(x^2y - xy + xy^2) - (2x^2y + 3xy)$ **56.** $(a^2b^2 + 2ab + 1) - (3 - ab)$

57. $(x^2y^2 - 2xy + 3) - (xy + 2)$ **58.** $(2g^2h + h - g) - (2g^2h + h)$

59. $(2xy^2 + 3xy - x) - (2xy + x)$ **60.** $(2ax^2 + 3ax + 4) - (2ax^2 - 3)$

61. $(x + y - z) + (x + y + 2z) - (x + y + z) + (3x - y + 2z)$

62. $(2x + y - z) + (x - 2y + z) - (x + y + 2z) - (x - 3y - 4z)$

63. $(a - b - c) + (a - b - c) - (a - b - c) + (a + b + c)$

64. $(2g + 3h - k) + (2g + h + k) - (2g + 2h + 2k) - (3g - h + k)$

65. $(2x + 2y - z) - (x + 2y - z) - (3x + 2y - z) + (x + 4y + 5z)$

66. $(a - b + c) - (2a + b - 2c) + (-a + b + c) - (a - 2b - 3c)$

Sample problem:

$$3x - 2y - (4x + 2y) + x$$

Remove ( ).

$$3x - 2y - 4x - 2y + x$$

Add.

Ans. $-4y$

67. $2x - y + (x + y)$ **68.** $3a - 2b + (2a + b)$

69. $2x + 3 - (x - 4)$ **70.** $(2x + 3) - x - 4$

71. $6a + 5b - (2a - 5b) - 2a$ **72.** $3c - 2d + 1 - (2 + 2c - d) + c - 1$

2.4 PRODUCTS OF SIGNED NUMBERS

To find the product of two signed numbers, we wish to adopt rules consistent with the rules for the multiplication of positive numbers and reflecting the properties of signed numbers.

If we consider multiplication as a form of addition, that is, if we think of $3(2)$ as meaning the sum of three 2's $(2 + 2 + 2)$, then $3(-2)$ would represent the sum of three -2's $(-2 - 2 - 2)$, which is -6. Thus it would appear that the product of a positive and a negative number should be a negative number.

To investigate the meaning of the product of two negative numbers, consider the sequence of products:

$$4(-2) = -8,$$
$$3(-2) = -6,$$
$$2(-2) = -4,$$
$$1(-2) = -2,$$
$$0(-2) = 0.$$

If we continue the sequence on the left and give meaning to the product $-1(-2)$, it seems plausible to continue the sequence on the right with the number 2. That is, the sequence would continue:

$$-1(-2) = 2,$$
$$-2(-2) = 4,$$
$$-3(-2) = 6, \text{ etc.}$$

It appears (at least intuitively) that the product of two negative numbers should be a positive number. Therefore we shall adopt the rule:

> *To find the product of two signed numbers, multiply the absolute values of the numbers. If the factors have like signs, the product is positive; if they have unlike signs, the product is negative.*

Thus,

$$(+a)(+b) = +(ab), \qquad (+a)(-b) = -(ab),$$
$$(-a)(-b) = +(ab), \quad \text{and} \quad (-a)(+b) = -(ab).$$

Using this rule, we can determine the sign of the product of any number of factors. For example,

$$(-2)(3)(4) = \quad (-6)(4) = -24,$$
$$(-2)(3)(-4) = (-6)(-4) = +24,$$
$$(-2)(-3)(-4) = \quad (6)(-4) = -24.$$

We observe that if we have an odd number of negative factors, the product is negative; if we have an even number of negative factors, the product is positive.

Again, we assume that the commutative and associative laws of multiplication hold for signed numbers.

EXERCISES 2.4

Multiply.

1. $+3$ $\underline{-2}$	**2.** -3 $\underline{+2}$	**3.** -4 $\underline{+3}$	**4.** -3 $\underline{+1}$
5. $+4$ $\underline{-4}$	**6.** -2 $\underline{-3}$	**7.** -2 $\underline{0}$	**8.** $+2$ $\underline{-1}$
9. 0 $\underline{-4}$	**10.** -3 $\underline{-7}$	**11.** $+2$ $\underline{+4}$	**12.** $+2$ $\underline{-7}$

Simplify.

13. $6(-2)$ **14.** $8(-9)$ **15.** $-2(-4)$

16. $2(4)$ **17.** $(-5)(-3)$ **18.** $(-6)0$

19. $(3)(2)(4)$ **20.** $(6)(-2)(3)$ **21.** $(4)(-2)(-1)$

22. $(-3)(-2)(-1)$ **23.** $(-2)(3)(-4)$ **24.** $(-3)(-1)(4)$

Sample problems:

a. $(-3x^2y)(2x)$ *b.* $(-2x^2y)(4x)(-3xy^2)$

$-$ $\qquad\qquad$ $+$ $\qquad\qquad$ Determine sign of product.

-6 $\qquad\qquad$ $+24$ $\qquad\qquad$ Multiply numerical factors.

$\qquad\qquad\qquad\qquad\qquad\qquad$ Multiply variable factors.

Ans. $-6x^3y$ $\qquad$ *Ans.* $+24x^4y^3$

25. $3x(2xy)$ **26.** $2x(-2xy)$ **27.** $2x(-x^2y)$

28. $-xy(xy^2)$ **29.** $(-x)(x^2y)(-y)$ **30.** $(xy)(-x)(-y)$

31. $(-a)(-2a)(3a^2)$ **32.** $(3ab)(a^2b)(-3b)$ **33.** $(-abc)(-ab)(-bc)(b)$

34. $(ab)(b^2)(-ab)(c)$ **35.** $(-2)(3b)(-b^2)(b^3)$ **36.** $(-4)(-2a)(-a^2)(a^3)$

Sample problems:

$\quad$ *a.* $(-3)^3$ $\qquad\qquad$ *b.* $(-x)^2(-xy)$ $\qquad\quad$ *c.* $-x^2 \cdot x$

$\qquad (-3)(-3)(-3)$ $\qquad\quad (-x)(-x)(-xy)$ $\qquad\quad -1 \cdot x \cdot x \cdot x$

$\qquad$ *Ans.* -27 $\qquad\qquad$ *Ans.* $-x^3y$ $\qquad\qquad$ *Ans.* $-x^3$

37. $(-2)^2$ **38.** $(-3)^3$ **39.** $-(-1)^2$

40. $-(2)^5$ **41.** $(-5)^2$ **42.** $-(4)^3$

43. $(-x)^3$ **44.** $(-a)^2(a)$ **45.** $-(a)^3$

46. $(-x)^3(-xy)$ **47.** $-(-xy)^2(xy^2)$ **48.** $(-a)^2(ab)(-b^3)$

49. $(-3)^2(-x)^2(-y)^2$ **50.** $-2(-x)^3(y^2)$ **51.** $-2x(-x)^2(-y)^2$

52. $2x(-y)(-xy)^2$ **53.** $-2x(-3y)(-z)^2$ **54.** $(-3x^2)^2(y^2)^3$

2.5 QUOTIENTS OF SIGNED NUMBERS

The quotient of two signed numbers is defined in the same way as the quotient of two natural numbers (Section 1.11); however, the sign of the quotient has to be consistent with the rule of signs for the multiplication of signed numbers. Recall that for natural numbers the quotient a/b is the number q, such that $(b)(q) = a$, and let us examine the quotient of two signed numbers by considering a simple numerical case.

$$\frac{+6}{+3} = +2, \text{ because } (+3)(+2) = +6;$$

$$\frac{+6}{-3} = -2, \text{ because } (-3)(-2) = +6;$$

$$\frac{-6}{+3} = -2, \text{ because } (+3)(-2) = -6;$$

$$\frac{-6}{-3} = +2, \text{ because } (-3)(+2) = -6.$$

We may formalize these results in the following rule:

To find the quotient of two signed numbers, find the quotient of the absolute values of the numbers. If the dividend and divisor have like signs, the quotient is positive; if they have unlike signs, the quotient is negative.

As always, division by 0 is meaningless.

EXERCISES 2.5

Simplify.

1. $\dfrac{-8}{-2}$ **2.** $\dfrac{-12}{-4}$ **3.** $\dfrac{-20}{5}$ **4.** $\dfrac{-4}{2}$

5. $\dfrac{0}{3}$ **6.** $\dfrac{0}{4}$ **7.** $-2 \div 0$ **8.** $-8 \div 0$

9. $-8 \div 1$ **10.** $1 \div (-1)$ **11.** $-3\overline{\smash{)}-27}$ **12.** $6\overline{\smash{)}-30}$

Sample problem:

$$\frac{-24x^3y^3}{6xy^2}$$

Determine sign of quotient.

$-$

Divide out common factors.

$$\frac{\overset{4}{\cancel{24}}\overset{x^2y}{\cancel{x^3}\cancel{y^3}}}{\underset{1\,1\,1}{\cancel{6}\cancel{x}\cancel{y^2}}}$$

Ans. $-4x^2y$

13. $\dfrac{3x}{-x}$

14. $\dfrac{-4x^2}{2x}$

15. $\dfrac{-x^2y^3}{-xy}$

16. $\dfrac{-16x^3}{-4x}$

17. $\dfrac{-6x}{6x}$

18. $\dfrac{12y^3}{-12}$

19. $\dfrac{16x^3}{-4x}$

20. $\dfrac{-2xy}{y}$

21. $\dfrac{-6x^2y^3}{-xy}$

22. $\dfrac{-x^3y^2}{-xy}$

23. $\dfrac{6x^3}{-3x^2}$

24. $\dfrac{3xy^3}{xy^2}$

25. $\dfrac{ax^2}{ax}$

26. $\dfrac{8bc}{4c}$

27. $\dfrac{-9xy^2}{3xy}$

28. $\dfrac{-12c^2d^2}{12c^2d}$

29. $\dfrac{18x^3y}{-6xy}$

30. $\dfrac{-36x^3y^3z^3}{18xy^2z^3}$

31. $\dfrac{x^2y^2z^2}{x^2y^2z^2}$

32. $\dfrac{26abc^2}{2ab}$

33. $\dfrac{-8x^2y^2}{-2xy}$

34. $\dfrac{-15a^3b^2}{-5a^3b^2}$

35. $\dfrac{30g^2h^3y^4}{15g^2h^2y^2}$

36. $\dfrac{24mn^2}{12mn}$

37. $\dfrac{-33x^2y}{11x^2y}$

38. $\dfrac{-26cd}{26c}$

39. $\dfrac{18xy^2z}{-xz}$

40. $\dfrac{-56x^2y^3z}{7x^2y^2z}$

Simplify. (Review Section 1.4 for order of operations.)

Sample problem:

$$y - \frac{3y + 5y}{4}$$

Combine like terms in numerator and divide.

$$y - \frac{\overset{2}{\cancel{8}}y}{\underset{1}{\cancel{4}}}$$

$$y - 2y$$

Combine like terms.

Ans. $-y$

41. $x - \dfrac{x + 2x}{x}$

42. $\dfrac{x^2 + 3x^2}{-2} - \dfrac{x^2}{x}$

43. $\dfrac{-3x + x}{-2} + x$

44. $x^2 + \dfrac{2x^2 - x^2}{x}$

45. $\dfrac{-xy}{x} + y$

46. $xy^2 + \dfrac{2x^3 - x^3}{x}$

47. $\dfrac{x^2 y}{-y} + x^2$

48. $\dfrac{x^3 y^3}{xy} - x^2$

49. $\dfrac{-xy^3}{y^3} - 2x$

50. $\dfrac{-y}{-y} - 6$

51. $\dfrac{x^2 y^2}{-y} + \dfrac{-x^3 y}{-x}$

52. $\dfrac{-y^2}{y} + \dfrac{-xy}{-x}$

53. $\dfrac{3x^2 - x^2}{-x^2} + \dfrac{4x^3 + 2x^3}{3x^3}$

54. $\dfrac{4y^3 + 8y^3}{6y^3 - 3y^3} - \dfrac{3x^3 + 7x^3}{5x^3 - 3x^3}$

55. $\dfrac{6xy^2 - 2xy^2}{2xy} + \dfrac{7x^2 y + 8x^2 y}{6x^2 - x^2}$

56. $\dfrac{14a^2 b^2 - 2a^2 b^2}{7ab - ab} - \dfrac{5ab^3 + 15ab^3}{(2b)^2}$

57. $\dfrac{24a(2b^3 - b^3)}{6b^2 - 2b^2} - \dfrac{15a^2 b^2 + 3a^2 b^2}{3a(4b - b)}$

58. $\left[\dfrac{(6a)^2 - (5a)^2}{10a + a} \right]^2 + \dfrac{7a^2 b - a^2 b}{4b - 10b}$

2.6 NUMERICAL EVALUATION

We may evaluate expressions using signed numbers in the same manner that we evaluate expressions using natural numbers. (See Section 1.5.)

EXERCISES 2.6

Find the value of each of the following expressions.

Given $x = -2$.

Sample problems:

$a.\ 2x^2 - 2x + 1$

$\qquad 2(-2)^2 - 2(-2) + 1$

$\qquad 2(4) + 4 + 1$

$\qquad 8 + 4 + 1$

$\qquad$ *Ans.* 13

$b.\ \dfrac{3x - 2}{4}$

$\qquad \dfrac{3(-2) - 2}{4}$

$\qquad \dfrac{-6 - 2}{4}$

$\qquad \dfrac{-8}{4}$

$\qquad$ *Ans.* -2

1. x^2

2. $-x^2$

3. $(-x)^2$

4. $-(-x)^2$

5. $x + 1$

6. $2x^2$

7. $-2x^3$

8. x^3

9. x^4

10. x^5

11. $2x^2 + x + 1$

12. $x^2 - x - 2$

13. $-x^2 + x + 2$ **14.** $3x^2 - 6x + 1$ **15.** $3x^2 + 6x - 1$ **16.** $\dfrac{2x^2 + 3x}{2}$

17. $\dfrac{2x + 2}{2} + 1$ **18.** $\dfrac{2x + 1}{3} - 2$ **19.** $\dfrac{x^2}{2} - \dfrac{2}{x}$ **20.** $\dfrac{6}{x} - \dfrac{4}{x^2}$

Given $x = 1$, $y = -2$.

Sample problems:

    a. $2x - 3y$ *b.* $2x^2 - 3xy + y^2$

        $2(1) - 3(-2)$ $2(1)^2 - 3(1)(-2) + (-2)^2$

        $2 + 6$ $2 + 6 + 4$

       Ans. 8   *Ans.* 12

21. xy **22.** $-2xy$ **23.** $x + y$

24. $x - y$ **25.** $2x + y$ **26.** x^2y

27. $-x^2y^2$ **28.** $3x^2y^3$ **29.** $-2x^3y^2$

30. $x^2 + y$ **31.** $2x^2 + y$ **32.** $x^2 - 2y^2$

33. $x^2 + xy + y^2$ **34.** $2x^2 - 3xy + y^2$ **35.** $-x^2 - y - y^2$

36. $2x^2 - (2y)^2$ **37.** $\dfrac{x - y}{3} + y^2$ **38.** $\dfrac{4x - 2y}{4} - 3y$

Given $a = 1$, $b = -2$, $c = -3$, $d = 0$.

39. $a + bc$ **40.** $a + b + c + d$ **41.** $2a + b - d$ **42.** $3a - 2b + 2c$

43. $-abc$ **44.** ab^2c **45.** $a^2b^2c^2d^2$ **46.** $-abc^2$

47. $-3a^2bc$ **48.** $4abcd$ **49.** $a^2 + b^2$ **50.** $a^2 - b^2 - c$

51. $ab^2 - cd^2$ **52.** $a^2 + ac - b^2$ **53.** $2a^2 - 3bc + 2d^2$ **54.** $\dfrac{3ab}{c}$

55. $\dfrac{a - b}{-c}$ **56.** $\dfrac{a + cd - b}{bc - 3a}$ **57.** $\dfrac{bd}{ac} + \dfrac{bc^2}{a^2}$ **58.** $\dfrac{cb^2}{a} - \dfrac{cd}{b}$

CHAPTER REVIEW

1. Graph the integers $-6, -2, -1, 2, 5, 7$ on a line graph.

2. Graph the odd integers between -6 and 4 on a line graph.

3. Arrange the following numbers in order from smallest to largest, $2, -3, 5, -4, 1, -6, 0$.

4. What is the value of $|-3|$?

5. Add: *a.* $+3$ *b.* -2 *c.* -6
$\underline{-5}$ $\underline{-4}$ $\underline{7}$

Simplify.

6. *a.* $(-2) + (-1)$ *b.* $(-3) + (0)$ *c.* $(-8) + (5)$

7. *a.* $5x + 7x$ *b.* $2x^2 + 5x^2 + 2x$ *c.* $3ab^2 - 2a^2b + ab^2 + 2a^2b$

8. Subtract the bottom number from the top number.

   a. 6 *b.* -7 *c.* 0
      $\underline{8}$ $\underline{-3}$ $\underline{-2}$

Simplify.

9. *a.* $(-4) - (+3)$ *b.* $(3x) - (2x)$ *c.* $(-2x) - (-3x)$

10. *a.* $-2x + x + 3x$ *b.* $6x^2 + 2xy + 2x^2 - 3y^2 - 3xy$
   c. $2xy^2 + 3xy + 3x^2y - 2x^2y + xy^2$

11. Subtract the bottom polynomial from the top polynomial.

   a. $3x^2 - 2x + 1$ *b.* $x^2 - 3x + 4$ *c.* $2x^2 + 3y^2 - z^2$
     $\underline{2x^2 - x + 2}$ $\underline{2x - 9}$ $\underline{3x^2 + z^2}$

Simplify.

12. *a.* $(x + y + 2z) - (x + 2y + z)$ *b.* $(2a + 3b - 4c) - (a + b + c)$
   c. $(x + y - 2z) + (2x + y - z) - (4x + 2y - 3z)$

13. *a.* $(3x)(4)$ *b.* $-3(-2x)$ *c.* $-(-2)^3$

14. *a.* $\dfrac{-15}{-3}$ *b.* $\dfrac{-8}{2}$ *c.* $\dfrac{-48}{-6}$

15. *a.* $\dfrac{xy}{-x}$ *b.* $\dfrac{-xyz}{xyz}$ *c.* $\dfrac{-4x}{-4}$

16. *a.* $\dfrac{3x - x}{2x} + 4$ *b.* $\dfrac{5x + 2x - 4x}{3x} - \dfrac{2x + 3x}{5x}$
   c. $\dfrac{3x^2 - 2x^2}{x} - \dfrac{2x^3 + 3x^3 + x^3}{2x^2}$

17. *a.* $\dfrac{3x^2 - 5x^2}{x} + 6x$ *b.* $\dfrac{-x^3}{x^2} - \dfrac{12x}{3}$ *c.* $\dfrac{3x^2 - 4x^2 + x^2}{7} + 1$

18. If $x = -2$, $y = 3$, $z = 4$, find the value of each expression.

   a. x^2 *b.* $\dfrac{2xy}{z}$ *c.* $\dfrac{3x + 2y}{z}$

19. If $x = -1$, $y = -2$, $z = 1$, find the value of each expression.

  $a.$ $\dfrac{-x^2y}{-z}$ $b.$ $\dfrac{x^2 - z^2}{-2y}$ $c.$ $\dfrac{x^2 - y}{z}$

20. What is the deviation (d) from the mean (M) of the measurement (m) if $d = m - M$, when

  $a.$ $m = 6$, $M = 8$? $b.$ $m = -3$, $M = 4$? $c.$ $m = 5$, $M = -2$?

CUMULATIVE REVIEW

1. Graph the prime numbers between 17 and 25 on a line graph.

2. Graph the integers between -7 and 7 on a line graph.

3. Write in exponential form: $2 \cdot yyy$.

4. Write in completely factored form without exponents: $36xy^3$.

5. If $x = 1$, $y = 2$, $w = -2$, find the value of $x^2y^2w^2$.

Simplify.

6. $(2x)(x^2) - 3y^3 + x^3 + y^3$ **7.** $(3x)(x^2)(-x)$

8. $\dfrac{-3m^2n^2}{m^2n}$ **9.** $(a - 2b + c) + (2a - b + c) - (a + b + c)$

10. $\dfrac{3a^2b + 5a^2b}{4a^2} + b$ **11.** $(3x - x)^2 - (x - 3x)^2$

12. The number of feet (s) that an object falls in seconds is given by the formula $s = 16t^2 + 24t$. How far will an object fall in 5 seconds?

13. Find the area and perimeter of a square with a side of length 6 inches.

14. Find the area and circumference of a circle with a radius of length 6 inches. (Use 3.14 for π.)

15. If -3 is one of two factors of -12, what is the other factor?

16. If 2 and -3 are two factors of 30, what is the other factor?

17. $-a + b - c$ can be rewritten as $-(\ \ ?\ \ )$.

18. $-a - b + c$ can be rewritten as $-(\ \ ?\ \ )$.

19. For what value of y will the expression $\dfrac{3}{y}$ be meaningless?

20. For what value of x will the expression $\dfrac{4 + x}{x + 2}$ be meaningless?

CHAPTER 3

FIRST-DEGREE EQUATIONS

3.1 EQUATIONS AS SYMBOLIC SENTENCES

In this chapter, we wish to develop certain techniques to assist us in solving problems stated in words. These techniques involve symbolic representations of stated problems. For example, the stated problem,

"Find a number which, when added to 3, yields 7"

may be symbolized

$$? + 3 = 7; \quad n + 3 = 7; \quad x + 3 = 7; \text{ etc.,}$$

where the symbols ?, n, or x are representations for the number we seek. We call such shorthand versions of stated problems **equations** or **symbolic sentences**.* The terms to the left of an equals sign are known as the **left-hand member** of the equation; those to the right comprise the **right-hand member**. Thus, in the equation $x + 3 = 7$, the left-hand member is $x + 3$ and the right-hand member is 7.

It is obvious that we do not need technical procedures to solve the equation $x + 3 = 7$, but simple examples are useful to illustrate concepts applicable to more complicated problems.

EXERCISES 3.1

Write an equation that expresses each word sentence symbolically.

Sample problem: A number added to three times itself is 20.

$$Ans. \ x + 3x = 20 \quad \text{or} \quad 3x + x = 20$$

1. The sum of 2 and a number is 8.

2. Three times a number is equal to the sum of 3 and twice the same number.

3. Two times a number added to five times the same number gives 21.

4. A certain number divided by 3 gives 4.

---

* Equations such as $x + 3 = 7$ are more specifically identified as **first-degree equations** since the variable has an exponent of 1.

5. A number subtracted from three times itself gives 10.

6. The sum of 3 and a certain number is equal to 13.

7. The sum of 3 and a certain number is equal to twice the number.

8. If a certain number is increased by 24, the result is three times the original number.

9. If twice a certain number is diminished by 5, the result is equal to the sum of 3 and the original number.

10. If 5 is subtracted from three times a certain number, the result is equal to the number increased by 5.

11. Three times a number exceeds the number by 12.

12. If the sum of a certain number and three times itself is divided by 2, the result is equal to the sum of the number and 3.

Write an equation that expresses each of the following word sentences. Use appropriate variables.

13. The area of a rectangle is equal to the product of its length and its width.

14. The area of a triangle is equal to one-half the product of its base and altitude.

15. The volume of a rectangular prism is found by multiplying its length times its width times its height.

16. The circumference of a circle is found by multiplying π times the length of its diameter.

17. The area of a circle is equal to π times the square of the length of its radius.

18. The perimeter of a rectangle is equal to the sum of twice its length and twice its width.

3.2   SOLUTIONS OF EQUATIONS

Equations may be true or false as are word sentences. The equation $x + 3 = 7$ will be false if any number except 4 is substituted for the variable. The value of the variable for which the equation is true (4 in this example) is called a **solution** or **root** of the equation. We may determine whether a given number is or is not a solution of a given equation by substituting the number in place of the variable and determining the truth or falsity of the result. A first-degree equation has only one solution.

EXERCISES 3.2

Determine whether each equation is true for the indicated value of the variable; that is, determine whether the given number is or is not the solution of the given equation.

Sample problems:

a. $2x + 3 = 9$, for $x = 3$ b. $x - 4 = 3x + 1$, for $x = -2$
  $2(3) + 3 = 9$ $(-2) - 4 = 3(-2) + 1$
     $9 = 9$ $-6 = -5$

Ans. 3 is the solution.   *Ans.* -2 is not the solution.

1. $x - 3 = 7$, for $x = 4$ 2. $2x + 1 = -5$, for $x = -3$
3. $0 = 3 + y$, for $y = -3$ 4. $y - 4 = 0$, for $y = 4$
5. $3a + 4 = 8 + a$, for $a = 3$ 6. $a - 3 = 2a + 1$, for $a = -1$
7. $3p - 2 = -p - 4$, for $p = 1$ 8. $4 - r = r$, for $r = 2$
9. $0 = 6r - 24$, for $r = -4$ 10. $0 = 2r + 12$, for $r = 6$

11. $\dfrac{x}{-5} = -3$, for $x = 15$ 12. $\dfrac{2x}{3} = x - 2$, for $x = 6$

13. $\dfrac{x}{4} - 3 = x + 2$, for $x = 8$ 14. $\dfrac{2}{3}x - 5 = \dfrac{3}{4}x - 6$, for $x = 12$

15. $\dfrac{x + 3}{4} = 2$, for $x = 5$ 16. $x + 2a = 5a$, for $x = 3a$

17. $2x - b = x + b$, for $x = 2b$ 18. $x + a = 3x + 5a$, for $x = -2a$

19. $2y - a = -5a$, for $y = -2a$ 20. $\dfrac{1}{2}x - b = 5b + x$, for $x = -12b$

3.3 SOLUTION OF EQUATIONS USING ADDITION AND SUBTRACTION PROPERTIES

Equivalent equations are equations that have identical solutions. Thus,

$$3x + 3 = x + 13, \quad 3x = x + 10, \quad 2x = 10, \quad \text{and} \quad x = 5$$

are equivalent equations, because 5 is the only solution of each of them. In solving any equation, we transform a given equation whose solution may not be obvious to an equivalent equation whose solution is readily discernible.

Since an equation is simply a statement that the left-hand and right-hand members are different names for the same number, like quantities added to or subtracted from each member will produce another equality. Thus, if

$$x + 3 = 7,$$

then

$$x + 3 - 3 = 7 - 3,$$

$$x = 4.$$

We formalize these properties in the following assumption or **axiom** as such statements are sometimes called.

If equal quantities are added to or subtracted from equal quantities, the resulting quantities are equal.

The addition or subtraction axiom can be applied to transform a given equation to an equivalent equation of the form $x = a$, from which the solution a can be obtained by inspection. For an equation such as

$$2x + 1 = x - 2,$$

we wish to obtain an equivalent equation in which all terms containing x are in one member and all terms not containing x are in the other in order to have x by itself as one member. If we first add -1 to each member, we obtain

$$2x + 1 - 1 = x - 2 - 1,$$

$$2x = x - 3.$$

If we now add $-x$ to each member, we obtain

$$2x - x = x - 3 - x,$$

$$x = -3,$$

from which the solution -3 is obvious. (Note that we are using color to indicate quantities to be added to or subtracted from each member of the equation.)

Since each equation obtained in the process is equivalent to the original equation, -3 is also a solution of $2x + 1 = x - 2$. The solution can be checked by substitution. Thus,

$$2(-3) + 1 = (-3) - 2,$$

$$-5 = -5.$$

The *symmetric property of equality* is also helpful in the solution of equations. This property asserts that

$$\text{if } a = b, \text{ then } b = a.$$

This enables us to interchange the members of an equation whenever we please without having to be concerned with any changes of sign. Thus,

$$\text{if } 4 = x + 2, \text{ then } x + 2 = 4;$$

$$\text{if } d = rt, \text{ then } rt = d;$$

$$\text{if } x + 3 = 2x - 5, \text{ then } 2x - 5 = x + 3; \text{ etc.}$$

EXERCISES 3.3

Write an equation equivalent to the given equation.

Sample problem :
$$x - 5 = 3, \quad \text{by adding 5 to each member.}$$
$$x - 5 + 5 = 3 + 5$$

Ans. $x = 8$

1. $x + 2 = 3$,   by adding -2 to each member.

2. $x - 3 = 7$,   by adding 3 to each member.

3. $3 - y = 0$,   by adding y to each member.

4. $7 = 4 + z$,   by adding -4 to each member.

5. $3x = 2x + 3$,   by adding $-2x$ to each member.

6. $x - 5 = 6$,   by adding 5 to each member.

Write an equation equivalent to the given equation.

Sample problem :
$$4x - 2 - 3x = 4 + 6, \quad \text{by } (a) \text{ combining like terms and}$$
$$(b) \text{ adding 2 to each member.}$$

$$x - 2 = 10$$
$$x - 2 + 2 = 10 + 2$$

Ans. $x = 12$

7. $2x - x + 3 = 6$,   by (a) combining like terms and
                           (b) adding -3 to each member.

8. $3x - 4 + 2 - 2x = 3$,   by (a) combining like terms and
                           (b) adding 2 to each member.

9. $2x = 7 + x$,   by (a) adding $-x$ to each member and
                           (b) combining like terms.

10. $3x + 7 - 2x = 8 + 3$,   by (a) adding -7 to each member and
                           (b) combining like terms.

11. $3x - 2 - 2x = 7$,   by (a) combining like terms and
                           (b) adding 2 to each member.

12. $3x - x = x + 1$,   by (a) combining like terms and
                           (b) adding $-x$ to each member.

Solve each equation.

Sample problem:
$$x + 7 = 12$$

Add -7 to each member.

$$x + 7 - 7 = 12 - 7$$

Combine like terms.

*Ans.** $x = 5$ *Check.* $(5) + 7 = 12$

13. $x + 2 = 5$ **14.** $3 + y = 7$ **15.** $x - 3 = 4$

16. $a - 2 = 0$ **17.** $2 + z = 7$ **18.** $-3 + x = 10$

Sample problem:
$$3x - x = 5 + x$$

Combine like terms.

$$2x = 5 + x$$

Add $-x$ to each member.

$$2x - x = 5 + x - x$$

Combine like terms.

Ans. $x = 5$

19. $-3 + y + 2 = 6$ **20.** $8 + c = 0$

21. $0 = z - 7$ **22.** $3 = 2x - x$

23. $3y - 2y = 7$ **24.** $3x = 3 + 2x$

25. $4z = 3z - 3$ **26.** $2x = 3 + x$

27. $2z + 3 = z$ **28.** $3 + 2x = 3x + 5$

29. $3k + 2k = 4 + 4k$ **30.** $6x - x = 4x$

31. $4v + 3 = 3v$ **32.** $5 = 4x + 3 - 5x$

33. $5r = 4r + 1$ **34.** $4x + 4 = 6 + 3x$

35. $8y - 4 = 9y$ **36.** $0 = 3x + 6 - 2x + 2$

37. $-2b - 2 + 3b = 0$ **38.** $5x - 4x = 3$

39. $4d - 3d = 7$ **40.** $5x - 2x + 4 = 2x + 4$

41. $2w + 5 = 3w - 5$ **42.** $7x - 6x - 7 + 6 = 0$

43. $5z + 3 + 6z - 1 = 5z + 3 + 2 + 5z$

44. $6t + 7 - 3t - 2 = 4t + 6 - 2t - 2$

---

* The solution of the original equation is the number 5; however, it is customary to display the answer in the form of the trivial equation $x = 5$.

45. $2(4t - t) + 6 = 2(2t + t) + 8 - t$

46. $-3(x - 3x) + 5 = -4(3x - x) + 7 + 13x$

47. $\dfrac{4x - 2x}{2} + 3(x + 2x) = 2(3x + x) + x$

48. $5(2x + x) - \dfrac{3(2x + x)}{9} = 2(3x + 4x) + x$

49. $\dfrac{3(6y - y)}{5 - 2} + \dfrac{8y - 2y}{3} = 2(5y - 2y) + 4$

50. $\dfrac{3(5y - y)}{4 + 2} - \dfrac{2^2(2y - y)}{2} = 8 + y$

3.4 SOLUTION OF EQUATIONS USING THE DIVISION PROPERTY

For reasons similar to those used in justifying the addition and subtraction axiom, we may divide each member of an equality by the same nonzero number and produce an equivalent equation. More formally, we have the following:

> *If equal quantities are divided by the same (nonzero) quantity, the quotients are equal.*

In solving equations, we use this axiom to produce equivalent equations in which the variable has a coefficient of 1.

EXERCISES 3.4

Write an equation equivalent to the given equation.

Sample problem:

$$-4x = 12, \qquad \text{by dividing each member by } -4.$$

$$\dfrac{\overset{1}{\cancel{-4}x}}{\underset{1}{\cancel{-4}}} = \dfrac{\overset{-3}{\cancel{12}}}{\underset{1}{\cancel{-4}}}$$

Ans. $x = -3$

1. $3x = 6,$ by dividing each member by 3.

2. $-3x = 9,$ by dividing each member by -3.

3. $3 = -x$,   by dividing each member by -1.

4. $14 = -7x$,   by dividing each member by -7.

5. $5x = -10$,   by dividing each member by 5.

6. $3x = 21$,   by dividing each member by 3.

Write an equation equivalent to each given equation.

7. $3x - x = 6$,   by (*a*) combining like terms and
  (*b*) dividing each member by 2.

8. $5x - x = 7 + 5$,   by (*a*) combining like terms and
  (*b*) dividing each member by 4.

9. $25 - 9 = 3x + 5x$,   by (*a*) combining like terms and
  (*b*) dividing each member by 8.

10. $7 + 5 = 5x - x$,   by (*a*) combining like terms and
  (*b*) dividing each member by 4.

11. $4x + 5x = 4 + 14$,   by (*a*) combining like terms and
  (*b*) dividing each member by 9.

12. $4x + 3x = 16 - 2$,   by (*a*) combining like terms and
  (*b*) dividing each member by 7.

Solve each equation.

Sample problem:
$$3x + x = 14 - 2$$

Combine like terms.

$$4x = 12$$

Divide each member by .

Ans. $x = 3$

Check. $3(3) + (3) = 14 - 2$
$9 + 3 = 14 - 2$
$12 = 12$

13. $3x = 15$	**14.** $6y = 18$	**15.** $-x = 8$
16. $3b = 9$	**17.** $-12 = 2c$	**18.** $-25 = 5x$
19. $3z + 2z = 10$	**20.** $5x + 2x = 35$	**21.** $8c - 2c = 6$
22. $7x - 2x = 20$	**23.** $2p + 4p = 6$	**24.** $2y + y = 6$

Sample problem:
$$2x + 5 = 5x - 4$$

Add $+4$ and $-2x$ to each member.

$$2x + 5 + 4 - 2x = 5x - 4 + 4 - 2x$$

Combine like terms.

$$9 = 3x$$

Divide each member by 3.

$$3 = x$$

Exchange members.

Ans. $x = 3$

25. $5 = 6p - 7$ **26.** $8 = 3y + 2$ **27.** $13 = 7x - 1$

28. $7 = 2p + 5$ **29.** $-5 = -2 - 3x$ **30.** $-20 = 1 - 7t$

31. $-6t = 3t$ **32.** $7r = 5r$ **33.** $2x - 2 = 6$

34. $4z - 3 = 9$ **35.** $-3Q + 4 = 2Q + 24$ **36.** $2x = -4x + 6$

37. $7x = 14 + 5x$ **38.** $5y + 3 = 13 - 5y$ **39.** $3d + 2 - 4d = 6$

40. $3x - 4 = 4x + 2$ **41.** $3 = 6x - 3 - 3x$ **42.** $30 = 6r - 24 + 3r$

43. $2t - 8 = 0$ **44.** $0 = 3t + 21$

45. $6(2y + y) - 2(3y - y) = 2y + 24$

46. $6(y - 3y) + 2(6y - y) + 8 = 3(2y - y) + 23$

47. $\dfrac{3(6y - 2y)}{4} + 2(3y + y) - 6 = 2(y + 2y) + 9$

48. $\dfrac{2(3t + 2t)}{7 - 2} - \dfrac{4(t + 2t)}{7 - 5} = 2(t + 3t) + \dfrac{4(2t - 6t)}{5 - 3}$

49. $\dfrac{3x(5 - 2)}{4 - 1} - 3(2x - 4x) = x(2^2 - 1) + 24$

50. $\dfrac{4(6z + 5z)}{5 - 3} - \dfrac{z(17 - 2)}{3 + 2} = 18(2z + z) - 70$

3.5 SOLUTION OF EQUATIONS USING THE MULTIPLICATION PROPERTY

For reasons identical with those discussed in the preceding two sections, we have the following:

> *If equal quantities are multiplied by the same quantity, their products are equal.*

In solving equations, we use this axiom to produce equivalent equations which are free of fractions.

EXERCISES 3.5

Write an equation equivalent to the given equation.

Sample problem:

$$\frac{x}{3} = -4, \qquad \text{by multiplying each member by 3.}$$

$$\overset{1}{\cancel{3}}\frac{x}{\cancel{3}} = 3(-4)$$
$${\scriptstyle 1}$$

Ans. $x = -12$ *Check.* $\dfrac{-12}{3} = -4$

1. $\dfrac{x}{2} = 4,$ by multiplying each member by 2.

2. $\dfrac{x}{3} = -2,$ by multiplying each member by 3.

3. $1 = \dfrac{x}{-5},$ by multiplying each member by -5.

4. $-3 = \dfrac{x}{-4},$ by multiplying each member by -4.

5. $\dfrac{x}{3} = 4,$ by multiplying each member by 3.

6. $\dfrac{x}{-2} = -1,$ by multiplying each member by -2.

Solve each equation.

Sample problems:

a. $\dfrac{1}{2}x = 10$ *b.* $\dfrac{3x}{5} = 9$

Multiply each member in Problem *a* by 2 and in Problem *b* by 5.

$$\overset{1}{\cancel{2}}\left(\frac{x}{\cancel{2}}\right) = 2(10) \qquad \overset{1}{\cancel{5}}\left(\frac{3x}{\cancel{5}}\right) = 5(9)$$
$${\scriptstyle 1} \qquad\qquad\qquad {\scriptstyle 1}$$

Ans. $x = 20$ $3x = 45$

In problem b, divide each member by 3.

$$Ans.\ x = 15$$

7. $\dfrac{1}{2}x = 4$ **8.** $\dfrac{x}{3} = 2$ **9.** $6 = \dfrac{x}{5}$ **10.** $2 = \dfrac{x}{4}$

11. $\dfrac{x}{3} = -2$ **12.** $\dfrac{x}{5} = 4$ **13.** $-7 = \dfrac{1}{3}x$ **14.** $-5 = \dfrac{1}{2}x$

15. $\dfrac{y}{-2} = 3$ **16.** $\dfrac{y}{-4} = 6$ **17.** $\dfrac{y}{3} = 0$ **18.** $\dfrac{y}{2} = 0$

19. $\dfrac{2a}{5} = 4$ **20.** $\dfrac{4}{5}a = -8$ **21.** $6 = \dfrac{3}{4}x$ **22.** $4 = \dfrac{2x}{3}$

23. $\dfrac{5x}{6} = -10$ **24.** $\dfrac{4}{3}x = -8$ **25.** $-8 = \dfrac{2}{3}y$ **26.** $-10 = \dfrac{5}{6}y$

27. $\dfrac{-x}{3} = 14$ **28.** $\dfrac{-x}{5} = 4$ **29.** $\dfrac{-2x}{3} = -10$ **30.** $\dfrac{-3x}{4} = -12$

31. $\dfrac{2a}{3} = -8$ **32.** $\dfrac{4a}{5} = -8$ **33.** $\dfrac{-b}{2} = 16$ **34.** $\dfrac{-b}{6} = 5$

35. $\dfrac{2}{3}y = -2$ **36.** $\dfrac{3}{4}x = -3$ **37.** $15 = \dfrac{3}{5}y$ **38.** $2 = \dfrac{1}{6}y$

39. $\dfrac{4t - t}{6} = 5$ **40.** $\dfrac{7z - z}{18} = -2$

41. $\dfrac{2(4t + 6t)}{40} = \dfrac{7 + 2}{3}$ **42.** $\dfrac{3(t - 3t)}{9} = \dfrac{2 - 18}{4}$

43. $\dfrac{3^2 + 4^2}{5} = \dfrac{2(3x + 5x)}{48}$ **44.** $\dfrac{7^2 - 5^2}{-6} = \dfrac{2y + 4}{9}$

3.6 FURTHER SOLUTIONS OF EQUATIONS

We are now in possession of all the techniques necessary to solve most first-degree equations. There is no specific order in which the axioms are to be applied. However, in simple equations, if more than one axiom is applicable, it is usually convenient to use the following order:

1. If like terms exist in the same member of an equation, combine them.
2. By application of the addition axiom, write the equation with all terms containing the unknown in one member and all terms not containing the unknown in the other.

3. Combine like terms in each member.

4. Apply the multiplication axiom to remove any fractional coefficients.

5. Apply the division axiom to obtain a coefficient of 1 for the variable.

The following exercises may require one or more of the above steps.

EXERCISES 3.6

Solve.

1. $3 = x + 7$ **2.** $7 = b + 6$ **3.** $4 = 2x$

4. $2z = 8$ **5.** $2a - 3a = 4$ **6.** $3x - 7x = 8$

7. $a = 6 - a$ **8.** $3x = 8 - x$ **9.** $\dfrac{1}{3} y = 6$

10. $\dfrac{1}{5} x = 7$ **11.** $7 - 2y = 1 + y$ **12.** $6 - 3x = 2 + x$

13. $2x = -3 + x$ **14.** $6r = 12 + 4r$ **15.** $-6 = \dfrac{3}{2} x$

16. $8 = \dfrac{2}{3} y$ **17.** $x - 3x = 4$ **18.** $2x - 6 = x + 5$

19. $\dfrac{4x - 2x}{2} = 3$ **20.** $\dfrac{x - 3x}{4} = 7$ **21.** $4x - 3 = 2x + 5$

22. $6x - 5 = 2x + 7$ **23.** $2x - 3 + 2x = 4 - x + 8$

24. $2y - 3 + 3y = 4y + 2$ **25.** $6z + 5 - 7z = 10 - 2z + 3$

26. $6a - 4 + 2 = 3a + 1$ **27.** $5y + 3 - y = 10 + y + 2$

28. $3x + 4 - 5x + 2 = 0$ **29.** $5x + 7 - 2x - 16 = 0$

30. $0 = 7 - 2x + 3 - 3x$ **31.** $0 = 3x + 5 - 7x + 3$

32. $-2x - 5x = 2x + 16 - x$ **33.** $\dfrac{3x + 2x}{2} = \dfrac{10 + 4}{2} - 2$

34. $\dfrac{5x - 3x}{4} = \dfrac{8 + 2}{5} - 2$ **35.** $\dfrac{4x + x}{3} = 10$

36. $0 = \dfrac{5x}{2} + 10$ **37.** $0 = 6 - \dfrac{2y}{3}$

38. $4 = 1 - \dfrac{3x}{7}$ **39.** $6 - x = 6 + 2x$

40. $8 + x = 8 - 5x$ **41.** $3x - 14 = 5x - 4x + 2$

42. $3y(7 - 2) + 17 = 16y + y - 1$ **43.** $\dfrac{(3z - z)}{6} + 3 = 2 + 9$

44. $\dfrac{5(4x - x)}{3} + x(3^2 - 1) = x - 36$

45. $\dfrac{8(2t + 5t)}{3^2 - 2} + \dfrac{2(3t + t)}{2^2} = 8(2t + t) + 28$

46. $\dfrac{6(5u - u)}{2^3} - \dfrac{5(u + 5u)}{3} = 3(2u - u) + 30$

47. Show by direct substitution that the solutions you obtained in Exercises 1–10 are correct.

48. Show by direct substitution that the solutions you obtained in Exercises 11–20 are correct.

49. Show by direct substitution that the solutions you obtained in Exercises 21–30 are correct.

50. Show by direct substitution that the solutions you obtained in Exercises 31–40 are correct.

3.7 LITERAL EQUATIONS—FORMULAS

It is often necessary to solve equations or formulas in which there is more than one variable. We may solve for any specified variable in terms of the others. The procedures used are identical to those developed in the preceding sections.

EXERCISES 3.7

Solve for x.

Sample problem:
$$5ax - 2c = 2ax$$

Add $-2ax$ and $+2c$ to each member.
$$5ax - 2c - 2ax + 2c = 2ax - 2ax + 2c$$

Combine like terms.
$$3ax = 2c$$

Divide each member by $3a$.
$$Ans. \ x = \frac{2c}{3a}$$

1. $x - a = 0$ **2.** $2x - x = 2a + a$ **3.** $3x - 3a = x - a$

4. $2x + 3a = 9a - x$ **5.** $5a - 2x = 2a - x$ **6.** $5a + x = 2x - a$

Solve for y.

7. $ay - b = 0$ **8.** $2ay + 2b = 4b + ay$

9. $3a - 2by = 9a + by$ **10.** $2aby + 6a = aby$

11. $5aby - 3b = 7b - aby$ **12.** $3ay - 4ab + ay = 0$

Solve for x or y.

13. $cx + a^2 = 0$ **14.** $dy - a^2 + 3dy = 0$ **15.** $bx + 2b = 5b - bx + b$

16. $ax - 2ar^2 = ar^2$ **17.** $\dfrac{a}{b}x - c = 0$ **18.** $0 = \dfrac{b}{c}y + a$

Solve each of the following formulas for the symbol in color.

Sample problem:

$$c = 2\pi r$$

Exchange members.

$$2\pi r = c$$

Divide each member by 2π.

$$\frac{\overset{11}{\cancel{2\pi}} r}{\cancel{2\pi}} = \frac{c}{2\pi}$$
$$11$$

$$Ans.\ r = \frac{c}{2\pi}$$

19. $d = rt$ **20.** $v = k + gt$ **21.** $v = lwh$ **22.** $f = ma$

23. $c = \pi d$ **24.** $I = prt$ **25.** $d = rt$ **26.** $v = lwh$

27. $v = lwh$ **28.** $f = ma$ **29.** $I = prt$ **30.** $I = prt$

31. $A = \pi r^2$ **32.** $c = 2\pi r$ **33.** $s = 2\pi rb$ **34.** $v = k + gt$

35. $v = k + gt$ **36.** $s = \dfrac{1}{2}at^2$ **37.** $F = \dfrac{kmM}{d^2}$ **38.** $F = \dfrac{kmM}{d^2}$

Solve for x.

39. $a(bx - 2bx) = a^2b$ **40.** $k(3cx + cx) = 8c^2k^2$

41. $\dfrac{c^2x + 2c^2x}{2c} = c^3 - cx$ **42.** $\dfrac{b^2x - 3b^2x}{b} = 6b^2 - 4bx$

43. $\dfrac{acx + 3acx}{2a} + \dfrac{4bcx + 6bcx}{20b} = c(4x - 2x) + c^2$

44. $\dfrac{2a^2bx + a^2bx}{ab} + \dfrac{6ab^2x - ab^2x}{12b^2} = a(4x - x) + 10a^2$

3.8 FINDING SYMBOLIC REPRESENTATIONS
FOR STATED PROBLEMS

In this section, we shall be concerned exclusively with representing word sentences symbolically, that is, in finding equations that represent stated problems. We shall leave their solution until the next section.

To aid in finding a correct symbolic representation of a stated problem, the following steps are suggested:

1. Represent the quantity you wish to find both as a symbol and as a word phrase.

2. Where applicable, draw a sketch and indicate all known quantities thereon.

3. Write an equation which represents symbolically a word sentence relating the known and unknown quantities. The equation may be obtained from:

    a. The problem itself, which may state the relationship explicitly. For example, "8 is the sum of what number and 5?" can be written as $x + 5 = 8$.

    b. From formulas or relationships which are a part of our general mathematical background, such as, $A = \pi r^2$, $d = rt$, etc.

It may prove helpful to write an actual word sentence before attempting to write out the symbolic sentence.

EXERCISES 3.8

In Exercises 1–10:

    a. Write a simple statement of what is to be found and represent the unknown quantities by appropriate symbols. Use a single variable.
    b. Write an equation relating unknown quantities with known quantities.

Sample problem : The sum of a number and 17 is 86. What is the number?

Ans. a. Let $x =$ the number.

b. $x + 17 = 86$

1. The sum of a number and 28 is 63. What is the number?

2. Six more than a certain number is 20. Find the number.

3. If a certain number is added to 23, the sum is 47. Find the number.

4. If four times a certain number is increased by one, the result is 29. What is the number?

5. What number added to four times itself is equal to the number plus 20?

Sample problem: The sum of two consecutive even integers is 26. What are the integers?

> *Ans. a.* Let x = the smaller even integer, then
> $x + 2$ = the next consecutive even integer.
> *b.* $x + (x + 2) = 26$

6. The sum of two consecutive even integers is 50. Find the integers.

7. The sum of three consecutive integers is 24. Find the integers.

8. The sum of two consecutive odd integers is 36. Find the integers.

9. The sum of three consecutive even integers equals four times the smallest integer. What are the integers?

10. The sum of three consecutive odd integers is equal to four times the smallest integer less one. Find the integers.

In Exercises 11–20:

a. Sketch the figure and label all known and unknown parts with appropriate symbols.

b. Write a simple statement of what is to be found and represent the unknown quantities by appropriate symbols. Use a single variable.

c. Write an equation relating the quantities that are known and those that are unknown.*

Sample problem: The length of a rectangle is three times its width. What are its dimensions if the perimeter is 48 feet?

a. Sketch the figure.

b. Represent the unknown quantities in terms of a single variable.

x = width
$3x$ = length

c. Write an equation relating known and unknown quantities.

$x + 3x + x + 3x = 48$

11. A board 24 feet long is cut into two pieces so that one piece is three times as long as the other. How long are the two pieces?

* Formulas for geometric relationships are available in Section 1.6.

12. A board 24 feet long is cut into three pieces of which the second is three times as long as the first, and the third is 4 feet longer than the first. How long are the three pieces?

13. The perimeter of a rectangle is 56 feet. What are its dimensions if the length is three times the width?

14. The length of a rectangle is five times its width. What are the dimensions of the rectangle if the perimeter is 36 feet?

15. How long is the side of a square whose perimeter is 24 feet?

16. The perimeter of a triangle is 104 inches. The second side is twice the first side, and the third side is 4 inches more than the second. How long is each side?

17. Two angles of a triangle are 40° and 70°. How large is the third angle?

18. Two angles of a triangle are equal, and the third angle is 40°. How large is each of the equal angles?

19. One angle of a triangle is 10° more than another, and the third is 20° more than the smallest. How large is each angle?

20. The largest angle of a triangle is three times the smallest, and the third angle is 30° smaller than the largest. How large is each angle?

3.9 SOLUTION OF WORD PROBLEMS

Although each word problem should be approached individually, the suggestions given in the preceding section should aid in solving most of them. The equation obtained should be solved and the solution checked to ensure that it meets the conditions of the problem.

EXERCISES 3.9

Solve.

Sample problem: The sum of a certain number and 12 is equal to three times the number. What is the number?

> Specify what the variable represents.

Let x = the number.

> Write an equation relating known and unknown quantities.

$x + 12 = 3x$

> Solve the equation.

$12 = 2x$

$6 = x$

Ans. The required number is 6.

(*Solution continued on the next page*)

Check.   Is the sum of 6 and 12 equivalent to the product of 3 and 6? Yes; the answer checks. Note that it is not sufficient that 6 satisfy the equation, since the equation itself may be in error.

(*Note.*   Problems 1–10 in Exercises 3.8 can now be solved completely.)

1. If 5 is added to twice a certain number, the result is 19. What is the number?
2. What number subtracted from three times itself gives a difference of 14?
3. The sum of two consecutive even integers is 86. Find the integers.
4. Find three consecutive even integers whose sum is 84.
5. Find three consecutive integers whose sum is -33.
6. Find three consecutive odd integers whose sum is -21.
7. One number is twice another. If 2 is added to the smaller and 16 is subtracted from the larger, the results are equal. Find the numbers.
8. One number is three times another. A third number is five more than the smaller of the other two. The sum of the three numbers is equal to the smallest number plus 29. What are the numbers?
9. At a recent election, the winning candidate received 50 votes more than his opponent. If there were 4376 votes cast in all, how many votes did each candidate receive?
10. There were 12,822 votes cast in a recent election. The winning candidate received 132 votes more than his opponent. How many votes did each candidate receive?

Sample problem: The perimeter of a rectangle is 120 feet. The length is 10 feet greater than the width. What are the dimensions of the rectangle?

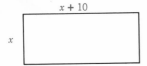

a. Sketch a figure and label.

b. Specify what the variable represents.

Let x = the width

Then $x + 10$ = the length

c. Write an equation relating the known and unknown quantities.

$$x + (x + 10) + x + (x + 10) = 120$$

d. Solve for x.

$$4x + 20 = 120$$
$$4x = 100$$
$$x = 25$$
$$x + 10 = 35$$

e. List both answers.

Ans. width: 25 feet   *Check.*   Does $25 + 35 + 25 + 35 = 120$? Yes;
      length: 35 feet   the answer checks.

(*Note.*   Problems 11–20 in Exercises 3.8 can now be solved completely.)

11. Where should a 39-inch board be cut so that one part will be 5 inches longer than the other?

12. A rectangle is 26 feet long and has an area of 169 square feet. Find the width of the rectangle.

13. A triangle whose base is 16 feet has an area of 144 square feet. Find the altitude of the triangle.

14. A man wishes to enclose a rectangular garden 18 feet longer than it is wide with 180 feet of wire fencing. What should be the dimensions of the garden?

15. A rectangle is 10 feet longer than it is wide and its perimeter is 164 feet. What are its dimensions?

16. A tennis court for singles is 24 feet longer than twice its width and its perimeter is 210 feet. Find its dimensions.

17. The perimeter of an isosceles triangle is 56 inches. The two equal sides are each 4 inches longer than the base. Find the length of each side.

18. One angle of a triangle is 10° larger than another, and the third angle is 20° larger than the smallest. How large is each angle?

19. One angle of a triangle is twice as large as another, and the third angle is 10° less than the larger of the other two. How large is each angle?

20. Two angles of a triangle are equal and the third is 20° less than the sum of the equal angles. How large is each angle?

CHAPTER REVIEW

1. Write an equation expressing the following:
   a. A number added to 3 equals two less than twice the same number.
   b. The volume of a sphere equals $\frac{4}{3}\pi$ times the radius cubed.
   c. Three-fourths of a number equals 21 less 6.

Solve.

2. *a.* $2 + x = 8$ *b.* $5y = 2 + 4y$ *c.* $\dfrac{2a + 4a}{3} = 5a + 3$

3. *a.* $4x + 3x = 35$ *b.* $4x - 4 = 2x - 4$ *c.* $8z + 6z = 2z - 12$

4. *a.* $\dfrac{2a}{3} = -12$ *b.* $\dfrac{b + 4b}{3} = 15$ *c.* $\dfrac{6x - 2x}{3} = -4$

5. *a.* $\dfrac{-9a - a}{2} = 10$ *b.* $\dfrac{3x + 5x}{2} = 6 + 3x$ *c.* $\dfrac{8x - 4x}{2} = \dfrac{8 + 10}{3}$

6. Show by direct substitution that the solutions you obtained in Exercises 2a, 2b, and 2c are correct.

7. Show by direct substitution that the solutions you obtained in Exercises 3a, 3b, and 3c are correct.

8. Solve each of the following formulas for the symbol in color.

$$a. \; f = ma \qquad b. \; v = k + gt \qquad c. \; M = \frac{a + b}{2}.$$

9. If an odd integer is represented by x, how may the next consecutive odd integer be represented in terms of x?

10. If an even integer is represented by x, how may the next consecutive even integer be represented in terms of x?

11. If an integer is represented by x, how may the next four consecutive integers be represented in terms of x?

12. If the width of a rectangle is represented by x, how may a length which is three times this width be represented in terms of x?

13. If a man's height is represented by x, how may the height of a second man be represented who is 7 inches taller? 7 inches shorter?

14. If a man's weight is represented by x, how may the weight of a second man be represented who weighs 18 pounds more? 12 pounds less?

15. The sum of four consecutive integers is 54. Find the integers.

16. The sum of three consecutive odd integers is five times the smaller integer. Find the integers.

17. It takes 144 feet of wire to enclose a rectangular garden of width 34 feet. What is the length of the garden?

18. A 32-foot board is cut into three pieces, so that one of the pieces is 3 feet longer than a second piece, and the third is 5 feet longer than the second. How long is each piece?

19. Five times a number diminished by three times the number equals the sum of the number and 5. What is the number?

20. One angle of a triangle is 15° larger than a second angle, and the third angle is 30° larger than the smaller of the other two. How large is each angle?

CUMULATIVE REVIEW

1. Simplify: $\dfrac{6^2 - 4^2}{2} - \dfrac{2^2 + 1}{5}.$

2. Which of the following are natural numbers?

$$3^2, \quad \frac{2^3}{3}, \quad \frac{4^2}{2}, \quad \frac{4 + 2^3}{12}, \quad 5^2 - 3^2$$

3. In the expression $3b^4$, the number 3 is called the ___?___ of b^4.

4. In the expression $3b^4$, the number 4 is called an ___?___ .

5. If two numbers have like signs, the sign of their product is ___?___ .

6. Which is greater, $|-5|$ or $|3|$?

7. If a is greater than b, and b is greater than c, then c is ___?___ a.

8. Simplify: *a.* $(x^3)(x^2)$.   *b.* $(x^3)^2$.

9. What is the value of $(-3)^4$? of -3^4?

10. The velocity v (in feet per second) of a falling body is related to time t (in seconds) by $v = 32t$. What is the velocity of the body after 6 seconds?

11. How long would it take a falling body to attain a velocity of 128 feet per second? $(v = 32t)$

12. The distance traveled in time t by a car moving with a constant velocity v is given by $d = vt$. How long will it take the car to travel 312 miles at 52 miles per hour?

13. The product of three numbers is $48xy^2$. If two of the numbers are -3 and $4x$, what is the third number?

14. In the simplification of arithmetic or algebraic expressions, multiplication operations are always performed ___?___ addition operations.

15. Like terms may be combined by adding the numerical ___?___ of the variable factors of the terms.

16. Two linear equations in one unknown which have the same solution are called ___?___ equations.

17. Find the number b that satisfies the equation $7b - 3 = 6 - 2b$.

18. Show by direct substitution that -2 is a solution of $-2a - 3 = 7 + 3a$.

19. Solve the equation $3y - b = y + 2$ for y.

20. The sum of three consecutive even integers is -48. What are the integers?

CHAPTER 4

PRODUCTS AND FACTORS

4.1 THE DISTRIBUTIVE LAW

In arithmetic, we obtained the product of a one-digit number and a two-digit number by multiplying the first number by each of the digits in the second number in turn. For example,

$$\begin{array}{r} 12 \\ \times 3 \\ \hline 36 \end{array}$$

is simply an abbreviated notation for the product

$$\begin{array}{r} 10 + 2 \\ \times\ 3 \\ \hline 30 + 6 \end{array}$$

which may be represented horizontally as

$$3(10 + 2) = 30 + 6 = 36.$$

This property of our number system is formalized as the **distributive law,** and may be represented symbolically by either

$$a(b + c) = ab + ac \quad \text{or} \quad (b + c)a = ab + ac.$$

By applying the distributive law to algebraic expressions containing parentheses, we can obtain equivalent expressions without parentheses.

EXERCISES 4.1

Remove parentheses and simplify.

Sample problems:

$a.\ 3a(a + 1)$ $\qquad b.\ -x(x^2 - 2x + 1)$ $\qquad c.\ xy(y - x + 1)$

$Ans.\ 3a^2 + 3a$ $\qquad Ans.\ -x^3 + 2x^2 - x$ $\qquad Ans.\ xy^2 - x^2y + xy$

1. $3(x + 1)$ 2. $2(y - 3)$ 3. $3(2x + 5)$

4. $2(3y - 4)$ 5. $-2(x + 3)$ 6. $-5(z - 2)$

7. $2a(x + a)$ 8. $5b(b - x)$ 9. $2\pi(R - r)$

10. $\pi(D - d)$ 11. $-6(-x + y)$ 12. $-3(-2x + y)$

13. $ab(a - b)$ 14. $b^2(a - b)$ 15. $-x(x - y)$

16. $-3x(x + y)$ 17. $2x(x^2 + x - 2)$ 18. $x^3(x^2 + x + a)$

19. $-x^3(x^2 + 2x - 3)$ 20. $-3y(x^2y + xy^2 + 1)$

21. $ax(2 - x - ax)$ 22. $ab(3 - a + b^2)$

23. $-3y^2(-2y - 3x + 1)$ 24. $-6x(-5x^2 - 2x + 3)$

Sample problems:

  a. $c(y - 3) + 2cy$ b. $a(3 - a) - 2(a + a^2)$

Remove parentheses.

  $cy - 3c + 2cy$ $3a - a^2 - 2a - 2a^2$

Combine like terms.

Ans. $3cy - 3c$ *Ans.* $a - 3a^2$

25. $-a(x + 1) + ax$ 26. $by - b(1 - y)$

27. $a(x + 1) + x(a + 1)$ 28. $2a(x + 3) - 3a(x - 3)$

29. $a(x + y) - 2(ax + y)$ 30. $3(x^2 + 2x - 1) - 2(x^2 + x - 2)$

31. $ax(x^2 + 2x - 3) - a(x^3 + 2x^2)$ 32. $3(x - 2y) - 2(x + 3y) + 2x$

33. $2x(3 - x) + 2(x^2 - 2x + 1) - 2$ 34. $3y(2y - 5) + 2y^2 - 5(y^2 + 2y)$

35. $3(y^2 - 2y + 1) + 3(1 + 2y - y^2)$ 36. $3(ax^2 + ax - a) - 2a(x^2 + x - 1)$

37. $3x^2(a - b + c) - 2x(ax - bx + cx)$

38. $2(x + 3y) - 2x(1 + y) + 2y(x - 2)$

39. $-3ab(x + y - 2) - 2a(bx - by + 2b) + b(ax + 1)$

40. $3ab^2(2 + 3a) - 2ab(3ab + 2b) - 2b^2(a^2 - 2a)$

Sample problems:

        a. $+(3a - 2b)$ b. $-(2a - 3b)$
           $+1(3a - 2b)$ $-1(2a - 3b)$

        Ans. $3a - 2b$ *Ans.* $-2a + 3b$

41. $-(a + c)$ 42. $-(2 - x)$

43. $+(a - 2b + c)$ 44. $+(2a + b - c)$

45. $-(3x + 2y - z)$ 46. $-(2r - s - t)$

47. $-(1 - 3x + x^2)$ 48. $-(3 + 3x - 2x^2)$

49. $-(a - b) + (a - b)$ **50.** $(a - 2b) - (a - b)$

51. $-(x - y) - (x + y)$ **52.** $-(x^2 - x) + (x^2 + x)$

4.2 FACTORING MONOMIALS FROM POLYNOMIALS

From the symmetric property of equality, we know that if

$$a(b + c) = ab + ac, \quad \text{then} \quad ab + ac = a(b + c).$$

Thus, if there is a monomial factor common to all terms in a polynomial, we may write the polynomial as the product of the common factor and another polynomial. For instance, since each term in $x^2 + 3x$ contains x as a factor, we may write the expression as the product $x(x + 3)$. The process of rewriting a polynomial in this way is called **factoring,** and the number x is said to be factored "from" or "out of" the polynomial $x^2 + 3x$.

To factor a monomial from a polynomial:

1. Write a set of parentheses preceded by the monomial common to each term in the polynomial.
2. Divide the monomial factor into each term in the polynomial and write the quotient in the parentheses.

Thus, to factor the common monomial $2x$ from the polynomial

$$4x^3 - 6x^2 + 2x,$$

we write

$$2x(\qquad\qquad),$$

and, upon dividing each term in the polynomial by $2x$, we obtain

$$2x(2x^2 - 3x + 1).$$

Generally polynomials of this type can be factored by inspection. The result can be checked by multiplying the factors obtained and verifying that the product is the original polynomial.

In this book, we shall restrict such factors to monomials consisting of numerical coefficients that are integers, and to integral powers of the variables. Such monomials can be determined by inspection. The choice of sign for the monomial factor is a matter of convenience, and we can use the sign most suitable to our purpose. Thus,

$$-3x^2 - 6x$$

may be factored either as

$$-3x(x + 2) \quad \text{or as} \quad 3x(-x - 2).$$

The first form is usually more convenient.

EXERCISES 4.2

Factor.

Sample problems:

a. $3a + 3b$	*b.* $6ab - 15a$	*c.* $x^3 + 2x^2 - x$
Ans. $3(a + b)$	*Ans.* $3a(2b - 5)$	*Ans.* $x(x^2 + 2x - 1)$

1. $2x + 4$ **2.** $3y - 6$ **3.** $6x + 3y$

4. $4a - 2b$ **5.** $4x^2 - 4x$ **6.** $3y^2 + 3y$

7. $ax^2 + a$ **8.** $by^2 - b$ **9.** $6ax^2 + 3x$

10. $2x^2 - 2x + 2$ **11.** $9by^2 + 6y$ **12.** $3y^2 - 9y - 3$

13. $ab + ac - ad$ **14.** $bx - by + bz$ **15.** $a^2 - a + ab$

16. $x + xy + x^2$ **17.** $3x^2 - 6xy + 9x$ **18.** $24xy - 12x + 36y$

19. $12ax^2y + 24axy^2 - 12axy$ **20.** $9a^2x^2y + 12ax^2y^2 - 3ax^2y$

Sample problems:

a. $-3x^2 - 3xy$	*b.* $-a - b + c$	*c.* $-x^2 - x + 1$
Ans. $-3x(x + y)$	*Ans.* $-1(a + b - c)$	*Ans.* $-1(x^2 + x - 1)$
	or $-(a + b - c)$	or $-(x^2 + x - 1)$

21. $-a^2 - ab$ **22.** $-a^2 - a$ **23.** $-x - x^2$

24. $-ab - ac$ **25.** $-abc - ab - bc$ **26.** $-b^2 - bc - ab$

27. $-6y^3 - 3y^2 - 3y$ **28.** $-2x^2 - 4x - 2$ **29.** $-x + x^2 - x^3$

30. $-3x^2 + 3xy - 3x$ **31.** $-xy^5 - xy^4 + xy^2$ **32.** $-x^2y + xy^2 - 3xy$

Factor the right-hand member of each of the following equations.

Sample problems:

a. $A = P + PRT$	*b.* $S = 4\pi R^2 - 4\pi r^2$
Ans. $A = P(1 + RT)$	*Ans.* $S = 4\pi(R^2 - r^2)$

33. $d = k + kat$ **34.** $A = \pi R^2 - \pi r^2$

35. $S = \frac{1}{3}\pi r^2h + \pi r^2$ **36.** $R = r + rat$

37. $V = 2ga^2D - 2ga^2d$ **38.** $L = 2an + n^2 - nd$

39. $A = ar^2 + br^2 + 6r^2 - \pi r^2$ **40.** $S = 2\pi r^2 + 2\pi rh$

4.3   BINOMIAL PRODUCTS I

The distributive law can be used to multiply two binomials. Although there is little necessity for multiplying binomials in arithmetic as shown in Example 1, the principle also applies to expressions containing variables.

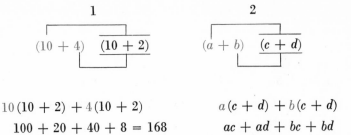

$$10(10 + 2) + 4(10 + 2) \qquad a(c + d) + b(c + d)$$
$$100 + 20 + 40 + 8 = 168 \qquad ac + ad + bc + bd$$

We observe that the final result in 2 can also be obtained by multiplying the individual terms in the following order:

$$(a + b) \quad (c + d),$$

and adding the resulting products. For example,

$$(x - 2) \quad (x + 3) = x^2 + 3x - 2x - 6$$
$$= x^2 + x - 6.$$

With practice, the second and third products can be added mentally.

EXERCISES 4.3

Write as a polynomial.

Sample problems:

a.

$$(x + 5) \quad (x - 3)$$

b.

$$(x - 3) \quad (x + 3)$$

Apply distributive law.

$$x^2 - 3x + 5x - 15 \qquad x^2 + 3x - 3x - 9$$

Simplify.

Ans. $x^2 + 2x - 15$ *Ans.* $x^2 - 9$

1. $(x + 2)(x + 3)$ 2. $(b - 3)(b + 1)$ 3. $(a + 2)(a - 5)$
4. $(a - 2)(a - 3)$ 5. $(x + 2)(x - 4)$ 6. $(x + 1)(x + 5)$
7. $(a + 1)(a + 3)$ 8. $(a - 2)(a + 1)$ 9. $(x - 3)(x + 1)$
10. $(y - 3)(y - 4)$ 11. $(x + 6)(x - 8)$ 12. $(y - 7)(y + 10)$
13. $(x + 2)(x - 2)$ 14. $(x - 3)(x + 3)$ 15. $(x + 2)(x + 2)$
16. $(y - 3)(y - 3)$ 17. $(x - 5)(x + 3)$ 18. $(x + 6)(x - 6)$
19. $(x - 10)(x + 10)$ 20. $(x + 2)(x - 1)$ 21. $(3 - x)(3 + x)$
22. $(10 - y)(10 + y)$ 23. $(8 - x)(8 - x)$ 24. $(5 + x)(5 + x)$

Sample problems:

a. $(x + 6)^2$ b. $(y - 3)^2$

Rewrite expression.

$(x + 6)(x + 6)$ $(y - 3)(y - 3)$

Apply distributive law.

$x^2 + 6x + 6x + 36$ $y^2 - 3y - 3y + 9$

Simplify.

Ans. $x^2 + 12x + 36$ *Ans.* $y^2 - 6y + 9$

25. $(x + 4)^2$ 26. $(y - 5)^2$ 27. $(x - 7)^2$ 28. $(y + 1)^2$
29. $(x - 1)^2$ 30. $(y + 8)^2$ 31. $(x + 2)^2$ 32. $(y - 10)^2$

Sample problems:

a. $(x - 2b)(x + 3b)$ b. $(y - a)(y + a)$

Apply distributive law.

$x^2 + 3bx - 2bx - 6b^2$ $y^2 + ay - ay - a^2$

Simplify.

Ans. $x^2 + bx - 6b^2$ *Ans.* $y^2 - a^2$

33. $(x - 3b)(x - b)$ 34. $(x - a)(x - 2a)$ 35. $(x + 2y)(x - y)$
36. $(x + b)(x + 2b)$ 37. $(x + 2a)(x + 2a)$ 38. $(x + 3b)(x + 3b)$
39. $(a - b)^2$ 40. $(x - y)^2$ 41. $(y - 6a)(y + 6a)$
42. $(x + 3z)(x - 3z)$ 43. $(x - t)(x + t)$ 44. $(y - c)(y + c)$

Sample problems:

a. $3(x - 2)(x + 3)$ b. $a(a + 1)(a + 3)$

Multiply binomial factors.

$3(x^2 + 3x - 2x - 6)$ $a(a^2 + 3a + a + 3)$

Simplify.

$3(x^2 + x - 6)$ $a(a^2 + 4a + 3)$

Multiply by monomial.

Ans. $3x^2 + 3x - 18$ *Ans.* $a^3 + 4a^2 + 3a$

45. $2(x + 1)(x + 2)$　　**46.** $4(x - 3)(x + 2)$　　**47.** $6(y + 5)(y + 5)$

48. $3(y - 7)(y + 1)$　　**49.** $6(x - 1)^2$　　　　**50.** $3(y + 3)^2$

51. $a(a - 1)(a + 5)$　　**52.** $b(b - 2)(b + 7)$　　**53.** $a(a - 2)(a + 2)$

54. $b(b + 3)(b - 3)$　　**55.** $x(y - 3)^2$　　　　**56.** $x^2(y - 4)^2$

4.4　FACTORING TRINOMIALS I

In the preceding section, we were concerned with finding the product of two binomials. In the present section, we propose to reverse this process, that is, given the product of two binomials, to find the binomials. The process involved is another example of factoring. As before, we shall confine our attention to factors containing only integral numerical coefficients. Such factors do not always exist, but we shall study cases where they do.

We observe that in multiplying two binomials,

$$(x + b)\ \ (x + a) = x^2 + ax + bx + ab = x^2 + (a + b)x + ab,$$

the first term in the trinomial is product 1; the last term in the trinomial is product 4; the middle term in the trinomial is the sum of the products 2 and 3. This then, is the process we wish to reverse.

We illustrate the factoring of a trinomial by example.

$x^2 - 3x - 10$

1. Write two first-degree factors whose product is the first term in the trinomial.

$(x \quad\quad)(x \quad\quad)$

2. Write two factors whose product is the last term of the trinomial. Consider all combinations.

$(x \quad 5)(x \quad 2)$
$(x \quad 10)(x \quad 1)$

3. Select the combination(s) which yield(s) the middle term of the trinomial upon the addition of products 2 and 3.

$(x \quad 5)(x \quad 2)$

4. Insert proper signs.
    a. If the third term of the trinomial is $(+)$, the signs on the last terms in the factors will be alike and will be the same as the sign of the second term of the trinomial.
    b. If the third term of the trinomial is $(-)$, the signs on the last terms in the factors will be opposite. The signs must be such as to yield the correct second term in the trinomial.

$(x - 5)(x + 2)$

5. Check the answer by multiplying the binomials.

$x^2 - 3x - 10$

Skill at factoring is usually the result of extensive practice. You will find that the more the process is applied, the clearer it will become. The second and third steps in the process outlined above should be done mentally if possible and the answer written directly.

EXERCISES 4.4

Factor.

Sample problem:

$x^2 - 6x - 16$

Write first-degree factors of x^2.

$(x \qquad)(x \qquad)$

Write all possible factors of 16.

$(x \quad 16)(x \quad 1)$
$(x \quad 8)(x \quad 2)$
$(x \quad 4)(x \quad 4)$

Select the combination(s) that will yield $6x$ upon the addition of products 2 and 3.

$(x \quad 8)(x \quad 2)$

Insert proper signs.

Ans. $(x - 8)(x + 2)$

Check by multiplying.

Check. $x^2 - 6x - 16$

1. $x^2 + 7x + 12$ 2. $x^2 - 8x + 12$ 3. $x^2 + 7x + 10$
4. $y^2 - 9y + 8$ 5. $y^2 - 5y + 6$ 6. $y^2 + 5y + 6$
7. $x^2 + 2x - 35$ 8. $a^2 - 19a - 20$ 9. $b^2 + 8b - 20$
10. $x^2 - 4x - 12$ 11. $a^2 + 10a - 24$ 12. $y^2 + y - 20$
13. $x^2 - 2x - 35$ 14. $y^2 + 11y + 30$ 15. $z^2 + 20z + 100$
16. $x^2 - 14x + 13$ 17. $y^2 - 5y - 50$ 18. $x^2 + 17x + 72$
19. $x^2 - x - 72$ 20. $x^2 - 4x - 45$ 21. $x^2 - 12x - 45$
22. $x^2 - 46x + 45$ 23. $x^2 + 14x + 45$ 24. $x^2 - 44x - 45$

Sample problem:

$$6 - 5x - x^2$$

Write all possible factors of 6 and first-degree factors of x^2.

$$(6 \quad x)(1 \quad x)$$
$$(3 \quad x)(2 \quad x)$$

Select combination(s) that yield $5x$ upon addition of products 2 and 3. In this case, both combinations might work.

$$(6 \quad x)(1 \quad x)$$

Inserting proper signs eliminates $(3 \quad x)(2 \quad x)$ since there exists no combination of signs that yield both the middle term and the last term of the trinomial.

Ans. $(6 + x)(1 - x)$

Check by multiplying.

Check. $6 - 5x - x^2$

25. $21 - 4x - x^2$ 26. $6 - x - x^2$ 27. $10 + 7c + c^2$
28. $30 - 11x + x^2$ 29. $63 - 2x - x^2$ 30. $18 + 7y - y^2$
31. $32 - 12z + z^2$ 32. $24 + 10x - x^2$ 33. $8 - 9x + x^2$

Sample problem:

$$x^2 - 12xy + 32y^2$$

Write first-degree factors of x^2.

$$(x \quad)(x \quad)$$

Write all first-degree factors of $32y^2$.

$(x \quad 32y)(x \quad y)$
$(x \quad 16y)(x \quad 2y)$
$(x \quad 8y)(x \quad 4y)$

Select combination(s) that yield $12xy$ upon addition of products 2 and 3.

$(x \quad 8y)(x \quad 4y)$

Insert proper signs.

Ans. $(x - 8y)(x - 4y)$

Check by multiplying.

Check. $x^2 - 12xy + 32y^2$

34. $a^2 - 2ab + b^2$ **35.** $x^2 + 4ax + 4a^2$ **36.** $x^2 - xy - 2y^2$

37. $a^2 - 3ab + 2b^2$ **38.** $r^2 + 4rx + 3x^2$ **39.** $s^2 + as - 6a^2$

40. $x^2 + 15xy + 36y^2$ **41.** $a^2b^2 - ab - 2$ **42.** $x^2y^2 + xy - 2$

Sample problem:
$x^2 - 16$

Write first-degree factors of x^2.

$(x \quad)(x \quad)$

Since there is no middle term in this expression, the first-degree products 2 and 3 must add to 0. The only factors of 16 to consider are 4 and 4.

$(x \quad 4)(x \quad 4)$

Insert proper signs.

Ans. $(x - 4)(x + 4)$

Check by multiplying.

Check. $x^2 - 16$

43. $x^2 - 9$ **44.** $y^2 - 25$ **45.** $x^2 - 1$

46. $x^2 - 81$ **47.** $z^2 - y^2$ **48.** $x^2 - 9y^2$

49. $x^2y^2 - 16$ **50.** $x^2y^2 - z^2$ **51.** $a^2x^2 - 49b^2$

52. $x^2 - 100a^2b^2$ **53.** $36 - x^2$ **54.** $b^2 - y^2$

4.5 BINOMIAL PRODUCTS II

In this section, we apply the procedure developed in Section 4.3 to multiply binomial factors whose first terms have numerical coefficients other than 1.

EXERCISES 4.5

Write as a polynomial.

Sample problems:

    a. $(2x - 3)(x + 1)$ *b.* $(3x - y)(3x + y)$

                                                    Multiply as indicated.

        $2x^2 + 2x - 3x - 3$ $9x^2 + 3xy - 3xy - y^2$

                                                    Combine like terms.

Ans. $2x^2 - x - 3$ *Ans.* $9x^2 - y^2$

1. $(5a + 1)(2a + 3)$	**2.** $(x - 2)(3x + 1)$	**3.** $(2y + 1)(3y - 1)$
4. $(b + 1)(2b + 1)$	**5.** $(2b - 1)^2$	**6.** $(2b + 1)^2$
7. $(2x + 3)(x + 2)$	**8.** $(3x + 1)(x - 2)$	**9.** $(2y + 3)^2$
10. $(3y - 1)^2$	**11.** $(4y + 6)^2$	**12.** $(3y + 1)^2$
13. $(3x + 1)(x - 4)$	**14.** $(x - 5)(3x + 7)$	**15.** $(3x - 7)(4x + 1)$
16. $(2x - 3)(3x - 2)$	**17.** $(5y + 7)(7y + 5)$	**18.** $(3a + 7)(2a - 7)$
19. $(2x - a)(x + 2a)$	**20.** $(2x - a)(x - a)$	**21.** $(x + a)(3x + a)$
22. $(y - x)(y - 4x)$	**23.** $(3x - a)(2x + a)$	**24.** $(2x - a)(3x - a)$
25. $(3x - 2y)(3x + 2y)$	**26.** $(5 - 2x)(5 + 2x)$	**27.** $(2x - 1)(2x + 1)$
28. $(5x + 9y)(5x - 9y)$	**29.** $(x - 2y)^2$	**30.** $(2x - 3y)^2$
31. $(3x - y)^2$	**32.** $(3x - 2y)^2$	**33.** $(8x + 3y)^2$
34. $(2x + y)^2$	**35.** $(2x + 3y)^2$	**36.** $(3x - 4y)^2$

Sample problems:

    a. $3(2x - 1)(x + 2)$ *b.* $x(x + 2)(3x - 5)$

                                                  Multiply binomials.

      $3(2x^2 + 4x - x - 2)$ $x(3x^2 - 5x + 6x - 10)$

                                                   Simplify.

      $3(2x^2 + 3x - 2)$ $x(3x^2 + x - 10)$

                                                Multiply by the monomial.

Ans. $6x^2 + 9x - 6$ *Ans.* $3x^3 + x^2 - 10x$

37. $2(3x + 1)(x - 3)$ **38.** $4(x - 2)(2x - 3)$ **39.** $3(2y + 1)(2y - 1)$

40. $6(3y + 2)(3y - 2)$ **41.** $3(2x - 5)^2$ **42.** $3(x + 1)^2$

43. $x(x - 2)(2x + 5)$ **44.** $y(y + 2)(y - 1)$ **45.** $x(2x - 1)^2$

46. $y(y + 1)^2$ **47.** $r(3r - 1)(3r + 1)$ **48.** $s(2s - 3)(2s + 3)$

4.6 FACTORING TRINOMIALS II

The factoring procedure developed in Section 4.4 is applicable to trinomials which have a coefficient other than 1 on their second-degree term. We illustrate by example:

$8x^2 + 2x - 15$

1. Consider all combinations of first-degree factors of the first term in the trinomial.

$(8x \qquad)(x \qquad)$
$(4x \qquad)(2x \qquad)$

2. Consider all combinations of factors of the last term of the trinomial. These factors must be considered in both possible orders and arranged with all combinations of the first terms.

$(8x \qquad 1)(x \qquad 15)$
$(8x \qquad 15)(x \qquad 1)$
$(8x \qquad 3)(x \qquad 5)$
$(8x \qquad 5)(x \qquad 3)$
$(4x \qquad 1)(2x \qquad 15)$
$(4x \qquad 15)(2x \qquad 1)$
$(4x \qquad 3)(2x \qquad 5)$
$(4x \qquad 5)(2x \qquad 3)$

3. Select the combination(s) which will yield the second term of the trinomial upon addition of products 2 and 3.

$(4x \qquad 5)(2x \qquad 3)$

4. Insert proper signs.

$(4x - 5)(2x + 3)$

5. Check by multiplying.

$8x^2 + 2x - 15$

With practice you will be able to check the combinations mentally and will not need to write out all of the possibilities.

EXERCISES 4.6

Factor.

Sample problem:

$9x^2 - 8 - 21x$

Write in decreasing powers of x.

$9x^2 - 21x - 8$

Write all possible first-degree factors of $9x^2$.

$(9x \quad)(\ x \quad)$
$(3x \quad)(3x \quad)$

Write all possible factors of 8. List factors in all possible orders.

$(9x \quad 8)(x \quad 1)$
$(9x \quad 1)(x \quad 8)$
$(9x \quad 2)(x \quad 4)$
$(9x \quad 4)(x \quad 2)$
$(3x \quad 8)(3x \quad 1)$
$(3x \quad 2)(3x \quad 4)$

Select the combination(s) that yield $21x$ upon addition of products 2 and 3.

$(3x \quad 8)(3x \quad 1)$

Insert proper signs.

Ans. $(3x - 8)(3x + 1)$

Check by multiplying.

Check. $9x^2 - 21x - 8$

1. $3a^2 + 4a + 1$
2. $2r^2 + 3r + 1$
3. $2x^2 - 3x + 1$
4. $2y^2 + 5y + 3$
5. $9b^2 - 6b + 1$
6. $4a^2 + 4a + 1$
7. $2x^2 - 3 + x$
8. $2x^2 + 3 + 7x$
9. $2x^2 - 3 - x$
10. $2x^2 - 7x + 3$
11. $6a^2 - 1 - a$
12. $1 + 6a^2 + 5a$
13. $4y^2 - 4y + 1$
14. $4y^2 - 5y + 1$
15. $4y^2 - 3y - 1$
16. $4y^2 + 3y - 1$
17. $4a^2 - 11a + 6$
18. $23a + 4a^2 - 6$
19. $4a^2 + a - 5$
20. $16x^2 - 5 - 16x$
21. $16x^2 - 2x - 5$
22. $16x^2 - 38x - 5$
23. $16x^2 - 11x - 5$
24. $16x^2 + 79x - 5$
25. $9x^2 - 21x - 8$
26. $64x^2 + 64x + 15$
27. $16y + 4y^2 + 15$
28. $10y - 8 + 25y^2$
29. $2t^2 - 5st - 3s^2$
30. $2a^2 + 5ab - 3b^2$

31. $3x^2 + 2a^2 - 7ax$ **32.** $9y^2 - 3yz - 2z^2$ **33.** $5by + 4y^2 + b^2$

34. $9a^2 + 9ab - 4b^2$ **35.** $4a^2 + 16ab + 15b^2$ **36.** $9x^2 + 3xy - 2y^2$

Sample problems:

        a. $9x^2 - 4$ *b.* $16a^2 - b^2y^2$

           $(9x^2 + 0x - 4)$ $(16a^2 + 0ab - b^2y^2)$

     Ans. $(3x - 2)(3x + 2)$ *Ans.* $(4a - by)(4a + by)$

37. $4b^2 - 9$ **38.** $9b^2 - 1$ **39.** $25x^2 - 16$

40. $4y^2 - 25$ **41.** $9 - 4x^2$ **42.** $25 - 9y^2$

43. $81 - 4x^2$ **44.** $9 - 64y^2$ **45.** $4a^2 - 121b^2$

46. $64x^2 - 9y^2$ **47.** $25y^2 - 49x^2$ **48.** $100x^2 - 81y^2$

49. $49a^2x^2 - 144b^2y^2$ **50.** $49a^2x^2 - 36b^2y^2$ **51.** $4x^2y^2 - 81$

52. $121 - 49x^2y^2$ **53.** $36a^2b^2 - 1$ **54.** $1 - 100a^2b^2$

4.7 FACTORING TRINOMIALS III

It is easier to factor a trinomial completely if any monomial factor common to each term of the trinomial is factored first. For example,

$$12x^2 + 36x + 24$$

might be factored as

$$(12x + 24)(x + 1),\ (12x + 12)(x + 2),\ (6x + 12)(2x + 2),$$

$$(2x + 4)(6x + 6),\ (4x + 8)(3x + 3),\ \text{or } (3x + 6)(4x + 4).$$

A monomial factor may then be factored from several of these binomial factors. However, first factoring the common factor 12 from the original expression yields

$$12(x^2 + 3x + 2),$$

from which we have

$$12(x + 2)(x + 1),$$

which is then said to be in **completely factored form.**

EXERCISES 4.7

Factor completely.

Sample problems:

    a. $3x^2 + 12x + 12$ *b.* $2b^3 - 8b^2 - 10b$ *c.* $4x^2 - 36$

      $3(x^2 + 4x + 4)$ $2b(b^2 - 4b - 5)$ $4(x^2 - 9)$

Ans. $3(x + 2)(x + 2)$ *Ans.* $2b(b - 5)(b + 1)$ *Ans.* $4(x - 3)(x + 3)$

1. $2x^2 + 10x + 12$ 2. $9a^2 - 15a - 6$

3. $y^3 - 2y^2 - 3y$ 4. $b^3 + 2b^2 + b$

5. $5c^2 - 25c + 30$ 6. $4a^2b + 12ab - 72b$

7. $6x^2 + 8x + 2$ 8. $6x^3 + 21x^2 + 9x$

9. $8ay^2 - 6ay - 2a$ 10. $18x^2 - 3x - 3$

11. $27y^3 - 9y^2 - 6y$ 12. $4a^2y^2 + 10a^2y + 6a^2$

13. $18x^2 - 9x - 27$ 14. $4x^3 - 10x^2y - 6xy^2$

15. $12ab^2 + 15a^2b + 3a^3$ 16. $27a^2b + 27ab^2 - 12b^3$

17. $50xy^3 + 20x^2y^2 - 16x^3y$ 18. $4a^2bx^2 - 2abx - 12b$

19. $5x^2 - 5$ 20. $2x^2 - 8$

21. $3x^3 - 3x$ 22. $3a^2 - 75$

23. $2x^2 - 8y^2$ 24. $3xy^2 - 12xb^2$

25. $x^3 - x^5$ 26. $a^2x^2y - 16y$

27. $3a^2b^2 - 12c^2d^2$ 28. $8x^2y^2z^2 - 18$

29. $\pi R^2 - \pi r^2$ 30. $2\pi R^3 - 2\pi r^2 R$

4.8 NUMERICAL EVALUATION

It is frequently easier to evaluate an algebraic expression or a formula by factoring it before making the numerical substitution.

EXERCISES 4.8

Given $x = -2$, $y = 3$, evaluate each of the following.
a. In the form given.   *b.* After factoring.

Sample problems: $x^3y - x^3$

a. Substitute directly	*b.* Factor first
$x^3y - x^3$	$x^3y - x^3$
$(-2)^3(3) - (-2)^3$	$x^3(y - 1)$
$(-8)(3) - (-8)$	$(-2)^3(3 - 1)$
$-24 + 8$	$(-8)(2)$
Ans. -16	*Ans.* -16

1. $xy + x$ 2. $x^2y - x^2$ 3. $yx + y^2$ 4. $x^2y^2 + y^2$

5. $x^3y - x^2$ 6. $4x^4y + x^2y$ 7. $17y^3 - 17y^2$ 8. $23x^2 - 23x$

9. $85xy + 85x^2y$ 10. $140x^2 + 70x$ 11. $44y^2 - 11xy$ 12. $48xy - 16y$

Evaluate each of the following.
a. In the form given.
b. After factoring the right-hand member. (Use $\frac{22}{7}$ for π.)

13. $P = 2l + 2w$ when $l = 8$, $w = 6$

14. $A = p + prt$ when $p = 75$, $r = \frac{1}{25}$, $t = 5$

15. $A = \pi R^2 - \pi r^2$ when $R = 5$, $r = 2$

16. $A = 2\pi rh + 2\pi r^2$ when $r = 3$, $h = 4$

17. $A = 2Bh + 2bh$ when $B = 20$, $b = 10$, $h = 4$

18. $V = 4\pi r^3 - 2\pi r$ when $r = 7$

19. $A = 6\pi D^2 - 3\pi d^2$ when $D = 6$, $d = 3$

20. $Q = 4a^2s^2 - 3as$ when $a = 2$, $s = 3$

4.9 EQUATIONS INVOLVING PARENTHESES

It is frequently necessary to solve equations in which the variable is included as a part of an expression enclosed in parentheses. These equations can be solved in the usual manner after they have been simplified by applying the distributive law to remove the parentheses.

EXERCISES 4.9

Solve.

Sample problem:

$$3(7 - 2x) + 7(2x + 1) = 44$$

Apply the distributive law.

$$21 - 6x + 14x + 7 = 44$$

Solve for x.

$$8x + 28 = 44$$
$$8x = 16$$

Ans. $x = 2$

1. $2(a + 5) = 16$

2. $4(2a + 6) = 48$

3. $3(a + 2) = 4a$

4. $2(2x + 3) = 14$

5. $6 = 2(2x - 1)$

6. $6x = 2(12 - x)$

7. $-2(3x + 5) - 15 = -7$

8. $5 = 9 + 2(3x + 7)$

9. $5b + 10(8 - b) = 65$

10. $3b = 110 - 2(50 - b)$

11. $7(c + 2) = 3c + 34$

12. $4c - 83 = -5(11 + 2c)$

13. $-x - (8 + x) = 2$

14. $3(7 + 2x) = 30 + 7(x - 1)$

15. $5x - (x + 2) = 7 + (x + 3)$

16. $4(y - 1) = 5(y - 2)$

17. $-2y + 5(y + 1) = 25 + 7y$

18. $25 + 5y = -2(y - 4) - 18$

19. $(a - 1) - (a + 2) = a + (a - 3)$ **20.** $3(2a - 1) + 2(a + 5) = 15$

21. $(b + 5) - (b - 1) = 3b$ **22.** $5a - 4(1 - a) = 11 - 6(a - 5)$

23. $b = 4(b + 6) + 3b$ **24.** $b = (b + 1) - (b - 5)$

Sample problem:

$$(x + 5)(x + 3) - x = x^2 + 1$$

Apply the distributive law.

$$x^2 + 8x + 15 - x = x^2 + 1$$

Solve for x.

$$7x = -14$$

$$Ans. \ x = -2$$

25. $(x - 1)(x + 2) = x^2 + 1$ **26.** $(x - 4)(x - 1) = 9 + x^2$

27. $(x + 2)(x - 2) = x^2 - 4x$ **28.** $(y + 3)(y + 1) = y^2 - 5$

29. $(y + 2)(y + 4) = y(y + 8)$ **30.** $(y - 4)(y + 4) = y^2 + 4y$

31. $a^2 = (a + 3)(a - 2) + 1$ **32.** $(a - 1)(a - 1) = a^2 - 11$

33. $(a - 2)(a + 2) + 3 = a^2 - a$ **34.** $2(a - 1)(a + 1) = 2a^2 + 2a$

35. $(a - 3)^2 = a^2 - 15$ **36.** $(a + 2)^2 = a^2 + 5a - 2$

4.10 WORD PROBLEMS

Parentheses are useful in representing products in which the variable is contained in one or more terms in any factor. As an example, consider an integer x and the next consecutive integer $x + 1$. Five times the smaller integer is represented as $5x$ and five times the larger integer is represented as $5(x + 1)$. As another example, the expression $2x - 1$ represents a number for a given value of x. Three times this number is represented as $3(2x - 1)$.

EXERCISES 4.10

In each of the following statements, assign a variable to one of the unknowns and represent all other unknowns in terms of this variable.

Sample problem: One number is three more than another number. If x represents the smaller number, represent in terms of x:

a. The larger number.

b. Five times the smaller number.

c. Five times the larger number.

Ans. $x + 3$ *Ans.* $5x$ *Ans.* $5(x + 3)$

1. One number is four more than a second number. If x represents the smaller number, represent in terms of x:

   a. The larger number.
   b. Five times the smaller number.
   c. Five times the larger number.

2. One number is six less than a second number. If n represents the larger number, represent in terms of n:

   a. The smaller number.
   b. Two times the smaller number.
   c. Two times the larger number.

3. One number is six more than another. If n represents the smaller number, represent in terms of n, three times the larger number.

4. One number is five less than another. If n represents the larger number, represent in terms of n, six times the smaller number.

5. The length of a rectangle is 3 feet longer than its width w. Represent in terms of w:

   a. The length.
   b. Three times the width.
   c. Two times the length.

6. The width of a rectangle is 6 feet less than its length l. Represent in terms of l:

   a. The width.
   b. Five times the width.
   c. Ten times the length.

7. The length of a rectangle is 6 feet more than the width w. Represent in terms of w, three times the length.

8. The width of a rectangle is 4 feet less than the length l. Represent in terms of l, five times the width.

Sample problem : The sum of two numbers is 13. If x represents the smaller number, represent in terms of x:

a. The larger number.	*b.* Five times the smaller number.	*c.* Five times the larger number.
Ans. $13 - x$	*Ans.* $5x$	*Ans.* $5(13 - x)$

9. The sum of two numbers is 27. If n represents the smaller number, represent in terms of n:

   a. The larger number.
   b. Three times the smaller number.
   c. Three times the larger number.

10. The sum of two numbers is 39. If n represents the larger number, represent in terms of n:

    a. The smaller number.
    b. Six times the smaller number.
    c. Four times the larger number.

11. The difference of two numbers is 16. If n represents the smaller number, represent in terms of n:

    a. The larger number.
    b. Five times the smaller number.
    c. Two times the larger number.

12. The difference of two numbers is 21. If n represents the larger number, represent in terms of n:

    a. The smaller number.
    b. Two times the larger number.
    c. Three times the smaller number.

13. A 10-foot board is divided into two pieces. If x represents the shorter piece, represent in terms of x:

    a. The longer piece.
    b. Two times the shorter piece.
    c. Five times the longer piece.

14. A 24-foot board is divided into two parts. If y represents the longer piece, represent in terms of y:

    a. The shorter piece.
    b. Three times the longer piece.
    c. Ten times the shorter piece.

Sample problem : Represent (in cents) the *value* of each of the following collections of coins.

a. Two dimes	*b.* x dimes	*c.* $(x + 3)$ dimes
Ans. 10(2) or 20 cents	*Ans.* $10x$ cents	*Ans.* $10(x + 3)$ cents
d. Three nickels	*e.* n nickels	*f.* $(n - 2)$ nickels
Ans. 5(3) or 15 cents	*Ans.* $5n$ cents	*Ans.* $5(n - 2)$ cents

15. In a collection of coins there are four more dimes than quarters. If x represents the number of quarters, represent in terms of x:

    a. The number of dimes.
    b. The value (in cents) of the quarters.
    c. The value (in cents) of the dimes.

16. In a collection of coins there are five fewer pennies than dimes. If n represents the dimes, represent in terms of n:

    a. The number of pennies.

    b. The value (in cents) of the dimes.

    c. The value (in cents) of the pennies.

17. In a collection of coins there are three less dimes than quarters and two more pennies than quarters. If n represents the number of quarters, represent in terms of n:

    a. The number of dimes.

    b. The number of pennies.

    c. The value (in cents) of the quarters.

    d. The value (in cents) of the dimes.

    e. The value (in cents) of the pennies.

18. In a collection of coins, there are four more dimes than pennies and two more nickels than dimes. If x represents the number of pennies, represent in terms of x:

    a. The number of dimes.

    b. The number of nickels.

    c. The value (in cents) of the pennies.

    d. The value (in cents) of the dimes.

    e. The value (in cents) of the nickels.

19. In a collection of coins, there are three more dimes than nickels. If n represents the number of nickels, represent in terms of n, the total value of the collection in cents.

20. In a collection of coins there are twice as many dimes as nickels and three more quarters than dimes. If n represents the number of nickels, represent in terms of n, the total value of the collection in cents.

Sample problem: One truck has a capacity 3 tons greater than another truck. If x represents the capacity of the smaller truck, represent in terms of x:

a. The capacity of the larger truck.	*b.* The total tons hauled by the smaller truck in three trips.	*c.* The total tons hauled by the larger truck in five trips.
Ans. $x + 3$	*Ans.* $3x$	*Ans.* $5(x + 3)$

21. One truck has a capacity of 4 tons less than another truck. If x represents the capacity of the larger truck, represent in terms of x:

    a. The capacity of the smaller truck.

    b. The total tons hauled by the larger truck in seven trips.

    c. The total tons hauled by the smaller truck in six trips.

22. One truck can carry 7 tons, and another truck can carry 10 tons. Let x represent the number of trips made by the larger truck. If the smaller truck makes four more trips than the larger truck, represent in terms of x:

   a. The number of trips made by the smaller truck.
   b. The total tons hauled by the larger truck.
   c. The total tons hauled by the smaller truck.

Solve each of the following problems completely.

23. One number is two less than a second number. The larger plus four times the smaller equals 17. Find the numbers.

24. One number is three more than a second number. Four times the second plus twice the first equals 42. Find the numbers.

25. One number is four more than another. A third number is six more than the smaller of the other two. If two times the smallest plus three times the largest equals six times the middle number, what are the numbers?

26. The length of a board is 24 feet. Where should the board be cut to make one piece 6 feet longer than the other? (Use a sketch.)

27. The length of a rectangle is 6 feet more than the width. The perimeter is 44 feet. Find the length and width. (Use a sketch.)

28. One side of a triangle is 2 inches shorter than a second side. The third side is twice as long as the shortest side. How long is each side if the perimeter is 22 inches? (Use a sketch.)

29. A board is 20 feet long. Where should it be cut so that one piece will be 4 feet shorter than the other? (Use a sketch.)

30. Where should a 30-foot cable be cut so that twice the longer piece is equal to three times the shorter? (Use a sketch.)

31. The sum of two numbers is 23. Twice the larger number is four more than five times the smaller. Find the numbers.

32. One number is three more than a second, while a third is thirty-four greater than the second. If the third number is equal to three times the sum of the first two, what are the numbers?

Sample problem: A collection of coins consisting of dimes and quarters has a value of $5.80. There are sixteen more dimes than quarters. How many dimes and quarters are in the collection?

> Represent the unknown quantities in terms of x.

Let x = the number of quarters
$x + 16$ = the number of dimes

> Write an equation relating the value of the quarters and dimes to the value of the entire collection.

$$\begin{bmatrix} \text{value of} \\ \text{quarters} \\ \text{in cents} \end{bmatrix} + \begin{bmatrix} \text{value of} \\ \text{dimes} \\ \text{in cents} \end{bmatrix} = \begin{bmatrix} \text{value of} \\ \text{collection} \\ \text{in cents} \end{bmatrix}$$

$$25x + 10(x + 16) = 580$$

Solve for x.

$$25x + 10x + 160 = 580$$
$$35x = 420$$
$$x = 12$$
$$x + 16 = 28$$

Ans. There are 12 quarters and 28 dimes in the collection.

33. A man had $1.80 in change. The change was entirely in the form of dimes and nickels. If he had three more dimes than nickels, how many of each coin did he have?

34. A man had $1.45 in change. The money consisted of quarters and dimes only. If he had four fewer quarters than he had dimes, how many of each coin did he have?

35. A man had $1.14 in change consisting of pennies, nickels, and dimes. He had six more nickels than pennies and six less dimes than pennies. How many of each coin did he have?

36. A man had $1.47 in change consisting of pennies, nickels, and quarters. He had three more pennies than quarters and one more nickel than pennies. How many of each coin did he have?

37. A man has the same number of nickels as he has dimes, and five more quarters than the sum of his nickels and dimes. If he has $2.55, how many of each coin does he have?

38. Three hundred tickets were sold at a baseball game. Adults paid 90 cents each for their tickets, and children paid 40 cents each. If the total receipts for the game were $200, how many tickets of each kind were sold?

39. One thousand tickets were sold at a football game. Adults paid $1.80 each for their tickets, and children paid 80 cents each. If the total receipts for the game were $1200, how many tickets of each kind were sold?

40. A man uses 60 pounds of fine powder worth 30 cents a pound and a coarse powder worth 25 cents a pound to make a mixture which he wishes to sell for 28 cents a pound. How many pounds of the coarse powder does he use?

41. Fine powder is worth 30 cents a pound, and coarse powder is worth 12 cents a pound. How many pounds of the fine powder should be mixed with 50 pounds of the coarse powder in order for the mixture to sell for 20 cents a pound?

42. A boy earns 60 cents per hour, and his older brother earns 90 cents per hour. One week the older boy worked 10 hours longer than his brother. How long did each boy work if their total income was $39?

43. Two trucks are carrying material to a road construction job. One truck can carry 4 tons more per trip than the other. If the smaller truck makes five trips and the larger truck makes seven trips, they can deliver a total of 112 tons of material. What is the capacity of each truck?

44. A 10-ton truck and a 12-ton truck are carrying material to a road construction job. If the smaller truck makes three trips more than the larger truck, how many trips does each make if together they deliver 140 tons?

CHAPTER REVIEW

Write as a polynomial.

1. *a.* $3x(x^2 + x)$ $\qquad$ *b.* $2xy(y - x)$ $\qquad$ *c.* $-(x^2 - y + 1)$

2. *a.* $a(2 - a)$ $\qquad$ *b.* $-b(a - b)$ $\qquad$ *c.* $3b(a + b + c)$

Factor.

3. *a.* $3a^2 - 6a^2b$ $\qquad$ *b.* $2x^3 + 4x^2 + 6x$ $\qquad$ *c.* $-y^2 - y^3$

4. *a.* $a^2 + a^2b$ $\qquad$ *b.* $4b - 4$ $\qquad$ *c.* $b - b^2 - b^3$

Write as a polynomial.

5. *a.* $(x - 2)(x + 3)$ $\qquad$ *b.* $(2a - 3)(3a - 4)$ $\qquad$ *c.* $(2a - 3)^2$

6. *a.* $(x + a)(x - 2a)$ $\qquad$ *b.* $(2x - b)(x + b)$ $\qquad$ *c.* $(2b + 1)^2$

Factor.

7. *a.* $x^2 - 4x - 21$ $\qquad$ *b.* $10a^2 + 17a + 3$ $\qquad$ *c.* $4x^2 - 9$

8. *a.* $a^2 - 10a + 21$ $\qquad$ *b.* $3b^2 + 4b + 1$ $\qquad$ *c.* $2b^2 + 3b - 2$

9. *a.* $2x^2 + 14x + 24$ $\qquad$ *b.* $3y^2 + 24y - 60$ $\qquad$ *c.* $4x^3 - 4x$

10. *a.* $x^2 - 3ax + 2a^2$ $\qquad$ *b.* $x^2 - a^2$ $\qquad$ *c.* $4b^2 + 6bc - 4c^2$

11. Solve.

a. $3(x - 5) = 45$ $\qquad\qquad$ *b.* $6(4 - b) + 8 = 4(3 + b)$

c. $7 - (b - 2) = 3(11 + b)$

12. Evaluate the following formula both before and after factoring the right-hand member: $A = 2\pi rh + 2\pi r^2$; $r = 7, h = 10$. (Use $\frac{22}{7}$ for π.)

13. The sum of two numbers is 24. If one of the numbers is represented by x, how can the second number be represented in terms of x?

14. How can the value (in cents) of x dimes be represented in terms of x?

15. How can the value (in cents) of $(x + 3)$ quarters be represented in terms of x?

16. How can the value of $(y - 2)$ nickels be represented in terms of y?

17. If oranges cost 30 cents per dozen, how can the cost of $(x + 4)$ dozen oranges be represented in terms of x?

18. One number is six more than a second number. Ten times the smaller minus four times the larger equals six. Find the numbers.

19. The length of a rectangle is 10 feet more than the width. The perimeter is 52 feet. Find the length and width.

20. A man had $2.65 in change, consisting of eight more nickels than dimes. How many of each coin did he have?

CUMULATIVE REVIEW

1. Graph on a line graph all natural numbers between 6 and 26 which are exactly divisible by 4.

2. Write $81x^3y^3$ in completely factored form.

3. If $a = 2$, $b = 3$, $c = -2$, find the value of $a^2c^2 - 8abc$.

Simplify.

4. $x^2 - 2x + 3 - 4x + 2 - 2x^2$

5. $(x^2 - 3) - (2x^2 + x)$

6. $x(x - 3) - 2x(x + 4) + 3x^2$

7. What is the area of a triangle with a base of 5 inches and an altitude equal to the side of a square with an area of 64 square inches?

8. Solve for x: $x - b = 2x + 3b$.

9. Show by substitution that the answer you obtained in Exercise 8 is correct.

10. Write an algebraic expression for the cost of n articles at c cents each.

11. The temperature dropped $y°$ from a maximum value of $80°$. Express the new temperature in terms of y.

12. The temperature dropped $6°$ from a maximum of $y°$. Express the new temperature in terms of y.

13. The minimum temperature of the day was y degrees; the maximum temperature was x degrees. Express the increase of temperature during the day in terms of x and y.

14. The sum of two numbers is 47. If x represents the smaller number, what expression in terms of x, represents the larger number?

15. The sides of a triangle are represented by x, $x + 3$, and $2x - 4$. Write an expression for the perimeter in terms of x.

16. Find three consecutive integers whose sum is 111.

17. The length of a rectangle is 6 feet less than three times the width, and the perimeter is 52 feet. What are the dimensions?

18. One side of a triangle is 4 inches longer than another, and the length of the third side is equal to 2 inches less than the sum of the lengths of the first two. If the perimeter is 26 inches, find the length of the sides.

19. A 35-foot board is cut into 3 pieces so that the two end pieces are each equal in length to one-third of the middle piece. How long is each piece? (*Hint:* The length of the middle piece is three times the length of each end piece.)

20. Three times one number is two more than a second number and the sum of the numbers is 22. Find the numbers.

CHAPTER 5

FRACTIONS

5.1 FRACTIONS AND THEIR GRAPHICAL REPRESENTATION

In arithmetic, the indicated quotient of two numbers is called a **fraction**. In algebra, we define a fraction to be the indicated quotient of two algebraic expressions. For example,

$$\frac{x}{3}, \quad \frac{x+y}{1}, \quad \text{and} \quad \frac{a^2-b}{a+b}$$

are fractions.

We may graph arithmetic fractions on a line graph in the same manner in which we graph integers. By dividing a unit on a number line into a number of equal divisions corresponding to the denominator of the fraction, we can locate the point corresponding to the fraction itself by counting off the number of divisions corresponding to the numerator. For example, the graphs of $-\frac{3}{2}$, $-\frac{1}{4}$, and $\frac{3}{4}$ are shown on the line graph in Figure 5.1 on page 90.

There are three signs associated with a fraction; the sign of the numerator, the sign of the denominator, and the sign of the fraction itself. We can divide all possible combinations of these signs into two categories— one where no negative signs or two negative signs are involved, and one where one or three negative signs are involved.

Zero or two $(-)$ signs:

$$+ \frac{+a}{+b} = + \left(+ \frac{a}{b} \right) = \frac{a}{b}$$

$$+ \frac{-a}{-b} = + \left(+ \frac{a}{b} \right) = \frac{a}{b}$$

$$- \frac{-a}{+b} = - \left(- \frac{a}{b} \right) = \frac{a}{b}$$

$$- \frac{+a}{-b} = - \left(- \frac{a}{b} \right) = \frac{a}{b}$$

One or three $(-)$ signs:

$$+ \frac{-a}{+b} = + \left(- \frac{a}{b} \right) = - \frac{a}{b}$$

$$+ \frac{+a}{-b} = + \left(- \frac{a}{b} \right) = - \frac{a}{b}$$

$$- \frac{+a}{+b} = - \left(+ \frac{a}{b} \right) = - \frac{a}{b}$$

$$- \frac{-a}{-b} = - \left(+ \frac{a}{b} \right) = - \frac{a}{b}$$

89

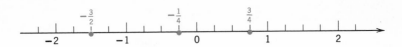

Figure 5.1

The foregoing chart may be summarized by the rule:

Any two of the three signs of a fraction may be changed without changing the value of the fraction.

In this book, the two forms $\frac{a}{b}$ and $\frac{-a}{b}$, which have positive signs on the denominator and on the fraction itself, will be considered standard forms for fractions.

EXERCISES 5.1

Represent each quotient in fractional form.

1. $3 \div 7$ 2. $7 \div 3$ 3. $3 \div a$ 4. $x \div y$

5. $5 \div (x + y)$ 6. $(x + y) \div 7$ 7. $2x \div (2 + x)$ 8. $3y \div (2x - 5)$

Graph each set of numbers on a line graph. Use a separate graph for each exercise.

9. $\dfrac{1}{4}, \dfrac{3}{4}$ 10. $\dfrac{1}{3}, \dfrac{2}{3}$ 11. $\dfrac{1}{2}, \dfrac{5}{2}$ 12. $-\dfrac{1}{4}, -\dfrac{3}{4}$

13. $-\dfrac{5}{6}, \dfrac{1}{6}$ 14. $-\dfrac{1}{2}, \dfrac{1}{2}$ 15. $-\dfrac{5}{2}, \dfrac{5}{4}$ 16. $3, \dfrac{3}{4}, \dfrac{3}{2}$

17. $-3, -\dfrac{3}{4}, \dfrac{3}{2}$ 18. $-\dfrac{2}{3}, \dfrac{1}{3}, 0$ 19. $\dfrac{2}{5}, \dfrac{3}{5}, \dfrac{4}{5}$ 20. $3, -\dfrac{5}{3}, 0$

Rewrite each fraction in standard form.

Sample problems:

$a. \ -\dfrac{1}{2}$ $b. \ \dfrac{-x}{-y}$ $c. \ \dfrac{x-1}{-3}$

$Ans. \ \dfrac{-1}{2}$ $Ans. \ \dfrac{x}{y}$ $Ans. \ \dfrac{-(x-1)}{3}$ or $\dfrac{1-x}{3}$

21. $\dfrac{-3}{-4}$ 22. $-\dfrac{-1}{2}$ 23. $-\dfrac{2}{-3}$ 24. $-\dfrac{-1}{-3}$

25. $\dfrac{3}{-5}$ 26. $-\dfrac{-2}{5}$ 27. $-\dfrac{-a}{-b}$ 28. $-\dfrac{-a}{b}$

29. $\dfrac{a}{-b}$ 30. $-\dfrac{a}{-b}$ 31. $\dfrac{-x}{y}$ 32. $-\dfrac{3y}{x}$

33. $-\dfrac{7x}{-8y}$ 34. $-\dfrac{2c}{-1}$ 35. $-\dfrac{-c}{-1}$ 36. $\dfrac{c}{-1}$

37. $-\dfrac{x+2}{4}$ 38. $\dfrac{x+3}{-3}$ 39. $\dfrac{-5}{-(x+2)}$ 40. $-\dfrac{x+2}{x-3}$

5.2 REDUCING FRACTIONS TO LOWER TERMS

In algebra, as in arithmetic, to reduce a fraction to lower terms, we use the fundamental principle:

> *If both the numerator and the denominator of a given fraction are divided by the same nonzero number, the resulting fraction is equivalent to the given fraction.*

In Section 1.11, we divided the numerator and the denominator of a fraction by the same number by writing the fraction in completely factored form and dividing out common factors. For example,

$$\frac{a^5}{a^2} = \frac{\cancel{a}\cancel{a}aaa}{\cancel{a}\cancel{a}} = a^3.$$

In cases such as this where no quotient is indicated above or below the factors "divided out," the quotient 1 is to be understood.

We observed on page 22, that in the general case, if m is greater than n, then

$$\frac{a^m}{a^n} = a^{m-n}.$$

The quotient a^{m-n} is obtained by subtracting the exponent in the denominator from the exponent in the numerator. If the greater exponent is in the denominator, that is, if n is greater than m, then

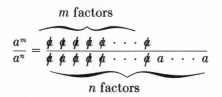

or

$$\frac{a^m}{a^n} = \frac{1}{a^{n-m}}.$$

Again, the principle of subtracting exponents applies only to powers of the same base. For example,

$$\frac{x^7}{x^3} = x^{7-3} = x^4$$

and

$$\frac{x^3}{x^7} = \frac{1}{x^{7-3}} = \frac{1}{x^4}.$$

However, the fractions

$$\frac{x^7}{y^3} \quad \text{and} \quad \frac{y^3}{x^7}$$

are in lowest terms.

EXERCISES 5.2

Reduce each fraction to an equivalent fraction in lowest terms by first completely factoring the numerator and the denominator and then dividing each by their common factors. Express your answer in standard form.

Sample problems:

a. $\dfrac{6}{9}$

$\dfrac{\cancel{3} \cdot 2}{\cancel{3} \cdot 3}$

Ans. $\dfrac{2}{3}$

b. $\dfrac{10y^2}{4y}$

$\dfrac{5 \cdot \cancel{2}\cancel{y}y}{2 \cdot \cancel{2}\cancel{y}}$

Ans. $\dfrac{5y}{2}$

c. $\dfrac{xy^2}{-x^2y}$

$\dfrac{\cancel{x}\cancel{y}y}{-1x\cancel{x}\cancel{y}}$

Ans. $\dfrac{-y}{x}$

d. $\dfrac{-6a^3b}{15ab^2}$

$\dfrac{-2 \cdot \cancel{3}\cancel{a}aa\cancel{b}}{\cancel{3} \cdot 5\cancel{a}\cancel{b}b}$

Ans. $\dfrac{-2a^2}{5b}$

1. $\dfrac{6}{8}$

2. $\dfrac{8}{12}$

3. $-\dfrac{21}{35}$

4. $-\dfrac{14}{28}$

5. $\dfrac{24}{15}$

6. $-\dfrac{36}{21}$

7. $\dfrac{4a^3}{12a^5}$

8. $\dfrac{6x^2}{15x^5}$

9. $\dfrac{-4y}{30y^4}$

10. $\dfrac{-3a}{12a^5}$

11. $\dfrac{21}{-15x^2}$

12. $\dfrac{49}{-14y^3}$

13. $\dfrac{xy^3}{y}$

14. $\dfrac{a^2b^3}{ab}$

15. $\dfrac{a}{-a^3b}$

16. $\dfrac{x}{-xy^2}$

17. $\dfrac{ax}{a}$

18. $\dfrac{bx^2}{b}$

19. $\dfrac{4xy}{-2z}$

20. $\dfrac{3x^3}{-6y^3}$

21. $\dfrac{4ab^2c^2}{6a^2c}$ **22.** $\dfrac{9a^2bc}{12ab^2}$ **23.** $\dfrac{-x^3y}{-x^3y}$ **24.** $\dfrac{-a^2bc}{-a^2b^2c}$

Sample problems:

a. $\dfrac{(x-2)(x+3)}{(x-5)(x+3)}$ *b.* $\dfrac{6x-4y}{12x-8y}$ *c.* $\dfrac{x^2+x-12}{x^2+2x-15}$

$\dfrac{(x-2)\cancel{(x+3)}}{(x-5)\cancel{(x+3)}}$ $\dfrac{\cancel{2}\cancel{(3x-2y)}}{\cancel{2}\cdot 2\cancel{(3x-2y)}}$ $\dfrac{(x+4)\cancel{(x-3)}}{(x+5)\cancel{(x-3)}}$

Ans. $\dfrac{x-2}{x-5}$ *Ans.* $\dfrac{1}{2}$ *Ans.* $\dfrac{x+4}{x+5}$

25. $\dfrac{3(a+b)}{4(a+b)}$ **26.** $\dfrac{4(a+2b)}{6(a+2b)}$ **27.** $\dfrac{12(x-y)}{-3}$ **28.** $\dfrac{15(a+b)}{-5}$

29. $\dfrac{(a-b)}{(a-b)}$ **30.** $\dfrac{(2x-y)}{(2x-y)}$ **31.** $\dfrac{2x+2y}{-(x+y)}$ **32.** $\dfrac{3x-3y}{-(3x+3y)}$

33. $\dfrac{2x-2a}{(x-a)^2}$ **34.** $\dfrac{3x-3a}{2(x-a)^2}$ **35.** $\dfrac{-4x}{4x^2+16x}$ **36.** $\dfrac{-3x}{6x^2+9x}$

37. $\dfrac{x+1}{x^2+2x+1}$ **38.** $\dfrac{x-4}{x^2-3x-4}$ **39.** $\dfrac{a-b}{a^2-2ab+b^2}$ **40.** $\dfrac{a-b}{a^2-b^2}$

41. $\dfrac{(a-b)^2}{a^2-b^2}$ **42.** $\dfrac{(x-2y)^2}{x^2-4y^2}$ **43.** $\dfrac{a^2-3a}{a^2-2a-3}$ **44.** $\dfrac{a^2-a}{a^2+a-2}$

45. $\dfrac{x^2+x-6}{x^2-9}$ **46.** $\dfrac{x^2+5x+6}{x^2-4}$ **47.** $\dfrac{a^2+6a+9}{a^2+2a-3}$ **48.** $\dfrac{x^2+5x+6}{x^2+6x+9}$

In Exercises 49–60, state whether the second is equivalent to the first expression.

Sample problems:

a. $\dfrac{(x-1)}{x^2-1},\ \dfrac{1}{x+1}$ *b.* $\dfrac{3a+a^2}{3a},\ a^2$

Simplify fractions.

$\dfrac{\cancel{(x-1)}}{\cancel{(x-1)}(x+1)},\ \dfrac{1}{x+1}$ $\dfrac{\cancel{a}(3+a)}{3\cancel{a}},\ a^2$

Compare fractions.

$\dfrac{1}{x+1},\ \dfrac{1}{x+1}$ $\dfrac{3+a}{3},\ a^2$

Ans. Yes, equivalent. *Ans.* No, not equivalent.

49. $\dfrac{x+y}{y},\ x$ **50.** $\dfrac{-2(x+y)}{-2x},\ -2y$ **51.** $\dfrac{2x+2}{2},\ x$

52. $\dfrac{x}{x + xy}, \dfrac{1}{1 + y}$

53. $\dfrac{x - 1}{x + 1}, -1$

54. $\dfrac{y^2}{y^3 - y^2}, \dfrac{1}{y - 1}$

55. $\dfrac{2b + 2a}{2a}, 2b$

56. $\dfrac{y^2 - 1}{y - 1}, y$

57. $\dfrac{y}{ay - by}, \dfrac{1}{a - b}$

58. $\dfrac{a^3}{a^4 - a^3}, \dfrac{1}{a - 1}$

59. $\dfrac{2 + y}{4}, \dfrac{y}{2}$

60. $\dfrac{6 + 2x}{12}, \dfrac{x}{2}$

5.3 QUOTIENTS OF POLYNOMIALS

In Section 5.2, we reduced fractions to lower terms by expressing the numerator and denominator in completely factored form and dividing out common factors. The same procedure may be used to divide a polynomial by a monomial, provided the monomial occurs as a factor in each term of the polynomial. For example,

$$\frac{2x^3 + 4x^2 + 2x}{2x} = \frac{2x(x^2 + 2x + 1)}{2x}$$
$$= x^2 + 2x + 1.$$

The same division can be accomplished in another manner. Because the sum of several fractions with common denominators may be expressed as a single fraction,

$$\frac{a}{d} + \frac{b}{d} + \frac{c}{d} = \frac{a + b + c}{d},$$

by the symmetric property of equality we have

$$\frac{a + b + c}{d} = \frac{a}{d} + \frac{b}{d} + \frac{c}{d}.$$

Thus, a fraction whose numerator is a polynomial may be expressed as the sum of a number of fractions whose numerators are the terms of the polynomial and whose denominators are the same as that of the original fraction. In the example above, we have

$$\frac{2x^3 + 4x^2 + 2x}{2x} = \frac{2x^3}{2x} + \frac{4x^2}{2x} + \frac{2x}{2x}$$

and the right-hand member may be simplified term by term to produce

$$x^2 + 2x + 1.$$

This particular approach has the advantage of being applicable to fractions where the numerator does not contain the denominator as a factor.

For example,

$$\frac{3x^2 + 2x + 1}{x} = \frac{3x^2}{x} + \frac{2x}{x} + \frac{1}{x}$$
$$= 3x + 2 + \frac{1}{x}.$$

In Section 5.2 we divided one polynomial by another polynomial in which the divisor was a factor of the dividend by first representing the division in fractional form and then dividing out common factors. A polynomial may also be divided by another polynomial in a manner similar to that used in long division in arithmetic as shown in the following example.

$21\overline{)672}$

Divide 2 into 6.

3
$21\overline{)672}$

Subtract product of
3 and 21 from 67.

3
$21\overline{)672}$
63
$\overline{4}$

"Bring down" 2.

3
$21\overline{)672}$
63
$\overline{42}$

Divide 2 into 4.

32
$21\overline{)672}$
63
$\overline{42}$

Subtract product of
2 and 21 from 42.

32
$21\overline{)672}$
63
$\overline{42}$
$\underline{42}$
$\overline{0}$

$x + 3\overline{)x^2 + x - 6}$

Divide x into x^2.

x
$x + 3\overline{)x^2 + x - 6}$

Subtract product of x and
$x + 3$ from $x^2 + x$.

x
$x + 3\overline{)x^2 + x - 6}$
$x^2 + 3x$
$\overline{- 2x}$

"Bring down" -6.

x
$x + 3\overline{)x^2 + x - 6}$
$x^2 + 3x$
$\overline{- 2x - 6}$

Divide x into $-2x$.

$x - 2$
$x + 3\overline{)x^2 + x - 6}$
$x^2 + 3x$
$\overline{- 2x - 6}$

Subtract product of -2
and $x + 3$ from $-2x - 6$.

$x - 2$
$x + 3\overline{)x^2 + x - 6}$
$x^2 + 3x$
$\overline{- 2x - 6}$
$\underline{- 2x - 6}$
$\overline{0}$

The result may be checked by multiplying the quotient and the divisor to ensure that the product is the dividend. As always, the division is not valid if the divisor is 0. Thus, in the example above, where the divisor is $x + 3$, we must restrict x from having a value of -3.

This process is most useful when the divisor is not a factor of the dividend. If such is the case, the division process will produce a remainder which can be expressed in terms of a fraction. For example, in dividing

$$(x^2 + x + 1) \quad \text{by} \quad (x + 2),$$

we have

$$
\begin{array}{r}
x - 1 \\
x + 2 \overline{\smash{)}x^2 + x + 1} \\
\underline{x^2 + 2x} \\
-x + 1 \\
\underline{-x - 2} \\
3
\end{array}
$$

The result can then be expressed as

$$x - 1 + \frac{3}{x + 2}.$$

EXERCISES 5.3

Rewrite each quotient in two ways as shown in the sample problem.

Sample problem:

$$\frac{6x - 8}{2} \qquad\qquad \frac{6x - 8}{2}$$

$$\frac{\cancel{2}(3x - 4)}{\cancel{2}} \qquad\qquad \frac{\cancel{6}x}{\cancel{2}}^{3} - \frac{\cancel{8}}{\cancel{2}}^{4}$$

$$Ans.\ 3x - 4 \qquad\qquad Ans.\ 3x - 4$$

1. $\dfrac{4x - 6}{2}$　　　　2. $\dfrac{14x - 2y}{2}$　　　　3. $\dfrac{x^2 + 3x}{x}$

4. $\dfrac{3x^2 - 6x}{3x}$　　　　5. $\dfrac{4y^2 - y}{y}$　　　　6. $\dfrac{xy - x}{x}$

7. $\dfrac{2x^3 + x^2 + 3x}{x}$　　　　8. $\dfrac{x^4 - 3x^3 + 2x^2}{x^2}$　　　　9. $\dfrac{4x^2y^2 - 2xy^2 + 2x^2y}{2xy}$

10. $\dfrac{6xy^2 - 2xy + x^2y}{xy}$ **11.** $\dfrac{9x^2y^3 - 3xy^2 + 3xy}{-3xy}$ **12.** $\dfrac{16xy - 4x - 4}{-4}$

Rewrite each quotient as shown in the sample problems.

Sample problems:

$a.$ $\dfrac{4x^2 + 2x + 1}{2}$

$$\dfrac{\cancel{4}x^2}{\cancel{2}} + \dfrac{\cancel{2}x}{\cancel{2}} + \dfrac{1}{2}$$

$Ans.$ $2x^2 + x + \dfrac{1}{2}$

$b.$ $\dfrac{2x^3 - x^2 - 4}{-x}$

$$\dfrac{2\cancel{x}^{3}}{-\cancel{x}} + \dfrac{-\cancel{x}^{2}}{-\cancel{x}} + \dfrac{-4}{-x}$$

$Ans.$ $-2x^2 + x + \dfrac{4}{x}$

13. $\dfrac{6y^2 + 3y - 2}{3}$ **14.** $\dfrac{8x^2 + 2x + 1}{2}$ **15.** $\dfrac{x^2 + x + 3}{x}$

16. $\dfrac{4y^2 + 2y + 1}{2y}$ **17.** $\dfrac{6y^4 - 3y^2 + 2}{3y^2}$ **18.** $\dfrac{6x^4 - 6x + 5}{6x}$

19. $\dfrac{x^3 + 2x^2 - x - 1}{x}$ **20.** $\dfrac{2y^3 - 4y^2 + 2y - 1}{2y}$ **21.** $\dfrac{x^2y - xy + y}{-xy}$

22. $\dfrac{x^3y^2 - x^2y + x}{-xy}$ **23.** $\dfrac{x^2y + xy^2 + x}{y}$ **24.** $\dfrac{x^3y^2 - x^2y + y}{x^2}$

Sample problems:

$a.$ $(x^2 - 3x - 4) \div (x + 1)$

$$\begin{array}{r} x - 4 \\ x+1\overline{)x^2 - 3x - 4} \\ \underline{x^2 + x} \\ -4x - 4 \\ \underline{-4x - 4} \\ 0 \end{array}$$

$Ans.$ $x - 4$

$b.$ $(x^2 - 1) \div (x + 1)$

$$\begin{array}{r} x - 1 \\ x+1\overline{)x^2 + 0x - 1} \\ \underline{x^2 + x} \\ -x - 1 \\ \underline{-x - 1} \\ 0 \end{array}$$

$Ans.$ $x - 1$

25. $(x^2 + 5x - 6) \div (x - 1)$ **26.** $(x^2 + x - 6) \div (x - 2)$

27. $(x^2 + 6x + 5) \div (x + 5)$ **28.** $(x^2 - 4x + 4) \div (x - 2)$

29. $(x^2 + 5x - 14) \div (x - 2)$ **30.** $(x^2 - 4) \div (x + 2)$

31. $(2x^2 - 7x - 4) \div (x - 4)$ **32.** $(2x^2 - x - 3) \div (x + 1)$

33. $(2x^2 + 5x - 3) \div (2x - 1)$ **34.** $(2x^2 - 9x - 5) \div (2x + 1)$

35. $(4x^2 + 4x - 3) \div (2x - 1)$ **36.** $(4x^2 - 8x - 5) \div (2x + 1)$

Sample problems :

a. $(x^2 - 3x + 1) \div (x + 2)$

$$
\begin{array}{r}
x - 5 \\
x + 2\overline{\smash{\big)}\,x^2 - 3x + 1} \\
\underline{x^2 + 2x} \\
-5x + 1 \\
\underline{-5x - 10} \\
11
\end{array}
$$

Ans. $x - 5 + \dfrac{11}{x + 2}$

b. $(2x^2 + 3x - 1) \div (2x - 1)$

$$
\begin{array}{r}
x + 2 \\
2x - 1\overline{\smash{\big)}\,2x^2 + 3x - 1} \\
\underline{2x^2 - x} \\
4x - 1 \\
\underline{4x - 2} \\
1
\end{array}
$$

Ans. $x + 2 + \dfrac{1}{2x - 1}$

37. $(x^2 + 3x + 1) \div (x + 2)$

38. $(x^2 - x + 3) \div (x + 1)$

39. $(x^2 + 3x - 9) \div (x + 5)$

40. $(x^2 - 2x - 2) \div (x - 3)$

41. $(x^2 + 5x - 7) \div (x + 6)$

42. $(x^2 - 6x - 10) \div (x - 7)$

43. $(2x^2 + x - 2) \div (x + 1)$

44. $(3x^2 - 8x - 1) \div (x - 3)$

45. $(4x^2 - 4x - 5) \div (2x + 1)$

46. $(6x^2 + x + 2) \div (3x + 2)$

5.4 LOWEST COMMON DENOMINATOR

The smallest natural number that is a multiple of each of the denominators of a set of arithmetic fractions is called the **lowest common denominator** (L.C.D.) of the set of fractions. For example, the lowest common denominator for $\frac{1}{6}$, $\frac{3}{10}$, and $\frac{5}{12}$ contains among its factors the factors of 6, 10, and 12. These factors are

$$
\begin{array}{ccc}
6 & 10 & 12 \\
2 \cdot 3 & 2 \cdot 5 & 2 \cdot 2 \cdot 3.
\end{array}
$$

Since the factor 2 occurs twice in 12, it must also occur twice in the L.C.D. Therefore, 2, 2, 3, and 5 are the factors, and it follows that 60 is the L.C.D.

The L.C.D. of a set of algebraic fractions is the simplest algebraic expression that is a multiple of each of the denominators in the set. Thus, the L.C.D. of the fractions

$$
\frac{3}{x}, \quad \frac{2}{x + 1}, \quad \text{and} \quad \frac{1}{x^2(x - 1)}
$$

is

$$
x^2(x + 1)(x - 1),
$$

because this is the simplest expression that is a multiple of each of the denominators.

In many cases, the lowest common denominator may be found by inspection. Where the L.C.D. is not evident by inspection, it may be found by the following procedure:

1. Completely factor each denominator.
2. Include in the L.C.D. each of these factors the greatest number of times it occurs in any single denominator.

EXERCISES 5.4

Find the lowest common denominator for each set of fractions.

Sample problem:

$$\frac{1}{6}, \qquad \frac{1}{8}, \qquad \frac{1}{36}$$

Completely factor each denominator.

$2 \cdot 3 \qquad 2 \cdot 2 \cdot 2 \qquad 2 \cdot 2 \cdot 3 \cdot 3$

Write as a product each different factor occurring in the denominator. Include each factor the greatest number of times it occurs in any *single* denominator.

$2 \cdot 2 \cdot 2 \cdot 3 \cdot 3$

Ans. 72

1. $\dfrac{1}{3}, \dfrac{1}{6}, \dfrac{1}{2}$ 　　　2. $\dfrac{1}{4}, \dfrac{1}{6}, \dfrac{1}{10}$ 　　　3. $\dfrac{1}{3}, \dfrac{1}{12}, \dfrac{1}{18}$

4. $\dfrac{1}{10}, \dfrac{1}{20}, \dfrac{1}{30}$ 　　　5. $\dfrac{1}{14}, \dfrac{1}{4}, \dfrac{1}{21}$ 　　　6. $\dfrac{1}{16}, \dfrac{1}{20}, \dfrac{1}{2}$

7. $\dfrac{1}{3}, \dfrac{1}{4}, \dfrac{1}{11}$ 　　　8. $\dfrac{1}{15}, \dfrac{1}{9}, \dfrac{1}{20}$ 　　　9. $\dfrac{1}{5}, \dfrac{1}{7}, \dfrac{1}{11}$

Sample problem:

$$\frac{1}{x}, \qquad \frac{3}{x^2 y}, \qquad \frac{5}{x^2 y^3}$$

Completely factor each denominator.

$x \qquad x \cdot x \cdot y \qquad x \cdot x \cdot y \cdot y \cdot y$

Write as a product each different factor occurring in the denominators. Include each factor the greatest number of times it occurs in any *single* denominator.

$xxyyy$

Ans. $x^2 y^3$

10. $\dfrac{1}{a}, \dfrac{1}{b}, \dfrac{1}{c}$ **11.** $\dfrac{2}{x}, \dfrac{3}{x^2}, \dfrac{1}{y}$ **12.** $\dfrac{a}{x^2}, \dfrac{a}{x^2y}, \dfrac{1}{z}$

13. $\dfrac{1}{xy}, \dfrac{2}{yz}, \dfrac{3}{xz}$ **14.** $\dfrac{a}{x^2y}, \dfrac{2}{xyz}, \dfrac{3}{yz^2}$ **15.** $\dfrac{3}{n}, \dfrac{2}{m^2n}, \dfrac{4}{mn^3}$

16. $\dfrac{3}{4x}, \dfrac{2}{6x^2}, \dfrac{1}{2y}$ **17.** $\dfrac{1}{8xy}, \dfrac{2}{3x^2}, \dfrac{2}{4xy}$ **18.** $\dfrac{2}{4xy}, \dfrac{3}{6yz^2}, \dfrac{1}{3xy^2z}$

Sample problem:

$$\dfrac{1}{x}, \qquad \dfrac{1}{x^2 - 1}, \qquad \dfrac{1}{x^2 + 2x + 1}$$

Completely factor each denominator.

$x \quad (x - 1)(x + 1) \quad (x + 1)(x + 1)$

Write as a product each different factor occurring in the denominators. Include each factor the greatest number of times it occurs in any *single* denominator.

$$x(x - 1)(x + 1)(x + 1)$$

Ans. $x(x - 1)(x + 1)^2$

19. $\dfrac{2}{x^2 - y^2}, \dfrac{1}{x - y}$ **20.** $\dfrac{3}{x^2 + 2x}, \dfrac{4}{x + 2}$

21. $\dfrac{3}{x^2}, \dfrac{4}{x^2 + 2x}$ **22.** $\dfrac{5}{x^2 + 2x + 1}, \dfrac{3}{x^2 + 4x + 3}$

23. $\dfrac{2}{x^2 + 3x - 4}, \dfrac{3}{(x - 1)^2}, \dfrac{2}{x + 4}$ **24.** $\dfrac{3}{a^2 - a - 6}, \dfrac{a + 2}{a^2 + 7a + 10}, \dfrac{3}{(a - 3)^2}$

5.5 BUILDING FRACTIONS

Just as it is often convenient to reduce fractions to lower terms, it is also often convenient to build fractions to higher terms. In algebra, as in arithmetic, we use the fundamental principle:

> *If both the numerator and denominator of a given fraction are multiplied by the same nonzero number, the resulting fraction is equivalent to the given fraction.*

When applying this principle, we are in effect multiplying a quantity by 1 because

$$\dfrac{2}{2}, \dfrac{3}{3}, \dfrac{4}{4}, \ldots \text{ are equivalent to 1.}$$

If we wish to express $\frac{3}{4}$ as a fraction with a denominator of 8, we multiply the numerator and denominator by 2 to obtain

$$\frac{3(2)}{4(2)} = \frac{6}{8}.$$

In general, to change $\frac{a}{b}$ to a fraction with a denominator bc:

1. Divide b, the denominator of the given fraction, into bc, the denominator to be obtained, to find the building factor c.

2. Multiply the numerator and denominator of the given fraction by the building factor c.

For example, to change

$$\frac{3}{x^2y} \quad \text{to} \quad \frac{?}{x^3y^2},$$

we can divide x^2y into x^3y^2 to obtain the building factor xy. Then, we can multiply the numerator and denominator by this building factor to obtain

$$\frac{3(xy)}{x^2y(xy)} = \frac{3xy}{x^3y^2}.$$

If negative signs are attached to any part of the fraction, it is usually convenient to write the fraction in standard form before building it.

EXERCISES 5.5

Express each fraction as an equivalent fraction with the indicated denominator.

Sample problem:

$$\frac{2}{3} = \frac{?}{9}$$

Obtain building factor.

$(9 \div 3 = 3)$

Multiply numerator and denominator of given fraction by building factor 3

$$\frac{2(3)}{3(3)}$$

Ans. $\frac{6}{9}$

1. $\dfrac{2}{3} = \dfrac{?}{6}$ **2.** $\dfrac{3}{4} = \dfrac{?}{12}$ **3.** $\dfrac{2}{7} = \dfrac{?}{21}$ **4.** $\dfrac{3}{5} = \dfrac{?}{25}$

5. $\dfrac{5}{12} = \dfrac{?}{48}$ **6.** $\dfrac{11}{3} = \dfrac{?}{6}$ **7.** $\dfrac{21}{5} = \dfrac{?}{15}$ **8.** $\dfrac{112}{3} = \dfrac{?}{12}$

Sample problem:

$$\frac{2}{-5a} = \frac{?}{10a^2}$$

Write in standard form.

$$\frac{-2}{5a}$$

Obtain building factor.

$$(10a^2 \div 5a = 2a)$$

Multiply numerator and denominator of given fraction by building factor $2a$.

$$\frac{-2(2a)}{5a(2a)}$$

Ans. $\dfrac{-4a}{10a^2}$

9. $\dfrac{5}{3x} = \dfrac{?}{6x}$ **10.** $\dfrac{6}{-7a} = \dfrac{?}{14a^2}$ **11.** $\dfrac{-a}{b} = \dfrac{?}{12b^3}$

12. $-\dfrac{3a}{5b} = \dfrac{?}{15ab}$ **13.** $\dfrac{-x^2}{y^2} = \dfrac{?}{3y^3}$ **14.** $\dfrac{-ax}{by} = \dfrac{?}{ab^2y}$

Sample problem:

$$ab = \frac{?}{ab^2}$$

Obtain building factor.

$$(ab^2 \div 1 = ab^2)$$

Multiply numerator and denominator of given fraction by building factor ab^2.

$$\frac{ab(ab^2)}{1(ab^2)}$$

Ans. $\dfrac{a^2b^3}{ab^2}$

15. $2 = \dfrac{?}{36}$ **16.** $-x = \dfrac{?}{y^2}$ **17.** $y = \dfrac{?}{xy}$

18. $3a = \dfrac{?}{9b^2}$ **19.** $x^2 = \dfrac{?}{3x^2y}$ **20.** $-2b^2 = \dfrac{?}{4a^2b}$

Sample problem :

$$\frac{1}{3} = \frac{?}{3(x-a)}$$

Obtain building factor.

$$[3(x-a) \div 3 = (x-a)]$$

Multiply numerator and denominator of given fraction by building factor $(x-a)$.

$$\frac{1(x-a)}{3(x-a)}$$

Ans. $\dfrac{x-a}{3(x-a)}$

21. $\dfrac{1}{2} = \dfrac{?}{2(x+y)}$ **22.** $\dfrac{2}{3} = \dfrac{?}{6(x-y)}$ **23.** $\dfrac{-2a}{5} = \dfrac{?}{5(a+4)}$

24. $\dfrac{3b}{-4} = \dfrac{?}{4(a+b)^2}$ **25.** $2a = \dfrac{?}{a+3}$ **26.** $3x = \dfrac{?}{6(x-2)}$

Sample problem :

$$\frac{2x}{x-y} = \frac{?}{(x-y)(x+y)}$$

Obtain building factor.

$$[(x-y)(\quad) \div (x-y) = (\quad)]$$

Multiply numerator and denominator of given fraction by building factor $(x+y)$.

Ans. $\dfrac{2x(x+y)}{(x-y)(x+y)}$

27. $\dfrac{3}{x-y} = \dfrac{?}{(x-y)(x+y)}$ **28.** $\dfrac{2x}{-(x-y)} = \dfrac{?}{(x-y)(x-y)}$

29. $-\dfrac{3}{2x-1} = \dfrac{?}{(x+1)(2x-1)}$ **30.** $\dfrac{-1}{a+b} = \dfrac{?}{(2a-b)(a+b)}$

31. $\dfrac{7a}{b+2} = \dfrac{?}{(b-3)(b+2)}$ **32.** $\dfrac{6x^2}{3x-4} = \dfrac{?}{(3x-4)(2x+5)}$

Sample problem :

$$\frac{3}{x-3} = \frac{?}{x^2-7x+12}$$

Factor denominator of each fraction.

Solution continued on the next page

$$\frac{3}{x - 3} = \frac{?}{(x - 3)(x - 4)}$$

Obtain building factor.

$$[(x - 3)(x - 4) \div (x - 3) = (x - 4)]$$

Multiply numerator and denominator of given fraction by building factor $(x - 4)$.

Ans. $\dfrac{3(x - 4)}{(x - 3)(x - 4)}$

33. $\dfrac{a}{a - 3} = \dfrac{?}{a^2 - 3a}$

34. $\dfrac{2}{b} = \dfrac{?}{b + b^2}$

35. $\dfrac{-3}{x + y} = \dfrac{?}{x^2 - y^2}$

36. $\dfrac{-2}{a - b} = \dfrac{?}{a^2 - b^2}$

37. $\dfrac{y}{y - 1} = \dfrac{?}{y^2 + y - 2}$

38. $\dfrac{-1}{x - 1} = \dfrac{?}{2x^2 - 4x + 2}$

39. $\dfrac{x + y}{x - y} = \dfrac{?}{x^2 - y^2}$

40. $\dfrac{y + 1}{y^2 - 1} = \dfrac{?}{(y - 1)(y^2 + 2y + 1)}$

In Exercises 41–60, change both fractions to equivalent fractions with lowest common denominator.

Sample problem:

$$\frac{1}{2x}, \qquad\qquad \frac{1}{15x^2}$$

Determine L.C.D.

$$2 \cdot 3 \cdot 5 \cdot x \cdot x = 30x^2$$

Obtain building factors.

$$(30x^2 \div 2x = 15x), \; (30x^2 \div 15x^2 = 2)$$

Multiply numerator and denominator of each fraction by the respective building factors; $15x$ for the first fraction and 2 for the second.

$$\frac{1(15x)}{2x(15x)} \qquad\qquad \frac{1(2)}{15x^2(2)}$$

Ans. $\dfrac{15x}{30x^2}, \dfrac{2}{30x^2}$

41. $\dfrac{1}{2}, \dfrac{1}{3}$

42. $\dfrac{2}{3}, \dfrac{3}{4}$

43. $\dfrac{1}{7}, \dfrac{3}{5}$

44. $\dfrac{-5}{6}, \dfrac{3}{4}$

45. $\dfrac{-5}{12}, \dfrac{3}{8}$

46. $\dfrac{6}{15}, \dfrac{2}{21}$

47. $\dfrac{-1}{a}, \dfrac{1}{3b}$

48. $\dfrac{a}{b}, \dfrac{3}{2a}$

49. $\dfrac{5a}{4b^2}, \dfrac{-2}{ab}$ **50.** $\dfrac{x}{y^2}, \dfrac{-3}{xy}$ **51.** $\dfrac{-a}{b^2}, \dfrac{2}{a^2b}$ **52.** $\dfrac{-b}{3}, \dfrac{-3}{b}$

Sample problem:

$$\dfrac{1}{a-1}, \qquad \dfrac{2a}{a^2-1}$$

Factor denominators where possible.

$$(a-1) \qquad (a+1)(a-1)$$

Determine L.C.D.

$$(a-1)(a+1)$$

Build first fraction to an equivalent fraction with the required denominator.

$$[(a-1)(a+1) \div (a-1) = (a+1)]$$

$$\dfrac{1(a+1)}{(a-1)(a+1)}$$

Ans. $\dfrac{a+1}{(a-1)(a+1)}, \dfrac{2a}{(a-1)(a+1)}$

53. $\dfrac{-3}{x-a}, \dfrac{2}{3}$ **54.** $\dfrac{2}{xy}, \dfrac{x}{x-y}$

55. $\dfrac{3}{ab}, \dfrac{a}{a+b}$ **56.** $\dfrac{-5}{a^2-b^2}, \dfrac{2}{(a+b)}$

57. $\dfrac{-x}{x^2+3x+2}, \dfrac{2x}{x^2+5x+4}$ **58.** $\dfrac{x+1}{x^2+x-2}, \dfrac{x}{x^2+5x+6}$

59. $\dfrac{3}{x^2-1}, \dfrac{x-2}{x^2+4x+3}$ **60.** $\dfrac{-5}{2x^2+3x-2}, \dfrac{4}{2x^2-3x+1}$

5.6 SUMS OF FRACTIONS WITH LIKE DENOMINATORS

We define the sum of two or more arithmetic or algebraic fractions with common denominators to be a fraction with the same denominator and a numerator which is the sum of the numerators of the original fractions. Thus,

$$\frac{4}{8} + \frac{9}{8} = \frac{13}{8},$$

$$\frac{2}{x} + \frac{5}{x} + \frac{3}{x} = \frac{10}{x},$$

$$\frac{3}{x+1} + \frac{x}{x+1} = \frac{3+x}{x+1}.$$

In general,

$$\frac{a}{c} + \frac{b}{c} = \frac{a+b}{c}.$$

A fraction not in standard form should be changed to standard form before adding.

EXERCISES 5.6

Write each sum as a single term.

Sample problems:

  a. $\dfrac{x}{7} + \dfrac{4}{7}$ b. $\dfrac{3}{5} - \dfrac{x}{5}$

                                Write in standard form.

                       $\dfrac{3}{5} + \dfrac{-x}{5}$

                                Add numerators.

  Ans. $\dfrac{x+4}{7}$ Ans. $\dfrac{3-x}{5}$

1. $\dfrac{1}{5} + \dfrac{2}{5}$ 2. $\dfrac{3}{7} + \dfrac{2}{7}$ 3. $\dfrac{3}{11} + \dfrac{2}{11}$

4. $\dfrac{6}{13} + \dfrac{5}{13}$ 5. $\dfrac{2x}{3} - \dfrac{4}{3} + \dfrac{5}{3}$ 6. $\dfrac{3}{2} - \dfrac{y}{2} - \dfrac{2}{2}$

Sample problem:

                $\dfrac{3}{2a} - \dfrac{1}{2a}$

                                Write in standard form.

                $\dfrac{3}{2a} + \dfrac{-1}{2a}$

                                Add numerators and simplify.

                $\dfrac{\cancel{2}}{\cancel{2}a}$

  Ans. $\dfrac{1}{a}$

7. $\dfrac{3}{2x} + \dfrac{3}{2x}$ 8. $\dfrac{4}{3y} + \dfrac{5}{3y}$ 9. $\dfrac{5a}{2b} - \dfrac{3a}{2b}$

10. $\dfrac{3y}{4x} - \dfrac{5y}{4x}$ 11. $\dfrac{6}{5y} + \dfrac{11}{5y} - \dfrac{2}{5y}$ 12. $\dfrac{8}{7x} - \dfrac{3}{7x} + \dfrac{9}{7x}$

13. $\dfrac{3a}{7b} + \dfrac{a}{7b} + \dfrac{5a}{7b}$ **14.** $\dfrac{2x}{3y} - \dfrac{x}{3y} + \dfrac{2x}{3y}$

Sample problems:

    a. $\dfrac{x-y}{a} + \dfrac{y}{a}$ *b.* $\dfrac{x+y}{x} + \dfrac{x-y}{x}$

                                                   Add numerators.

      $\dfrac{x-y+y}{a}$ $\dfrac{x+y+x-y}{x}$

                                                   Simplify.

                          $\dfrac{2\cancel{x}}{\cancel{x}}$

Ans. $\dfrac{x}{a}$ *Ans.* 2

15. $\dfrac{x+1}{2} + \dfrac{3}{2}$ **16.** $\dfrac{x-2}{5} + \dfrac{3}{5}$

17. $\dfrac{x-2y}{3x} + \dfrac{x+3y}{3x}$ **18.** $\dfrac{3-x}{2y} + \dfrac{4-x}{2y}$

19. $\dfrac{x+1}{2a} + \dfrac{x-1}{2a}$ **20.** $\dfrac{2x-y}{3y} + \dfrac{2x+2y}{3y}$

21. $\dfrac{x^2-x}{2} + \dfrac{x^2}{2} + \dfrac{3x}{2}$ **22.** $\dfrac{2x-y}{3} + \dfrac{x-y}{3} + \dfrac{x+y}{3}$

23. $\dfrac{2x+y}{y} + \dfrac{x-2y}{y} + \dfrac{x+y}{y}$ **24.** $\dfrac{x-2y}{2x} + \dfrac{x+y}{2x} + \dfrac{2x+y}{2x}$

Sample problem:

    $\dfrac{x-2}{a+b} - \dfrac{2x+1}{a+b}$

                 Insert parentheses and write in standard form.

    $\dfrac{(x-2)}{a+b} + \dfrac{-(2x+1)}{a+b}$

                 Add numerators.

    $\dfrac{(x-2)-(2x+1)}{a+b}$

                 Remove parentheses.

    $\dfrac{x-2-2x-1}{a+b}$

                 Simplify.

Solution continued on the next page

Ans. $\dfrac{-x - 3}{a + b}$

25. $\dfrac{2x + 3}{2} - \dfrac{x - 3}{2}$

26. $\dfrac{2x - y}{3} - \dfrac{3x - y}{3}$

27. $\dfrac{2a + b}{a - b} - \dfrac{a - 2b}{a - b}$

28. $\dfrac{2a - b}{b} - \dfrac{a - 2b}{b}$

29. $\dfrac{3}{a + b} - \dfrac{a + 3}{a + b}$

30. $\dfrac{b - 1}{a} - \dfrac{b + 1}{a}$

31. $\dfrac{2x - y}{x + y} - \dfrac{x - 3y}{x + y} + \dfrac{2x}{x + y}$

32. $\dfrac{2u - 3v}{u + 2} - \dfrac{u + 2v}{u + 2} + \dfrac{u}{u + 2}$

33. $\dfrac{3}{x + 2y} - \dfrac{x + 3}{x + 2y} + \dfrac{x + 1}{x + 2y}$

34. $\dfrac{2x - y}{x - y} + \dfrac{x - 2y}{x - y} - \dfrac{3x - 3y}{x - y}$

Sample problem:

$$\dfrac{2x - y}{2a + 2b} + \dfrac{2x - 3y}{2a + 2b}$$

Add numerators.

$$\dfrac{(2x - y) + (2x - 3y)}{2a + 2b}$$

Remove parentheses and combine like terms.

$$\dfrac{4x - 4y}{2a + 2b}$$

Factor numerator and denominator and reduce.

$$\dfrac{\overset{2}{\cancel{4}}(x - y)}{\underset{}{\cancel{2}}(a + b)}$$

Ans. $\dfrac{2(x - y)}{a + b}$

35. $\dfrac{2a + b}{3} + \dfrac{4a - 2b}{3}$

36. $\dfrac{6x - 6y}{5} + \dfrac{4x - 4y}{5}$

37. $\dfrac{2x + y}{2} + \dfrac{4x + y}{2}$

38. $\dfrac{x - y}{4} + \dfrac{3x - 7y}{4}$

39. $\dfrac{3u + 2v}{4u - 2v} - \dfrac{u + 2v}{4u - 2v}$

40. $\dfrac{u + 7}{2u - 4v} + \dfrac{u - 5}{2u - 4v}$

41. $\dfrac{x}{2x + 4} - \dfrac{2 - x}{2x + 4}$

42. $\dfrac{x + y}{2(x - y)} + \dfrac{2x - 2y}{2(x - y)} + \dfrac{x - 3y}{2(x - y)}$

Sample problem:

$$\frac{3}{x^2 + 2x + 1} - \frac{2 - x}{x^2 + 2x + 1}$$

Insert parentheses and write in standard form.

$$\frac{3}{x^2 + 2x + 1} + \frac{-(2 - x)}{x^2 + 2x + 1}$$

Add numerators and simplify.

$$\frac{3 - (2 - x)}{x^2 + 2x + 1}$$

$$\frac{x + 1}{x^2 + 2x + 1}$$

Factor denominator and reduce to lowest terms.

$$\frac{\cancel{(x + 1)}}{\cancel{(x + 1)}(x + 1)}$$

Ans. $\dfrac{1}{(x + 1)}$

43. $\dfrac{x + 1}{x^2 - 2x + 1} - \dfrac{5 - 3x}{x^2 - 2x + 1}$

44. $\dfrac{2x + 1}{x^2 - x - 6} + \dfrac{1 - x}{x^2 - x - 6}$

45. $\dfrac{2x - 3y}{x^2 + 3xy - 4y^2} - \dfrac{x - 7y}{x^2 + 3xy - 4y^2}$

46. $\dfrac{u + 3v}{u^2 - v^2} + \dfrac{3u + v}{u^2 - v^2}$

47. $\dfrac{x^2 - 2}{x^2 - x} - \dfrac{2 - 4x}{x^2 - x} - \dfrac{1}{x^2 - x}$

48. $\dfrac{3x^2 - 4}{x^2 - 4} - \dfrac{x^2}{x^2 - 4} - \dfrac{4}{x^2 - 4}$

5.7 SUMS OF FRACTIONS WITH UNLIKE DENOMINATORS

We add fractions with unlike denominators by building the fractions to equivalent fractions with like denominators and adding as in the preceding section. The process is identical with that used in arithmetic. As an example, consider the sum $\frac{1}{2} + \frac{2}{5}$ and the sum $\frac{a}{2} + \frac{b}{5}$. In each case, we first determine the lowest common denominator, 10, and build each fraction to a fraction with that denominator. Thus,

$$\frac{(5)1}{(5)2} + \frac{(2)2}{(2)5} \quad \text{and} \quad \frac{(5)a}{(5)2} + \frac{(2)b}{(2)5}$$

are equivalent to

$$\frac{5}{10} + \frac{4}{10} \quad \text{and} \quad \frac{5a}{10} + \frac{2b}{10},$$

from which we obtain

$$\frac{9}{10} \quad \text{and} \quad \frac{5a + 2b}{10}.$$

EXERCISES 5.7

Rewrite each sum as a single term.

Sample problem:

$$\frac{5}{3x} - \frac{5}{6x}$$

Write in standard form; find L.C.D. $6x$ and build each fraction to a fraction with denominator $6x$.

$$\frac{(2)5}{(2)3x} + \frac{-5}{6x}$$

$$\frac{10}{6x} + \frac{-5}{6x}$$

Add numerators.

$Ans.$ $\dfrac{5}{6x}$

1. $\dfrac{1}{2} + \dfrac{1}{4}$

2. $\dfrac{3}{8} - \dfrac{1}{4}$

3. $\dfrac{x}{6} - \dfrac{2x}{3}$

4. $\dfrac{3a}{2} - \dfrac{a}{6}$

5. $\dfrac{2}{a} - \dfrac{3}{2a}$

6. $\dfrac{1}{bc} + \dfrac{3}{c}$

7. $\dfrac{1}{ax} - \dfrac{2}{x}$

8. $\dfrac{3}{ax} - \dfrac{2}{a}$

9. $\dfrac{2}{3} - \dfrac{4}{3a}$

10. $\dfrac{5}{6} - \dfrac{1}{6r}$

11. $\dfrac{2}{x} - \dfrac{3}{x^2} + \dfrac{1}{x^3}$

12. $\dfrac{15}{x^3} - \dfrac{7}{x^2} + \dfrac{3}{x}$

Sample problem:

$$\frac{2}{3x} - \frac{3}{4x}$$

Write in standard form; find L.C.D. $12x$ and build each fraction to a fraction with denominator $12x$.

$$\frac{(4)2}{(4)3x} + \frac{-3(3)}{4x(3)}$$

$$\frac{8}{12x} + \frac{-9}{12x}$$

Add numerators.

$Ans. \dfrac{-1}{12x}$

13. $\dfrac{1}{3} + \dfrac{1}{2}$ **14.** $\dfrac{2}{3} + \dfrac{1}{4}$ **15.** $\dfrac{3x}{5} - \dfrac{x}{3}$

16. $\dfrac{x}{4} - \dfrac{2x}{5}$ **17.** $\dfrac{3a}{4} + \dfrac{a}{3}$ **18.** $\dfrac{3y}{4} - \dfrac{y}{3}$

19. $\dfrac{1}{2x} - \dfrac{1}{3x}$ **20.** $\dfrac{2}{3a} - \dfrac{1}{4a}$ **21.** $\dfrac{2}{3y} + \dfrac{3}{x}$

22. $\dfrac{2a}{5b} + \dfrac{4}{3}$ **23.** $\dfrac{1}{a} + \dfrac{1}{b} + \dfrac{1}{c}$ **24.** $\dfrac{2}{r} - \dfrac{3}{s} + \dfrac{4}{t}$

Sample problem:

$$\dfrac{x-1}{4} - \dfrac{2x+5}{2}$$

Insert parentheses and write in standard form; find L.C.D. 4 and build each fraction to a fraction with denominator 4.

$$\dfrac{(x-1)}{4} + \dfrac{-(2x+5)(2)}{2(2)}$$

Add numerators.

$$\dfrac{(x-1) - 2(2x+5)}{4}$$

Remove parentheses and simplify.

$$\dfrac{x - 1 - 4x - 10}{4}$$

$Ans. \dfrac{-3x - 11}{4}$

25. $\dfrac{x-2}{6} - \dfrac{x+1}{3}$ **26.** $\dfrac{2x+1}{3} - \dfrac{x-1}{9}$ **27.** $\dfrac{3y-2}{3} + \dfrac{2y-1}{6}$

28. $\dfrac{3x+4}{2} + \dfrac{4x-1}{4}$ **29.** $\dfrac{2-x}{6} + \dfrac{3+x}{2}$ **30.** $\dfrac{y+2}{3} - \dfrac{y-4}{6}$

31. $\dfrac{5x+1}{6x} + \dfrac{3x-2}{2x}$ **32.** $\dfrac{2b-c}{2c} + \dfrac{c+a}{c}$ **33.** $\dfrac{x-y}{2x} - \dfrac{x+y}{3x}$

34. $\dfrac{4y-9}{3y} - \dfrac{3y-8}{4y}$ **35.** $\dfrac{2a-b}{4b} - \dfrac{a-3b}{6a}$ **36.** $\dfrac{a-b}{ab} - \dfrac{b-c}{bc}$

Sample problem:

$$\frac{1}{x+1} - \frac{1}{2x+2}$$

Write in standard form.

$$\frac{1}{x+1} + \frac{-1}{2x+2}$$

Factor denominators where possible.

$$\frac{1}{x+1} + \frac{-1}{2(x+1)}$$

Find L.C.D. $2(x+1)$ and build each fraction to a fraction with denominator $2(x+1)$.

$$\frac{(2)1}{(2)(x+1)} + \frac{-1}{2(x+1)}$$

Add numerators.

Ans. $\dfrac{1}{2(x+1)}$

37. $\dfrac{2}{x+y} - \dfrac{1}{2x+2y}$

38. $\dfrac{2}{x+1} - \dfrac{3}{2x+2}$

39. $\dfrac{5}{6x+6} - \dfrac{3}{2x+2}$

40. $\dfrac{7}{5y-10} - \dfrac{5}{3y-6}$

41. $\dfrac{3}{2a+b} - \dfrac{2}{4a+2b} + \dfrac{1}{8a+4b}$

42. $\dfrac{3}{2x+3y} - \dfrac{5}{4x+6y} + \dfrac{1}{8x+12y}$

Sample problem:

$$\frac{x}{x+2} - \frac{1}{x-1}$$

Write in standard form.

$$\frac{x}{x+2} + \frac{-1}{x-1}$$

Find L.C.D. $(x-1)(x+2)$ and build each fraction to a fraction with denominator $(x-1)(x+2)$.

$$\frac{(x-1)x}{(x-1)(x+2)} + \frac{-1(x+2)}{(x-1)(x+2)}$$

Add numerators.

$$\frac{x(x-1) - 1(x+2)}{(x-1)(x+2)}$$

Remove parentheses and simplify.

$$\frac{x^2 - x - x - 2}{(x - 1)(x + 2)}$$

$Ans.$ $\dfrac{x^2 - 2x - 2}{(x - 1)(x + 2)}$

43. $\dfrac{x}{x + 3} + \dfrac{x}{x - 3}$

44. $\dfrac{2}{x + 2} - \dfrac{3}{x + 3}$

45. $\dfrac{3}{3x - 4} - \dfrac{5}{5x + 6}$

46. $\dfrac{1}{x + y} - \dfrac{1}{x - y}$

47. $\dfrac{1}{2a + 1} - \dfrac{3}{a - 2} + \dfrac{2}{2a + 1}$

48. $\dfrac{x}{2x - y} + \dfrac{y}{x - 2y} + \dfrac{y}{2x - y}$

Sample problem:

$$\frac{x + 1}{x + 2} - \frac{x - 1}{x - 2}$$

Enclose numerators and denominators in parentheses and write in standard form.

$$\frac{(x + 1)}{(x + 2)} + \frac{-(x - 1)}{(x - 2)}$$

Find L.C.D. $(x - 2)(x + 2)$ and build each fraction to a fraction with denominator $(x - 2)(x + 2)$.

$$\frac{(x - 2)(x + 1)}{(x - 2)(x + 2)} + \frac{-(x - 1)(x + 2)}{(x - 2)(x + 2)}$$

Add numerators.

$$\frac{(x - 2)(x + 1) - (x - 1)(x + 2)}{(x - 2)(x + 2)}$$

Perform indicated multiplication. *Write products in parentheses.*

$$\frac{(x^2 - x - 2) - (x^2 + x - 2)}{(x - 2)(x + 2)}$$

Remove parentheses and Simplify.

$$\frac{x^2 - x - 2 - x^2 - x + 2}{(x - 2)(x + 2)}$$

$Ans.$ $\dfrac{-2x}{(x - 2)(x + 2)}$

49. $\dfrac{x-2}{x+2} - \dfrac{x+2}{x-2}$

50. $\dfrac{y-4}{y-2} - \dfrac{y-7}{y-5}$

51. $\dfrac{x+1}{x+2} - \dfrac{x+2}{x+3}$

52. $\dfrac{x+y}{x-y} - \dfrac{x-y}{x+y}$

53. $\dfrac{2x-3y}{x+y} + \dfrac{x+y}{x-y}$

54. $\dfrac{a+2b}{2a-b} - \dfrac{2a+b}{a-2b}$

Sample problem:

$$\frac{x}{x^2-9} - \frac{1}{x^2+4x-21}$$

Factor denominators and write in standard form.

$$\frac{x}{(x-3)(x+3)} + \frac{-1}{(x+7)(x-3)}$$

Find L.C.D. $(x+7)(x-3)(x+3)$ and build each fraction to a fraction with this denominator.

$$\frac{(x+7)x}{(x+7)(x-3)(x+3)} + \frac{-1(x+3)}{(x+7)(x-3)(x+3)}$$

Add numerators.

$$\frac{x(x+7)-(x+3)}{(x+7)(x-3)(x+3)}$$

Remove parentheses.

$$\frac{x^2+7x-x-3}{(x+7)(x-3)(x+3)}$$

Simplify.

Ans. $\dfrac{x^2+6x-3}{(x+7)(x-3)(x+3)}$

55. $\dfrac{1}{x^2-x-2} - \dfrac{1}{x^2+2x+1}$

56. $\dfrac{2}{x^2-5x+6} - \dfrac{5}{x^2+2x-15}$

57. $\dfrac{3x}{x^2+3x-10} - \dfrac{2x}{x^2+x-6}$

58. $\dfrac{2}{x^2-x-6} + \dfrac{3}{x^2-9}$

59. $\dfrac{5x}{x^2+3x+2} - \dfrac{3x-6}{x^2+4x+4}$

60. $\dfrac{8}{x^2-4y^2} + \dfrac{2}{x^2-5xy+6y^2}$

5.8 PRODUCTS OF FRACTIONS

The product of two fractions is defined to be a fraction whose numerator is the product of the numerators and whose denominator is the product of the denominators of the given fractions. Thus,

$$\frac{a}{b} \cdot \frac{c}{d} = \frac{ac}{bd}.$$

Any common factor occurring in both a numerator and a denominator of either fraction may be divided out either before or after multiplying. For example,

$$\frac{\cancel{3}}{\cancel{4}} \cdot \frac{\cancel{2}}{\cancel{3}} = \frac{1}{2} \cdot \frac{1}{1} = \frac{1}{2}$$
$$2$$

or

$$\frac{3}{4} \cdot \frac{2}{3} = \frac{\cancel{6}}{\cancel{12}} = \frac{1}{2}.$$
$$2$$

If any of the factors contain negative signs, it is advisable to proceed with the problem as if all the factors were positive and then attach the appropriate sign to the solution. A positive sign is attached to the solution if there are no negative signs or an even number of negative signs on the factors; a negative sign is attached to the solution if there are an odd number of negative signs on the factors.

In algebra, an expression such as $a\left(\dfrac{b}{c}\right)$ is often rewritten as an equivalent expression as follows:

$$a\left(\frac{b}{c}\right) = \frac{a}{1} \cdot \frac{b}{c} = \frac{ab}{c}.$$

The form most convenient for use in a particular problem should be employed.

EXERCISES 5.8

Change each of the following to the form $\dfrac{ab}{c}$.

Sample problems:

$a.\ \dfrac{2}{3}\,x$ $\qquad$ $b.\ \dfrac{2}{y}\,x$ $\qquad$ $c.\ \dfrac{3}{4}\,(a+b)$ $\qquad$ $d.\ -\dfrac{1}{2}\,y$

Ans. $\dfrac{2x}{3}$ $\qquad$ *Ans.* $\dfrac{2x}{y}$ $\qquad$ *Ans.* $\dfrac{3(a+b)}{4}$ $\qquad$ *Ans.* $-\dfrac{y}{2}$

1. $\dfrac{3}{4}\,x$ $\qquad$ **2.** $-\dfrac{2}{3}\,b$ $\qquad$ **3.** $-\dfrac{3}{5}\,r$ $\qquad$ **4.** $\dfrac{1}{5}\,c$

5. $\dfrac{5}{7}\,(x-y)$ $\qquad$ **6.** $-\dfrac{4}{7}\,(b-a)$ $\qquad$ **7.** $-\dfrac{7}{4}\,(b-a)$ $\qquad$ **8.** $\dfrac{1}{3}\,(x+y)$

Change each of the following to the form $\dfrac{a}{b}\,c$.

Sample problems:

$a.\ \dfrac{3x}{5}$ $\qquad$ $b.\ \dfrac{r}{6}$ $\qquad$ $c.\ \dfrac{-3t}{4}$ $\qquad$ $d.\ \dfrac{-6(x-y)}{7}$

Ans. $\dfrac{3}{5}\,x$ $\qquad$ *Ans.* $\dfrac{1}{6}\,r$ $\qquad$ *Ans.* $-\dfrac{3}{4}\,t$ $\qquad$ *Ans.* $-\dfrac{6}{7}\,(x-y)$

9. $\dfrac{2a}{3}$ $\qquad$ **10.** $\dfrac{4x}{7}$ $\qquad$ **11.** $\dfrac{-y}{3}$ $\qquad$ **12.** $\dfrac{-b}{5}$

13. $\dfrac{2(x+3)}{5}$ $\qquad$ **14.** $\dfrac{3(y-2)}{7}$ $\qquad$ **15.** $\dfrac{-5(a-b)}{7}$ $\qquad$ **16.** $\dfrac{-3(a+b)}{4}$

Write each product as a single term.

Sample problem:

$\dfrac{3}{8}\cdot\dfrac{12}{27}$

Factor numerators and denominators and divide numerators and denominators by common factors.

$\dfrac{\not{3}}{2\cdot2\cdot2}\cdot\dfrac{\not{2}\cdot\not{2}\cdot\not{3}}{\not{3}\cdot\not{3}\cdot3}$

Multiply remaining factors of numerators and remaining factors of denominators.

Ans. $\dfrac{1}{6}$

17. $\dfrac{1}{2}\cdot\dfrac{3}{4}$ $\qquad$ **18.** $\dfrac{16}{38}\cdot\dfrac{19}{12}$ $\qquad$ **19.** $\dfrac{81}{121}\cdot\dfrac{99}{90}$

20. $\dfrac{3}{5}\cdot\dfrac{8}{12}$ $\qquad$ **21.** $\dfrac{24}{30}\cdot\dfrac{20}{36}\cdot\dfrac{3}{4}$ $\qquad$ **22.** $\dfrac{18}{30}\cdot\dfrac{6}{8}\cdot\dfrac{4}{20}$

Sample problem:
$$\frac{12x^2}{5y} \cdot \frac{-10y^3}{3x^2y}$$

Divide numerator and denominator by common factors.

$$\frac{\overset{4}{\cancel{12x^2}}}{\cancel{5y}} \cdot \frac{\overset{2y}{-\cancel{10y^3}}}{\cancel{3x^2y}}$$

Multiply remaining factors of numerators and remaining factors of denominators. Prefix appropriate sign to the answer.

Ans. $-8y$

23. $\dfrac{1}{3} \cdot \dfrac{3y}{1}$

24. $\dfrac{2}{3} \cdot \dfrac{9x^2}{4}$

25. $\dfrac{6x^3}{5} \cdot \dfrac{2}{3x}$

26. $\dfrac{7a}{3} \cdot \dfrac{1}{a^3}$

27. $6x^2y \cdot \dfrac{2}{3x^2}$

28. $5x^2y^2 \cdot \dfrac{1}{x^3y^3}$

29. $\dfrac{-6xy}{3} \cdot \dfrac{4x}{8xy^2}$

30. $\dfrac{-24ab^2}{8a} \cdot \dfrac{21a^2b}{14b}$

31. $\dfrac{-21r^2s}{8t} \cdot \dfrac{-14t^2}{3rs}$

32. $\dfrac{-12a^2b}{5c} \cdot \dfrac{10bc^2}{24a^3b}$

33. $\dfrac{-6xyz}{4a^2b} \cdot \dfrac{10ab^2}{15xyz^2}$

34. $\dfrac{-56x^3yz^2}{24xy^2} \cdot \dfrac{-48z}{28x^2z^3}$

Sample problem:
$$\frac{2x-4}{3x+6} \cdot \frac{2x+3}{x-2}$$

Factor numerators and denominators and divide numerators and denominators by common factors.

$$\frac{2\cancel{(x-2)}}{3(x+2)} \cdot \frac{(2x+3)}{\cancel{(x-2)}}$$

Multiply remaining factors of numerators and remaining factors of denominators.

Ans. $\dfrac{2(2x+3)}{3(x+2)}$

35. $\dfrac{3x-9}{5x-15} \cdot \dfrac{10x-5}{8x-4}$

36. $\dfrac{2x+4}{3x-9} \cdot \dfrac{x-3}{x+2}$

37. $\dfrac{5a+25}{2a} \cdot \dfrac{4a}{2a+10}$

38. $\dfrac{2a-4b}{8a+24b} \cdot \dfrac{2a+6b}{4a-8b}$

39. $\dfrac{2x+3y}{x-2y} \cdot \dfrac{3x-6y}{x-2y} \cdot \dfrac{x-2y}{6x+9y}$

40. $\dfrac{7x+14}{14x-28} \cdot \dfrac{2x-4}{x+2} \cdot \dfrac{x-3}{x+1}$

Sample problem:

$$\frac{x^2 - 2x - 3}{x^2 - 9} \cdot \frac{x^2 + 5x + 6}{x^2 - 1}$$

Factor numerators and denominators and divide numerators and denominators by common factors.

$$\frac{\cancel{(x-3)}\cancel{(x+1)}}{\cancel{(x-3)}\cancel{(x+3)}} \cdot \frac{\cancel{(x+3)}(x+2)}{(x-1)\cancel{(x+1)}}$$

Multiply remaining factors of numerators and remaining factors of denominators.

$$Ans. \ \frac{x+2}{x-1}$$

41. $\dfrac{x^2 - 3x - 10}{x^2 + 2x - 35} \cdot \dfrac{x^2 + 4x - 21}{x^2 + 9x + 14}$

42. $\dfrac{4y^2 - 1}{y^2 - 16} \cdot \dfrac{y^2 - 4y}{2y + 1}$

43. $\dfrac{6x^2 - x - 2}{12x^2 + 5x - 2} \cdot \dfrac{8x^2 - 6x + 1}{4x^2 - 1}$

44. $\dfrac{y^2 - y - 20}{y^2 + 7y + 12} \cdot \dfrac{y^2 + 9y + 18}{y^2 - 7y + 10}$

45. $\dfrac{x^2 + xy - 2y^2}{x^2 - 3xy + 2y^2} \cdot \dfrac{x^2 - xy - 2y^2}{x^2 + 5xy + 6y^2}$

46. $\dfrac{x^2 + x - 6}{2x^2 + 6x} \cdot \dfrac{8x^2}{x^2 - 5x + 6}$

47. $\dfrac{x^2 - 4}{x^2 - 1} \cdot \dfrac{x - 1}{2x^2 + 4x}$

48. $\dfrac{a^2 + a}{2a + 1} \cdot \dfrac{10a + 5}{3a + 3}$

49. $\dfrac{x^2 - 4}{x^2 - 5x + 6} \cdot \dfrac{x^2 - 2x - 3}{x^2 + 3x + 2}$

50. $\dfrac{x^2 + 3x}{x^2 - 3x - 4} \cdot \dfrac{x^2 - 5x + 4}{x^2 + 2x - 3}$

51. $\dfrac{y^2 - y - 20}{y^2 - 6y + 5} \cdot \dfrac{y^2 + 5y - 6}{y^2 + 7y + 12} \cdot \dfrac{y^2 - 9}{y^2 - 36}$

52. $\dfrac{x^2 - xy}{xy + y^2} \cdot \dfrac{x^2 - 4y^2}{x^2 - y^2} \cdot \dfrac{x^2 - 2xy - 3y^2}{x^2 - 5xy + 6y^2}$

5.9 QUOTIENTS OF FRACTIONS

In dividing one fraction by another, we seek a number which, when multiplied by the divisor, yields the dividend. This is precisely the same motion as that of dividing one integer by another; $b \div a$ means that we seek a number q, the quotient, such that $aq = b$.

To divide $\dfrac{1}{2}$ by $\dfrac{2}{3}$, we seek a number q such that $\dfrac{2}{3} q = \dfrac{1}{2}$. In order to solve this equation for q, we multiply each member of the equation by

$\frac{3}{2}$, which is the reciprocal* of $\frac{2}{3}$. Thus,

$$\left(\frac{3}{2}\right)\frac{2}{3}q = \left(\frac{3}{2}\right)\frac{1}{2},$$

$$q = \frac{3}{4}.$$

This is a perfectly general procedure. The quotient

$$\frac{a}{b} \div \frac{c}{d}$$

is a number q such that

$$\frac{c}{d}q = \frac{a}{b}.$$

Multiplying each member by $\frac{d}{c}$, the reciprocal of $\frac{c}{d}$, we have

$$\left(\frac{d}{c}\right)\frac{c}{d}q = \left(\frac{d}{c}\right)\frac{a}{b},$$

$$q = \frac{a}{b} \cdot \frac{d}{c}.$$

Therefore,

$$\frac{a}{b} \div \frac{c}{d} = \frac{a}{b} \cdot \frac{d}{c}.$$

Thus, to divide one fraction by another, the dividend can be multiplied by the reciprocal of the divisor. This is the same technique employed in arithmetic; that is, "invert the divisor and multiply."

As in multiplication, when fractions have signs attached, it is advisable to proceed with the problem as if all the factors were positive and then attach the appropriate sign to the solution.

EXERCISES 5.9

Write each quotient as a single term.

Sample problems:

$$a. \; 4 \div \frac{2}{3} \qquad b. \; \frac{2}{3} \div \frac{7}{12}$$

Invert divisor and multiply.

Solution continued on the next page

---

* The reciprocal of any nonzero number a is the number $\frac{1}{a}$. The reciprocal of any fraction may be obtained by "inverting" the fraction.

$$\frac{\cancel{4}^{2}}{1}\cdot\frac{3}{\cancel{2}}$$

$$\frac{2}{\cancel{8}}\cdot\frac{\cancel{12}^{4}}{7}$$

Ans. 6

Ans. $\dfrac{8}{7}$

1. $\dfrac{2}{3} \div \dfrac{2}{9}$

2. $\dfrac{5}{6} \div \dfrac{7}{12}$

3. $\dfrac{3}{4} \div 6$

4. $\dfrac{3}{4} \div 3$

5. $\dfrac{9}{8} \div \dfrac{9}{4}$

6. $\dfrac{7}{8} \div \dfrac{21}{32}$

Sample problems:

a. $\dfrac{3a^2x}{2by} \div \dfrac{6ax^2}{b^2y^2}$

b. $\dfrac{-a^2}{b} \div a^3$

Invert divisor and multiply.

$$\frac{\cancel{3a^2x}^{a}}{\cancel{2by}}\cdot\frac{\cancel{b^2y^2}^{b\,y}}{\cancel{6ax^2}}$$
$$\qquad 2\ x$$

$$\frac{-\cancel{a^2}^{a}}{b}\cdot\frac{1}{\cancel{a^3}}$$
$$\qquad a$$

Ans. $\dfrac{aby}{4x}$

Ans. $\dfrac{-1}{ab}$

7. $\dfrac{2c}{3d} \div \dfrac{4c}{6d}$

8. $\dfrac{c^2}{d} \div \dfrac{c^4}{d^2}$

9. $\dfrac{15}{27ab} \div \dfrac{16b}{9a}$

10. $\dfrac{a}{b^2} \div \dfrac{ab^2}{b^3}$

11. $\dfrac{-x^2y^2}{u^2v^2} \div \dfrac{xy^2}{u^2v}$

12. $\dfrac{14a^2b^3}{15x^2y} \div \dfrac{-21a^2b^2}{35xy}$

13. $16y^2 \div \dfrac{4y}{3}$

14. $ax^2 \div \dfrac{x^2}{b}$

15. $\dfrac{3}{4}xy \div (-12y^2)$

16. $\dfrac{36x^3}{7y} \div (-3x^2)$

17. $\dfrac{9x^2y}{ab} \div \dfrac{3xy^2}{b^2}$

18. $\dfrac{xy}{a^2b} \div \dfrac{x^3y}{ab}$

Sample problem:

$$\frac{3xy + x}{y^2 - y} \div \frac{3y + 1}{y}$$

Invert divisor.

$$\frac{3xy + x}{y^2 - y} \cdot \frac{y}{3y + 1}$$

Factor where possible and multiply.

$$\frac{x\cancel{(3y+1)}}{\cancel{y}(y-1)} \cdot \frac{\cancel{y}}{\cancel{3y+1}}$$

$$Ans. \quad \frac{x}{y-1}$$

19. $\dfrac{a^2 - ab}{ab} \div \dfrac{2a - 2b}{ab}$

20. $\dfrac{2x - 2y}{xy} \div \dfrac{4x - 4y}{xy}$

21. $\dfrac{6a - 12}{3a + 9} \div \dfrac{4a - 8}{5a + 15}$

22. $\dfrac{x^2 + xy}{x^2 - xy} \div \dfrac{x + y}{4x - 4y}$

23. $\dfrac{10x^2 - 5x}{12x^3 + 24x^2} \div \dfrac{2x^2 - x}{2x^2 + 4x}$

24. $\dfrac{ax - ay}{bx + by} \div \dfrac{cx - cy}{dx + dy}$

Sample problem:

$$\frac{x^2 - 2x - 8}{x^2 + x - 2} \div \frac{2x^2 - 5x + 2}{x^2 - 3x + 2}$$

Invert divisor.

$$\frac{x^2 - 2x - 8}{x^2 + x - 2} \cdot \frac{x^2 - 3x + 2}{2x^2 - 5x + 2}$$

Factor where possible and multiply.

$$\frac{(x - 4)\cancel{(x + 2)}}{\cancel{(x + 2)}\cancel{(x - 1)}} \cdot \frac{\cancel{(x - 2)}\cancel{(x - 1)}}{(2x - 1)\cancel{(x - 2)}}$$

$$Ans. \quad \frac{x - 4}{2x - 1}$$

25. $\dfrac{4x^2 - y^2}{x^2 - 4y^2} \div \dfrac{2x - y}{x - 2y}$

26. $\dfrac{x^2 - x - 6}{x^2 + 2x - 15} \div \dfrac{x^2 - 4}{x^2 - 25}$

27. $\dfrac{y^2 - 6y + 5}{y^2 + 8y + 7} \div \dfrac{y^2 - 3y - 10}{y^2 + 3y + 2}$

28. $\dfrac{x^2 - 8x + 15}{x^2 + 9x + 14} \div \dfrac{x^2 + 4x - 21}{x^2 - 6x - 16}$

29. $\dfrac{2x^2 - x - 28}{3x^2 - x - 2} \div \dfrac{4x^2 + 16x + 7}{3x^2 + 11x + 6}$

30. $\dfrac{y^2 + 7y + 10}{y^2 + 7y + 12} \div \dfrac{y^2 + 6y + 5}{y^2 + 8y + 16}$

31. $\dfrac{3y + 2}{5y^2 - y} \cdot \dfrac{2y^2 - y}{2y^2 - y - 1} \div \dfrac{6y^2 + y - 2}{10y^2 + 3y - 1}$

32. $\dfrac{x^2 + 4x + 3}{x^2 - 8x + 7} \cdot \dfrac{x^2 - 2x - 35}{x^2 - 7x - 8} \div \dfrac{x^2 + 8x + 15}{x^2 - 9x + 8}$

33. $\dfrac{3x^2 + 2x - 5}{2x^2 + x - 6} \cdot \dfrac{2x - 3}{3x + 5} \div \dfrac{x^2 + 2x - 3}{2x^2 + 3x - 2}$

34. $\dfrac{x^2 - x}{x^2 - 2x - 3} \cdot \dfrac{x^2 + 2x + 1}{x^2 + 4x} \div \dfrac{x^2 - 3x - 4}{x^2 - 16}$

35. $\dfrac{a^2 + 11a + 18}{a^2 + 4a - 5} \cdot \dfrac{a^2 - 6a - 7}{a^2 + 8a + 12} \div \dfrac{a^2 - 7a - 8}{a^2 + 2a - 15}$

36. $\dfrac{2y^2 - 5y - 3}{18y^2 + 3y - 1} \cdot \dfrac{6y^2 + 5y + 1}{2y + 1} \div \dfrac{2y^2 - 7y + 3}{36y^2 - 1}$

5.10 COMPLEX FRACTIONS

A fraction which contains a fraction or fractions in either its numerator or denominator or both is called a **complex fraction**. For example,

$$\frac{\dfrac{1}{2}}{\dfrac{3}{4}}, \quad \frac{2}{\dfrac{2}{a}}, \quad \text{and} \quad \frac{a + \dfrac{a}{3}}{2}$$

are complex fractions.

We may simplify a complex fraction by multiplying the numerator and denominator by the same number. If the number is the L.C.D. of all fractions in the numerator and denominator, the result of this multiplication is a simple fraction equivalent to the given complex fraction.

EXERCISES 5.10

Simplify.

Sample problems:

$$a. \ \frac{\dfrac{2}{3}}{\dfrac{4}{9}} \qquad\qquad b. \ \frac{\dfrac{3c^2}{4d^4}}{\dfrac{5c^3}{12d^4}}$$

Find the L.C.D. for all fractions in numerator and denominator; 9 in problem a and $12d^4$ in problem b; multiply numerator and denominator by the L.C.D.

$$\frac{\overset{3}{(\cancel{9})} \ \dfrac{2}{\cancel{3}}}{\underset{}{(\cancel{9})} \ \dfrac{4}{\cancel{9}}}, \qquad\qquad \frac{\overset{3}{(\cancel{12d^4})} \ \dfrac{3c^2}{\cancel{4d^4}}}{(\cancel{12d^4}) \ \dfrac{5c^3}{\cancel{12d^4}}}$$

Divide numerator and denominator by common factors.

$$\cfrac{\cfrac{3}{\cancel{6}}}{\cfrac{\cancel{4}}{2}}$$

Ans. $\dfrac{3}{2}$

$$\cfrac{\cfrac{9\cancel{c}}{5\cancel{c}}}{c}$$

Ans. $\dfrac{9}{5c}$

1. $\cfrac{\dfrac{3}{5}}{\dfrac{4}{1}}$

2. $\cfrac{\dfrac{4}{5}}{\dfrac{3}{2}}$

3. $\cfrac{\dfrac{1}{6}}{\dfrac{2}{3}}$

4. $\cfrac{\dfrac{5}{8}}{\dfrac{15}{16}}$

5. $\cfrac{\dfrac{3}{5}}{\dfrac{11}{10}}$

6. $\cfrac{\dfrac{8}{7}}{\dfrac{16}{15}}$

7. $\cfrac{\dfrac{rs}{rt}}{\dfrac{s^2}{t}}$

8. $\cfrac{\dfrac{b}{ax}}{\dfrac{bx}{9}}$

9. $\cfrac{\dfrac{2c}{3d}}{\dfrac{4c}{6d}}$

10. $\cfrac{\dfrac{a}{b^2}}{\dfrac{a}{b}}$

11. $\cfrac{\dfrac{4x^2}{6y}}{\dfrac{8x}{2y}}$

12. $\cfrac{\dfrac{35a^3}{24b^3}}{\dfrac{5a}{4b^2}}$

Sample problem :

$$\frac{1 - \dfrac{1}{3}}{2 + \dfrac{5}{6}}$$

Find the L.C.D. for all fractions in numerator and denominator, 6. Multiply each term in numerator and each term in denominator by 6.

$$\frac{(6)1 - (\cancel{6})\overset{2}{\cancel{3}}\dfrac{1}{\cancel{3}}}{(6)2 + (\cancel{6})\dfrac{5}{\cancel{6}}}$$

Simplify.

$$\frac{6 - 2}{12 + 5}$$

Ans. $\dfrac{4}{17}$

13. $\dfrac{\dfrac{2}{3}}{3 - \dfrac{1}{3}}$ **14.** $\dfrac{1 + \dfrac{1}{5}}{\dfrac{2}{5}}$ **15.** $\dfrac{1 - \dfrac{1}{3}}{2 + \dfrac{2}{3}}$ **16.** $\dfrac{3 + \dfrac{1}{10}}{2 + \dfrac{3}{5}}$

17. $\dfrac{\dfrac{1}{2} - \dfrac{3}{8}}{\dfrac{5}{4} + \dfrac{1}{2}}$ **18.** $\dfrac{\dfrac{2}{3} - \dfrac{1}{6}}{\dfrac{1}{3} + \dfrac{5}{6}}$ **19.** $\dfrac{\dfrac{1}{2} + \dfrac{1}{3}}{\dfrac{1}{3} - \dfrac{1}{6}}$ **20.** $\dfrac{\dfrac{3}{4} - \dfrac{1}{2}}{\dfrac{1}{6} + \dfrac{1}{3}}$

Sample problem:

$$\dfrac{x + \dfrac{y}{z}}{x - \dfrac{z}{y}}$$

Find the L.C.D. for all fractions in numerator and denominator, yz. Multiply each term in numerator and each term in denominator by yz.

$$\dfrac{(yz)x + (y\!\!\!/z)\,\dfrac{y}{\not z}}{(yz)x - (y\!\!\!/z)\,\dfrac{z}{\not y}}$$

Simplify.

Ans. $\dfrac{xyz + y^2}{xyz - z^2}$

21. $\dfrac{\dfrac{2}{y} + \dfrac{1}{2y}}{y + \dfrac{y}{2}}$ **22.** $\dfrac{4 - \dfrac{1}{x^2}}{2 - \dfrac{1}{x}}$ **23.** $\dfrac{y - \dfrac{1}{y}}{y + \dfrac{1}{y}}$ **24.** $\dfrac{a + \dfrac{a}{b}}{1 + \dfrac{1}{b}}$

25. $\dfrac{\dfrac{x}{3y} - \dfrac{1}{2}}{\dfrac{4}{3y} - \dfrac{2}{x}}$ **26.** $\dfrac{2 - \dfrac{a}{b}}{2 - \dfrac{b}{a}}$ **27.** $\dfrac{\dfrac{3}{2b} - \dfrac{1}{b}}{\dfrac{4}{a} + \dfrac{3}{2a}}$ **28.** $\dfrac{\dfrac{1}{ab} - \dfrac{1}{b}}{\dfrac{1}{b} - \dfrac{1}{ab}}$

5.11 FRACTIONAL EQUATIONS

To solve an equation containing fractions, it is generally easiest to find first an equivalent equation which is free of fractions. We do this by multiplying each member of an equation by the lowest common denominator of the fractions. Thus, to solve the equation

$$\frac{x}{3} - 2 = \frac{4}{5},$$

each member can be multiplied by the L.C.D. 15 to obtain an equivalent equation which does not contain a fraction. Thus we have

$$(\cancel{15})^5 \left(\frac{x}{\cancel{3}}\right) - 15(2) = \cancel{15}^3 \left(\frac{4}{\cancel{5}}\right)$$

$$5x - 30 = 12,$$

$$5x = 42,$$

$$x = \frac{42}{5}.$$

The solution of any equation in which each member has been multiplied by an expression containing the variable should be checked. For example, multiplying each member of

$$6 + \frac{4}{x - 3} = \frac{x + 1}{x - 3}$$

by $x - 3$, we obtain

$$(x - 3)6 + (x - 3)\frac{4}{x - 3} = (x - 3)\frac{x + 1}{x - 3},$$

$$6x - 18 + 4 = x + 1,$$

$$5x = 15,$$

$$x = 3.$$

Substituting 3 for x in the original equation yields

$$6 + \frac{4}{0} = \frac{3 + 1}{0}.$$

Therefore, 3 is *not* a solution. The equation does not have a solution.

EXERCISES 5.11

Solve.

Sample problem:

$$5x - 2 = \frac{7}{2} - \frac{x}{2}$$

Multiply each member by L.C.D. 2.

Solution continued on the next page

$$(2)5x - (2)2 = (2)\frac{7}{2} - (2)\frac{x}{2}$$

Complete the solution.

$$10x - 4 = 7 - x$$
$$11x = 11$$
$$Ans.\ x = 1 \qquad Check. \quad 5(1) - 2 = \tfrac{7}{2} - \tfrac{1}{2}$$
$$3 = 3$$

1. $\dfrac{5x}{2} - 1 = x + \dfrac{1}{2}$ **2.** $y - \dfrac{3}{10} = \dfrac{1}{2} + \dfrac{3y}{5}$ **3.** $\dfrac{5y}{6} - \dfrac{1}{6} = \dfrac{2y}{3} + \dfrac{5}{6}$

4. $\dfrac{2t}{3} - \dfrac{1}{4} = \dfrac{25}{12} + \dfrac{t}{3}$ **5.** $\dfrac{x}{6} - \dfrac{7}{3} = \dfrac{2x}{9} - \dfrac{x}{4}$ **6.** $\dfrac{8x}{3} - 3 = \dfrac{2x}{3} - 6$

7. $4 + \dfrac{4}{y} = \dfrac{12}{y}$ **8.** $1 + \dfrac{3}{x} = \dfrac{12}{x}$ **9.** $2 + \dfrac{5}{z} = \dfrac{11}{z}$

10. $2 + \dfrac{5}{2x} = \dfrac{3}{x} + \dfrac{3}{2}$ **11.** $3 - \dfrac{1}{x} = \dfrac{7}{5x} - \dfrac{9}{5}$ **12.** $\dfrac{1}{3} - \dfrac{1}{4} = \dfrac{10}{3x} - \dfrac{1}{18}$

Sample problem:

$$\frac{x + 11}{6} - \frac{11 - x}{3} = 1$$

Enclose numerators in parentheses and write in standard form.

$$\frac{(x + 11)}{6} + \frac{-(11 - x)}{3} = 1$$

Multiply each member by L.C.D. 6.

$$\frac{(6)(x + 11)}{6} + \frac{-\overset{2}{(6)}(11 - x)}{3} = (6)1$$
$$(x + 11) - 2(11 - x) = 6$$

Complete the solution.

$$x + 11 - 22 + 2x = 6$$
$$3x - 11 = 6$$
$$3x = 17$$
$$Ans.\ x = \frac{17}{3}$$

13. $\dfrac{y + 12}{9} = \dfrac{y - 9}{2}$ **14.** $\dfrac{y + 1}{4} - \dfrac{3}{2} = \dfrac{2y - 9}{10}$

15. $\dfrac{x - 1}{10} + \dfrac{19}{15} = \dfrac{x}{3}$ **16.** $\dfrac{2x}{3} - \dfrac{2x + 5}{6} = \dfrac{1}{2}$

17. $\dfrac{x + 6}{2} - 1 = 5$

18. $\dfrac{2x - 2}{2} + 2 = \dfrac{1}{2}$

19. $\dfrac{x - 2}{x} = \dfrac{14}{3x} - \dfrac{1}{3}$

20. $\dfrac{3}{2x} - \dfrac{x - 3}{2x} = \dfrac{5}{2x} - 1$

21. $\dfrac{2 - y}{5y} = \dfrac{4}{15y} - \dfrac{1}{6}$

22. $\dfrac{2z - 5}{z} - \dfrac{3}{z} = -\dfrac{2}{3}$

23. $\dfrac{x - 3}{2x} + \dfrac{3x - 7}{2x} = \dfrac{1}{3}$

24. $\dfrac{4}{x} + \dfrac{5}{2} = \dfrac{4x + 5}{2x} - \dfrac{2x - 3}{5x}$

Sample problem:

$$\frac{2}{x + 10} = \frac{1}{x + 3}$$

Multiply each term in the equation by L.C.D. $(x + 10)(x + 3)$.

$$\cancel{(x + 10)}(x + 3)\,\frac{2}{\cancel{(x + 10)}} = (x + 10)\cancel{(x + 3)}\,\frac{1}{\cancel{(x + 3)}}$$

$$2(x + 3) = (x + 10)$$

Complete the solution.

$$2x + 6 = x + 10$$

$$Ans.\ x = 4$$

$$Check.\ \frac{2}{4 + 10} = \frac{1}{4 + 3};\ \frac{1}{7} = \frac{1}{7}$$

25. $\dfrac{3}{5} = \dfrac{x}{x + 2}$

26. $\dfrac{2}{x + 4} = \dfrac{2}{3x}$

27. $\dfrac{3}{2y - 1} = \dfrac{7}{3y + 1}$

28. $\dfrac{7}{4 - x} = \dfrac{4}{7 + x}$

29. $\dfrac{2}{x - 9} = \dfrac{9}{x + 12}$

30. $\dfrac{4}{y - 5} = \dfrac{-5}{y + 4}$

Solve for x in terms of the other variables.

Sample problem:

$$\frac{a + b}{x} = \frac{3}{c}$$

Multiply each member of the equation by L.C.D. xc.

$$(\cancel{x}c)\,\frac{(a + b)}{\cancel{x}} = (x\cancel{c})\,\frac{3}{\cancel{c}}$$

Simplify and complete solution.

Solution continued on the next page

$$ca + cb = 3x$$
$$3x = ca + cb$$

Ans. $x = \dfrac{ca + cb}{3}$ or $x = \dfrac{c(a + b)}{3}$

Check. $\dfrac{a + b}{\dfrac{c(c + b)}{3}} = \dfrac{3}{c}; \dfrac{3}{c} = \dfrac{3}{c}$

31. $\dfrac{a}{x} + \dfrac{b}{x} = 2$

32. $\dfrac{a + c}{x} = \dfrac{2}{b}$

33. $\dfrac{a}{x + 1} = \dfrac{2a}{x - 2}$

34. $\dfrac{2x + a}{x - b} = \dfrac{3}{2}$

35. $\dfrac{3}{4 - x} = \dfrac{a}{b}$

36. $\dfrac{3}{x - a} - \dfrac{2}{x + b} = 0$

37. $\dfrac{x}{x - 3} = \dfrac{3}{x - 3} + 2$

38. $\dfrac{x}{x - 2} - 7 = \dfrac{2}{x - 2}$

39. $\dfrac{a}{x + b} - \dfrac{a}{x} = \dfrac{3}{x}$

40. $\dfrac{a + b}{x + 4} - \dfrac{a}{x} = \dfrac{-b}{x}$

41. $\dfrac{x + 2b}{x + b} = \dfrac{b}{x + b} + 2$

42. $\dfrac{a}{x - a} = 2 - \dfrac{x + 2a}{x - a}$

5.12   WORD PROBLEMS

The word problems in the following exercises lead to equations which involve fractions.

EXERCISES 5.12

Sample problem: If two-thirds of a certain number is added to three-fourths of the number, the result is 17. Find the number.

Represent the unknown quantity symbolically.

Let x = the number

Write an equation representing the word sentence.

$$\frac{2}{3}x + \frac{3}{4}x = 17$$

Solve the equation.

$$(\cancel{12})^{4}\frac{2}{\cancel{3}}x + (\cancel{12})^{3}\frac{3}{\cancel{4}}x = (12)(17)$$
$$8x + 9x = 204$$
$$17x = 204$$
$$x = 12$$

Ans. The number is 12.

1. If one-half of a certain number is added to three times the number, the result is $3\frac{5}{2}$. Find the number.

2. If two-thirds of a certain number is subtracted from twice the number, the result is 20. Find the number.

3. Find two consecutive integers such that the sum of one-half the first and two-thirds of the next is 17.

4. Find two consecutive integers such that twice the second less one-half of the first is 14.

5. If two-thirds of the sum of a certain number and 5 is 10, find the number.

6. If seven-eighths of the difference between a certain positive number and 8 is 21, find the number.

7. If twice a certain number is divided by 2 less than the number, the result is 3. Find the number.

8. If a certain number increased by 8 is divided by the number decreased by 2, the result is $\frac{9}{4}$. Find the number.

9. The denominator of a certain fraction is 6 more than the numerator and the fraction is equivalent to $\frac{3}{4}$. Find the numerator.

10. The width of a rectangle is two-fifths of the length. What are the dimensions if the perimeter is 112 feet?

11. The length of one side of a triangle is two-thirds the length of each of the other sides which are equal. How long is each of the sides if the perimeter is 16 inches?

12. One angle of a triangle is 90°. If two-thirds of one acute angle is added to one-half of the second acute angle, the result is 50°. Find the number of degrees in each acute angle.

13. If one-half of one of the acute angles of a right triangle is equal to seven-fourths of the other, how large is each acute angle?

14. If one of the equal angles in an isosceles triangle is two-fifths of the vertex angle, how large is each angle in the triangle?

Sample problem : An express train travels 180 miles in the same time that a freight train travels 120 miles. If the express goes 20 miles per hour faster than the freight, find the rate of each.

Given: time $= \dfrac{\text{distance}}{\text{rate}}$.

Represent the unknown quantities in terms of r.

Let $r =$ rate of freight train;
then $r + 20 =$ rate of express train.

Solution continued on the next page

Since the fact that the times are equal is the significant equality in the problem, express the time of each train for the trip in terms of r.

Freight train's time: $t_1 = \dfrac{\text{distance}}{\text{rate}} = \dfrac{120}{r}$.

Express train's time: $t_2 = \dfrac{\text{distance}}{\text{rate}} = \dfrac{180}{r + 20}$.

Equate the expressions for time.

$$t_1 = t_2$$
$$\frac{120}{r} = \frac{180}{r + 20}$$

Clear fractions by multiplying each term by the L.C.D. of all of the fractions, $r(r + 20)$.

$$\cancel{r}(r + 20)\,\frac{120}{\cancel{r}} = r\cancel{(r + 20)}\,\frac{180}{\cancel{r + 20}}$$

Solve for r.

$$120(r + 20) = 180r$$
$$120r + 2400 = 180r$$
$$2400 = 60r$$
$$r = 40$$

Ans. $r = 40$ mph, freight train's speed

$r + 20 = 60$ mph, express train's speed

15. A man drives 120 miles in the same time that another man drives 80 miles. If the speed of the first driver is 20 miles per hour greater than the speed of the second driver, find the speed of each.

16. An airplane travels 630 miles in the same time that an automobile covers 210 miles. If the speed of the airplane is 120 miles per hour greater than the speed of the automobile, find the speed of each.

17. A man rides 15 miles on his bicycle in the same time it takes him to walk 7 miles. If his rate riding is 2 miles per hour more than his rate walking, how fast does he walk?

18. A man rides 10 miles in a car and then walks 4 miles on foot. If his rate driving is 20 times his rate walking, and if the whole trip takes him $2\frac{1}{4}$ hours, how fast does he walk?

19. Two men drive from town A to town B, a distance of 300 miles. If one man drives twice as fast as the other, and arrives at town B 5 hours ahead of the other, how fast was each driving?

20. Two trains traveled from town A to town B, a distance of 400 miles. If one train traveled twice as fast as the other and arrived at town B 4 hours ahead of the other, how fast was each traveling?

5.13 RATIO AND PROPORTION

The quotient of two numbers, $a \div b$ or $\frac{a}{b}$, is sometimes referred to as a **ratio** and read "the ratio of a to b." This is a convenient way to compare two numbers. A statement that two ratios are equal, for example,

$$\frac{2}{3} = \frac{4}{6} \quad \text{or} \quad \frac{a}{b} = \frac{c}{d},$$

is called a **proportion** and read "2 is to 3 as 4 is to 6" and "a is to b as c is to d." The numbers a, b, c, and d respectively are called the first, second, third, and fourth terms of the proportion. The first and fourth terms are called the **extremes** of the proportion, and the second and third terms are called the **means** of the proportion.

If each ratio in the proportion $\frac{a}{b} = \frac{c}{d}$ is multiplied by bd, the result is $ad = bc$. That is:

In any proportion, the product of the extremes is equal to the product of the means.

A proportion is a special type of fractional equation. The above rule to obtain an equivalent equation without denominators is a special case of our general approach using the multiplication axiom.

EXERCISES 5.13

Express each of the following as a ratio.

Sample problems:

a. 1 to 8	*b.* 10 to 40	*c.* 12 to 30
	$\dfrac{\cancel{10}}{\cancel{40}}$	$\dfrac{\cancel{12}^{2}}{\cancel{30}_{5}}$
	4	
Ans. $\dfrac{1}{8}$	*Ans.* $\dfrac{1}{4}$	*Ans.* $\dfrac{2}{5}$

1. 5 cents to 25 cents.

2. 3 pounds to 30 pounds.

3. 2 tons to 8 tons.

4. 3 quarts to 9 quarts.

5. 6 quarts to 2 quarts.

6. 12 miles to 2 miles.

7. 8 to 20   **8.** 10 to 30   **9.** 6 to 20

10. 12 to 30   **11.** 16 to 10   **12.** 20 to 6

Express each of the following as a proportion.

Sample problems:

$a.$ 2 is to 5 as 4 is to 10. $b.$ 4 is to 9 as x is to 27.

$$Ans. \ \frac{2}{5} = \frac{4}{10}$$ $$Ans. \ \frac{4}{9} = \frac{x}{27}$$

13. 8 is to 3 as 24 is to 9.   **14.** 18 is to 4 as 9 is to 2.

15. 21 is to 24 as 7 is to 8.   **16.** 6 is to 12 as 4 is to 8.

17. 15 is to x as 10 is to 4.   **18.** 12 is to 6 as 4 is to x.

19. 6 is to 2 as x is to $x + 1$.   **20.** $x + 3$ is to x as 15 is to 3.

Solve each proportion for x.

Sample problems:

$a.$ $\dfrac{4}{5} = \dfrac{x}{20}$ $b.$ $\dfrac{14}{12} = \dfrac{x}{x - 1}$

Set the product of the extremes equal to the product of the means and solve equation.

$(4)(20) = 5x$ $14(x - 1) = 12x$

$80 = 5x$ $14x - 14 = 12x$

$2x = 14$

$Ans. \ x = 16$ $Ans. \ x = 7$

21. $\dfrac{3}{x} = \dfrac{1}{5}$ **22.** $\dfrac{2}{7} = \dfrac{x}{28}$ **23.** $\dfrac{x}{21} = \dfrac{5}{7}$

24. $\dfrac{6}{11} = \dfrac{x}{22}$ **25.** $\dfrac{3}{14} = \dfrac{x}{7}$ **26.** $\dfrac{12}{5} = \dfrac{6}{x}$

27. $\dfrac{x}{x + 2} = \dfrac{2}{3}$ **28.** $\dfrac{x}{x - 2} = \dfrac{14}{10}$ **29.** $\dfrac{1}{3} = \dfrac{x + 3}{x + 5}$

30. $\dfrac{1}{2} = \dfrac{x}{6 - x}$ **31.** $\dfrac{3}{4} = \dfrac{x + 2}{12 - x}$ **32.** $\dfrac{x - 7}{14 + x} = \dfrac{-3}{4}$

Solve each problem using a proportion.

Sample problem   It takes 2 hours to address 70 envelopes. At the same rate, how many envelopes can be addressed in 5 hours?

Represent the unknown quantity symbolically.

x = number of envelopes addressed in 5 hours.

Set up proportion. The ratio of the times is equal to the ratio of the number of envelopes addressed.

$$\frac{2}{5} = \frac{70}{x}$$

Set the product of the extremes equal to the product of the means and solve equation.

$$2x = 350$$

Ans. x = 175 envelopes

33. How many pounds of coffee will be required to make 3000 cups of coffee if 3 pounds will make 225 cups?

34. Five pounds of sugar costs 60 cents. How many pounds can be purchased for $4.20?

35. A car uses 8 gallons of gas to travel 110 miles. How many gallons would be required to drive 500 miles?

36. A man earns $4200 in 30 weeks. At the same rate of earnings, how much could he anticipate earning in one year (52 weeks)?

37. A family uses 3 quarts of milk every two days. How many quarts will be used in 3 months (90 days)?

38. If $\frac{3}{4}$ inch on a map represents 10 miles, how many miles does 6 inches represent?

39. If 660 bricks are required for 24 linear feet of a wall, how many bricks will be required for 30 linear feet?

40. The sum of two numbers is 48 and their ratio is $\frac{5}{19}$. What are the numbers?

41. If 20 pounds of apples cost $1.60, how much would 28 pounds of apples cost?

42. A typist takes 1 hour and 20 minutes to type 12 pages of manuscript. If she types at the same rate, how long would it take her (in hours) to type 50 pages?

43. A sample of 92 parts in a manufacturing plant proved to contain 3 defective parts. If the sample was a valid sample, how many defective parts would you expect to find in a run of 276 parts?

44. The acute angles of a right triangle are in the ratio 5 to 13. How large is each angle?

CHAPTER REVIEW

1. Graph the following numbers.

$$\frac{-27}{4}, \frac{-5}{2}, 2, \frac{11}{2}, \frac{37}{4}$$

2. Change to equivalent fractions in standard form.

a. $-\dfrac{3}{x+y}$ *b.* $-\dfrac{-a}{x}$ *c.* $-\dfrac{b-2}{4}$

3. Rewrite in the form $\dfrac{ac}{b}$.

a. $\dfrac{2}{3}(x-3)$ *b.* $-\dfrac{1}{3}(x^2+1)$ *c.* $-\dfrac{3}{4}(2x+y)$

4. Reduce to lowest terms.

a. $\dfrac{x^2y^2z^2}{xy^3}$ *b.* $\dfrac{b-3}{b^2-2b-3}$ *c.* $\dfrac{a^2+a}{a^3-a}$

5. Build each fraction to an equivalent fraction.

a. $\dfrac{3}{x-y}, \dfrac{}{2(x-y)}$ *b.* $\dfrac{3}{a+3}, \dfrac{}{a^2+5a+6}$ *c.* $\dfrac{x}{x-2}, \dfrac{}{x^2-3x+2}$

6. Change both fractions to equivalent fractions with identical denominators.

a. $\dfrac{2}{3}, \dfrac{3}{5}$ *b.* $\dfrac{3}{x^2y}, \dfrac{-2}{xy^2}$ *c.* $\dfrac{a}{a^2-1}, \dfrac{3}{a+1}$

Simplify.

7. *a.* $\dfrac{2}{5}-\dfrac{1}{5}+\dfrac{3}{5}$ *b.* $\dfrac{x+3}{y}-\dfrac{3}{y}$ *c.* $\dfrac{a-2}{3}-\dfrac{a+3}{3}$

8. *a.* $\dfrac{3}{x}-\dfrac{2}{3x}$ *b.* $\dfrac{3}{r}+\dfrac{4}{2s}$ *c.* $\dfrac{2}{ab^2}-\dfrac{3}{a^2b}$

9. *a.* $\dfrac{3}{a-b}+\dfrac{1}{a+b}$ *b.* $\dfrac{a}{a^2-1}-\dfrac{1}{a^2+a}$ *c.* $\dfrac{1}{x^2-25}+\dfrac{5}{x^2-4x-5}$

10. *a.* $\dfrac{2xy^2}{3}\cdot\dfrac{x}{4y^2}$ *b.* $\dfrac{x^2-2x}{5}\cdot\dfrac{25}{x^2}$ *c.* $\dfrac{x^2-7x+6}{x^2-1}\cdot\dfrac{x+1}{x-6}$

11. *a.* $\dfrac{2r}{3s}\div\dfrac{2r^2}{21s^2}$ *b.* $\dfrac{a^2-b^2}{4}\div\dfrac{a^2+ab}{4a-4}$ *c.* $\dfrac{2x^2-5x-3}{2x^2+x}\div\dfrac{x-3}{x^4}$

12. *a.* $\dfrac{\dfrac{3}{6}}{\dfrac{2}{9}}$ *b.* $\dfrac{\dfrac{2}{3}+\dfrac{1}{6}}{\dfrac{1}{3}+\dfrac{5}{6}}$ *c.* $\dfrac{1+\dfrac{1}{2}}{3-\dfrac{1}{4}}$

13. *a.* $\dfrac{1 - \dfrac{a}{b}}{1 + \dfrac{2}{b}}$ *b.* $\dfrac{x - \dfrac{x}{y}}{y - \dfrac{y}{x}}$ *c.* $\dfrac{\dfrac{1}{y} + 3}{2 - \dfrac{3}{y}}$

Solve.

14. *a.* $\dfrac{x}{2} = -1 + \dfrac{2x}{3}$ *b.* $\dfrac{x}{3} + \dfrac{7}{9} = \dfrac{1}{3}$ *c.* $\dfrac{x+1}{2} = \dfrac{2x-9}{5} + 3$

15. *a.* $\dfrac{6}{x} = \dfrac{16}{x+5}$ *b.* $\dfrac{2+y}{y} = \dfrac{3}{2}$ *c.* $\dfrac{y-2}{2y} = \dfrac{5}{2}$

16. *a.* $\dfrac{10}{x+4} - \dfrac{6}{x} = \dfrac{-4}{x}$ *b.* $\dfrac{14}{x-1} + \dfrac{1}{x} = \dfrac{8}{x}$ *c.* $1 - \dfrac{3+y}{2y} = \dfrac{3-y}{y}$

17. Solve for x.

   a. $\dfrac{b}{3} = \dfrac{2ax}{4}$ *b.* $\dfrac{b-x}{4} - \dfrac{b}{3} = \dfrac{x}{2}$ *c.* $\dfrac{a}{x-1} = \dfrac{2a}{x}$

18. If three times a certain number is divided by 10 more than that number, the result is $\frac{1}{2}$. What is the number?

19. The width of a rectangle is $\frac{3}{8}$ of the length. What are the dimensions if the perimeter is 22 feet?

20. One car travels 90 miles in the same time that another car travels 60 miles. If the slower car is traveling 10 mph slower than the other car, find the rate of each.

CUMULATIVE REVIEW

1. The relation between centigrade and Fahrenheit temperatures is given by $F = \frac{9}{5}C + 32$. Solve for C in terms of F.

2. Show by direct substitution that 4 is a solution of the equation

$$\frac{2x}{5} + \frac{2(x-3)}{5} = 2.$$

3. If a and b represent numbers, then $a + b = b + a$. This statement is called the __?__ law of addition.

4. If the number represented by $(24 \cdot 5) + (24 \cdot 8)$ is divided by 24, the quotient is __?__ .

5. The sum of the integers between -5 and $+5$ is __?__ .

6. Write $(300 \cdot 3) + (70 \cdot 3) + (5 \cdot 3)$ as $(? \cdot 3)$.

7. The reciprocal of $\frac{13}{42}$ is __?__ .

8. If $x = -2$ and $y = 4$, find the numerical value of $x^3 - 5y$.

9. Simplify: $(3 - x) + (2 + x) - (1 - x)$.

10. Factor completely: $x^4 - 16$.

11. Factor completely: $5b^3 + 10b^2 + 5b$.

12. Divide $(x^2 - 6x + 8)$ by $(x - 2)$.

In Exercises 13–16, solve for x.

13. $1 - \dfrac{x}{3} = \dfrac{2}{5}.$

14. $\dfrac{x + 1}{2x + 4} = \dfrac{3}{7}.$

15. $\dfrac{x}{3} + \dfrac{x}{2} = x - 1.$

16. $\dfrac{x}{b} = \dfrac{a}{c}.$

17. Find the altitude of a triangle whose area is 200 square inches and base is 40 inches.

18. Fifty coins in nickels and dimes amount to $3.50. How many of each are there?

19. The sum of three consecutive even integers is 16 more than the next even integer. What are the integers?

20. A man gave $\frac{1}{3}$ of his money to one son and $\frac{1}{4}$ to another son. He has $10 left. How much did he have to start with?

CHAPTER 6

FIRST-DEGREE EQUATIONS IN TWO VARIABLES

The language of mathematics is particularly effective in representing relationships between two or more variables. We have used many examples of such relationships in previous chapters. As another example, let us consider the distance traveled in a certain length of time by a car moving at a constant speed of 40 miles per hour. We can represent this relationship by:

1. A word sentence: The distance traveled in miles is equal to forty times the number of hours traveled.
2. An equation: $d = 40t$.
3. A tabulation of values.
4. A graph showing the relationship between time and distance.

We have already used word sentences and equations to describe such relationships; in this chapter we shall give our attention to tabular and graphical representations.

6.1   SOLUTIONS OF EQUATIONS IN TWO VARIABLES

The equation $d = 40t$ serves to pair with each time t a distance d. Thus,

$$\text{if } t = 1, \text{ then } d = 40,$$
$$\text{if } t = 2, \text{ then } d = 80,$$
$$\text{if } t = 3, \text{ then } d = 120, \text{ etc.}$$

The pair of numbers 1 and 40, considered together, is called a **solution** of the equation in two variables $d = 40t$. If we agree to refer to paired numbers in a specified order, we may abbreviate the above solutions as

(1, 40), (2, 80), (3, 120), etc., where it is understood that the first number refers to time, whereas the second refers to distance. We call such pairs of numbers **ordered pairs,** and refer to the first and second numbers in the pairs as **components.** With this agreement, solutions of the equation $d = 40t$ are ordered pairs (t, d) whose components satisfy the equation. Some such ordered pairs are

$$(0, 0),\ (1, 40),\ (2, 80),\ (3, 120),\ (4, 160),\ \text{and}\ (5, 200).$$

In a relationship of this type, we note that the variables d and t may be replaced by *any one* of a given set of numbers. On the other hand, symbols such as 40, that are limited to one specific value, are called **constants.** In any particular discussion involving two variables, when we assign a value to one of the variables, the value for the other variable is determined and therefore dependent upon the first. It is convenient to speak of the variable associated with the first component of an ordered pair as the **independent variable** and the variable associated with the second component of an ordered pair as the **dependent variable.**

EXERCISES 6.1

1. The equation $C = 2\pi r$ shows the way the circumference (C) of a circle is related to the length (r) of the radius of the circle.

   a. Which symbols are constants?
   b. Which symbols are variables?
   c. What is the effect on C of increasing r?
   d. Which symbol is the independent variable, if a solution is given by (r, C)?
   e. Which symbol is the dependent variable?
   f. If r is assigned the value 3, what is the value of C? (Use 3.14 for π.)

2. The equation $d = 4t$ shows the way the distance traveled by a person walking 4 miles per hour is related to the length of time he walks.

   a. Which symbols are constants?
   b. Which symbols are variables?
   c. What is the effect on d of increasing t?
   d. Which symbol is the independent variable if a solution is given by (t, d)?
   e. Which symbol is the dependent variable.
   f. If t is assigned the value 3, what is the value of d?

In Exercises 3–12, find the value for the dependent variable y that is associated with each given value x. Express your answer as an ordered pair (x, y).

3. $y = x + 2.$

Sample problem: $(-4, \quad)$

$$\text{Replace } x \text{ with } -4.$$

$$y = (-4) + 2$$
$$y = -2$$

$$Ans. \ (-4, -2)$$

   a. (1,)   *b.* (3,)   *c.* (0,)   *d.* (−2,)   *e.* (−1,)   *f.* (−6,)

4. $y = 2x - 1$
   a. (2,)   *b.* (1,)   *c.* (0,)   *d.* (−1,)   *e.* (−2,)   *f.* (−3,)

5. $y = 3x + 2$
   a. (10,)   *b.* (5,)   *c.* (0,)   *d.* (−5,)   *e.* (−1,)   *f.* (−15,)

6. $y = 4 - 2x$
   a. (2,)   *b.* (1,)   *c.* (0,)   *d.* (−1,)   *e.* (−2,)   *f.* (−3,)

7. $y = 4x$
   a. (2,)   *b.* (1,)   *c.* (0,)   *d.* (−1,)   *e.* (−2,)   *f.* (−3,)

8. $y = -x$
   a. (2,)   *b.* (1,)   *c.* (0,)   *d.* (−1,)   *e.* (−2,)   *f.* (−3,)

9. $y - 2x = 5$

Sample problem: $(2, \quad)$

$$\text{Solve } y - 2x = 5 \text{ explicitly for } y.$$

$$y = 2x + 5$$

$$\text{Replace } x \text{ with } .$$

$$y = 2(2) + 5$$
$$y = 9$$

$$Ans. \ (2, 9)$$

   a. (4,)   *b.* (1,)   *c.* (0,)   *d.* (−1,)   *e.* (−2,)   *f.* (−3,)

10. $y + 3x - 5 = 0$
   a. (2,)   *b.* (1,)   *c.* (0,)   *d.* (−1,)   *e.* (−2,)   *f.* (−3,)

11. $2x - 3y = 6$

Sample problem: $(2, \quad)$

$$\text{Solve } 2x - 3y = 6 \text{ explicitly for } y.$$

$$2x - 6 = 3y$$
$$3y = 2x - 6$$
$$y = \frac{2x - 6}{3}$$

$$\text{Replace } x \text{ with } 2.$$

Solution continued on the next page

$$y = \frac{2(\;) - 6}{3}$$

$$y = -\frac{2}{3}$$

$$Ans. \left(2, \; -\frac{2}{3}\right)$$

   a. (10,)   *b.* (5,)   *c.* (0,)   *d.* (−5,)   *e.* (−10,)   *f.* (−15,)

12. $3x + 2y = 4$

   a. (2,)   *b.* (1,)   *c.* (0,)   *d.* (−1,)   *e.* (−2,)   *f.* (−3,)

6.2 GRAPHS OF ORDERED PAIRS

Just as a correspondence exists between numbers and points on a line, a correspondence exists between ordered pairs of numbers and points on a plane. By constructing a pair of perpendicular line graphs, called **axes,** at some point in a plane, we may assign an ordered pair of numbers to each point in the plane by referring to the perpendicular distance of the point from each of the intersecting line graphs. If the first component is positive, the point lies to the right of the vertical axis; if negative, it lies to the left. If the second component is positive, the point lies above the horizontal axis; if negative, it lies below. The point of intersection of the axes is called the **origin,** the distance y that the point is located from the x-axis is called the **ordinate** of the point, and the distance x that the point is located from the y-axis is called the **abscissa** of the point. The abscissa and ordinate together are called the **rectangular** or **Car-**

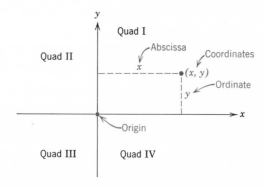

Figure 6.1

tesian coordinates of the point. Each of the four regions into which the axes divide the plane is called a **quadrant,** generally referred to by the number indicated in Figure 6.1.

EXERCISES 6.2

In Exercises 1–8, plot each set of ordered pairs on a rectangular coordinate system.

Sample problem:

a. $(2, 3)$
b. $(-2, 1)$
c. $(0, -2)$
d. $(-4, 4)$
e. $(3, -1)$
f. $(-3, -3)$

1. a. $(1, 2)$ b. $(-2, 3)$ c. $(3, -1)$ d. $(-4, 5)$ e. $(4, 4)$ f. $(0, 5)$
2. a. $(3, 4)$ b. $(-2, 0)$ c. $(2, -1)$ d. $(0, 5)$ e. $(4, -1)$ f. $(-5, 1)$
3. a. $(0, 0)$ b. $(0, 2)$ c. $(0, 5)$ d. $(0, -2)$ e. $(-5, 0)$ f. $(5, 0)$

In Exercises 4 and 5, let the distance between successive marks on your axes represent 5 units.

4. a. $(10, 5)$ b. $(-10, 5)$ c. $(25, -5)$
   d. $(0, 20)$ e. $(-20, -20)$ f. $(25, 15)$

5. a. $(0, 30)$ b. $(-25, 0)$ c. $(0, -20)$
   d. $(30, -25)$ e. $(-5, 0)$ f. $(5, -30)$

In Exercises 6, 7, and 8, let the distance between successive marks on the x-axis represent 1 unit and on the y-axis 5 units.

6. a. $(3, 25)$ b. $(-1, 20)$ c. $(5, 0)$
   d. $(-2, -20)$ e. $(0, -10)$ f. $(-5, -30)$

7. a. $(2, -10)$ b. $(1, -5)$ c. $(0, 0)$
   d. $(-1, 5)$ e. $(-2, 10)$ f. $(-3, 15)$

8. a. $(3, -24)$ b. $(2, -16)$ c. $(1, -8)$
   d. $(0, 0)$ e. $(-1, 8)$ f. $(-2, 16)$

9. Connect the points plotted in Exercise 7. What do you observe?
10. Connect the points plotted in Exercise 8. What do you observe?

11. In the rectangular coordinate system, name the (perpendicular) distance from a given point to: *a.* The *x*-axis. *b.* The *y*-axis.

12. Which component of the ordered pair (x, y) represents the (perpendicular) distance of a point from: The *x*-axis? The *y*-axis?

13. Name the point corresponding to $(0, 0)$.

14. Describe the location of the graphs of all ordered pairs $(0, y)$ and $(x, 0)$.

15. Describe the location of the graphs of all ordered pairs (a, a); i.e., all points whose first and second components are equal.

16. Graph $(1, 2)$ and $(3, 6)$ and draw a line connecting the points.

    a. Does the graph of $(2, 4)$ lie on the line?
    b. If you extended the graph in both directions would the graphs of $(4, 8)$ and $(-1, -2)$ lie on the line?
    c. Is the graph of $(0, 0)$ on this line?

17. Locate the graphs of $(2, 3)$ and $(2, 5)$ and draw a line connecting them.

    a. Does the graph of $(2, 4)$ lie on this line?
    b. Does the graph of $(1, 3)$ lie on this line?
    c. If you extended the graph in both directions, would the graphs of $(2, 6)$ and $(2, -1)$ lie on the line?
    d. Is the graph of $(0, 0)$ on the line?

18. How many points lie on any line in the plane?

19. What would be the least number of points necessary to determine a (straight) line?

20. Which axis, the horizontal or the vertical is usually employed to represent:

    a. The independent variable?   *b.* The dependent variable?

6.3 GRAPHING FIRST-DEGREE EQUATIONS

In Section 6.1, we observed that a solution of an equation in two variables is an ordered pair. In Section 6.2, we observed that the components of an ordered pair are the coordinates of a point in a plane. Thus, to graph an equation in two variables, we need only plot the set of ordered pairs that are solutions to the equation. For example, we may find some representative solutions to the first degree equation $y = x + 2$, say

$$(0, 2), \quad (-3, -1), \quad (-2, 0), \quad \text{and} \quad (3, 5).$$

If we graph the points determined by these ordered pairs and pass a straight line through them, we obtain the graph of all solutions of $y = x + 2$ as shown in Figure 6.2. The graphs of first-degree equations

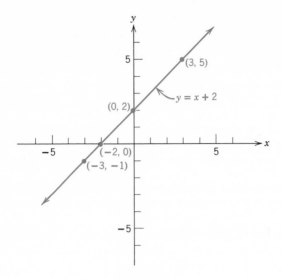

Figure 6.2

are always straight lines; therefore such equations are also referred to as linear equations.

Only two points are necessary to determine the graph of any first-degree equation. A third point is usually obtained as a check.

The following procedure is suggested in graphing a first-degree equation.

1. Construct a set of rectangular axes showing the scale and the variable represented by each axis.

2. Find two ordered pairs that are solutions of the equation to be graphed. Assign any convenient value to one variable and determine the corresponding value of the other variable.

3. Graph these ordered pairs.

4. Pass a straight line through the points.

5. Check by graphing a third ordered pair that is a solution of the equation and verify that it lies on the line.

EXERCISES 6.3

1. Given $d = 4t$ (see Section 6.1, Exercise 2), find the value of d corresponding to each value of t and express your answer in the form of an ordered pair (t, d). Then graph each of the ordered pairs and connect them with a straight line.

    a. (0, ?)   *b.* (2, ?)   *c.* (4, ?)

    d. Where are all points located whose coordinates satisfy $d = 4t$?

    e. Check by obtaining additional solutions (1, ?) and (3, ?) and graphing these.

2. What is the minimum number of points necessary to determine the line representing $d = 4t$?

In Exercises 3–14:

  (1) Find any two ordered pairs that are solutions of the given equation.

  (2) Graph these points and draw a straight line through them.

  (3) Check your result by finding a third solution of the equation and verify that its graph is a point on the line. Graph each equation on a separate set of axes.

Sample problem : $2x + 3y = 6$

                                Solve explicitly for y.

$$y = \frac{6 - 2x}{3}$$

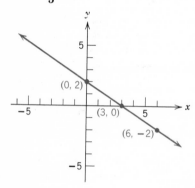

Take any two numbers for the first components, say 0 and 6.

Find the second components of (0, ?) and (6, ?) so that the ordered pairs are solutions of the equation.

Graph the ordered pairs (0, 2) and (6, −2) which are obtained and draw a straight line through them.

Check by noting that the graph of a third ordered pair (3, 0) that satisfies the equation also lies on the line.

3. $y = x + 2$ **4.** $y = x - 2$ **5.** $y = 2x + 1$

6. $y = 3x - 1$ **7.** $y = 2x - 1$ **8.** $y + x = 4$

9. $y - 3x = 0$ **10.** $2y = 3x + 4$ **11.** $3y = 4 - x$

12. $3y + 2x = 12$ **13.** $2y + x - 6 = 0$ **14.** $y - 2x - 6 = 0$

15. Consider the two ordered pairs (5, 2) and (2, 2).

    a. Graph these ordered pairs and draw a straight line through their graphs.

    b. Are the graphs of (1, 2), (3, 2), (4, 2), (−2, 2) on the line?

    c. Would the graph of $(x, 2)$ lie on the line for any (all) x?

    d. Does the value of x have anything to do with the fact that a point lies on this line?

e. Is $y = 0x + 2$ an equation for the line?

f. Does $y = 2$ give a complete description of the line?

16. Consider the two ordered pairs (3, 5) and (3, 2).

a. Graph these ordered pairs and draw a straight line through their graphs.

b. Are the graphs of (3, −1), (3, 4), (3, 6) on the line?

c. Would the graphs of (3, *y*) lie on the line for any (all) *y*?

d. Does the value of *y* have anything to do with the fact that a point lies on this line?

e. Is $x = 0y + 3$ an equation for the line?

f. Does $x = 3$ give a complete description of the line?

Graph each of the following equations:

Sample problem: $y = 3$

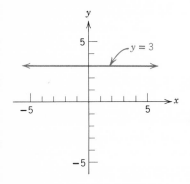

The equation $y = 3$ is equivalent to $y = 0x + 3$. For each x, the value of y is 3. Thus, the graph is a line parallel to the x-axis at a distance of 3 units above this axis.

17. $x = 4$	**18.** $y = -1$	**19.** $x = -3$	**20.** $y = 5$
21. $x = -2$	**22.** $y = -5$	**23.** $x = 0$	**24.** $y = 0$

6.4 INTERCEPT METHOD OF GRAPHING

In Section 6.3 we assigned values to x in equations in two variables to find the corresponding values of y. The solutions of an equation in two variables that are generally easiest to find are those in which either the first component or the second component is 0. For example, if we substitute 0 for x in the equation

$$3x + 4y = 12 \qquad (1)$$

we have

$$3(0) + 4y = 12,$$

$$4y = 12,$$

$$y = 3.$$

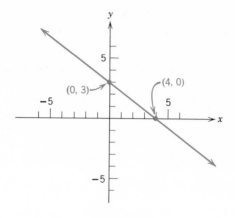

Figure 6.3

Hence a solution of Equation (1) is (0, 3). We can also find ordered pairs that are solutions of equations in two variables by assigning values to y and determining the corresponding values of x. In particular, if we substitute 0 for y in Equation (1) we obtain

$$3x + 4(0) = 12,$$

$$3x = 12,$$

$$x = 4,$$

and a second solution of the equation is (4, 0). The ordered pairs (0, 3) and (4, 0) can now be used to graph Equation (1). The graph is shown in Figure 6.3. The numbers 4 and 3 are called the **x-intercept,** and the **y-intercept** of the graph, respectively.

The foregoing method of drawing the graph of a linear equation is called the **intercept method of graphing.**

If the graph intersects the axes at the origin or near the origin, the intercept method is not satisfactory. It is then necessary to graph an ordered pair that is a solution of the equation and whose graph is not the origin or is not near the origin.

EXERCISES 6.4

Graph each equation by the intercept method.

$2x - y = 6$ (1)

Substitute 0 for x and solve for y.

$2(0) - y = 6$

$- y = 6$

$y = -6$

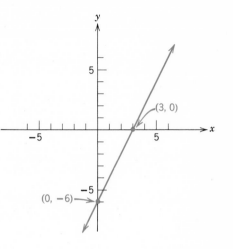

The ordered pair $(0, -6)$ is a solution of Equation (1). Substitute 0 for y in Equation (1) and solve for x.

$2x - (0) = 6$

$2x = 6$

$x = 3$

The ordered pair $(3, 0)$ is a solution of Equation (1).

Graph $(0, -6)$ and $(3, 0)$ and complete the graph of Equation (1).

1. $x + y = 5$	**2.** $x - y = 4$	**3.** $2x + y = 8$
4. $x + 2y = 6$	**5.** $3x - y = 6$	**6.** $x - 2y = 4$
7. $2x + 3y = 12$	**8.** $3x + 5y = 15$	**9.** $3x - 4y = 12$
10. $4x - 5y = 20$	**11.** $y = x + 6$	**12.** $y = x + 4$
13. $y = 2x - 4$	**14.** $y = 3x + 9$	**15.** $y = 2x + 5$
16. $y = 3x - 7$	**17.** $x = 4 + y$	**18.** $x = 6 - 2y$
19. $x = 3y - 10$	**20.** $x = 5y + 5$	**21.** $2x - y = 0$
22. $x - 3y = 0$	**23.** $2x + 3y = 1$	**24.** $4x - 3y = 1$

6.5 GRAPHICAL SOLUTION OF SYSTEMS OF LINEAR EQUATIONS

It is frequently useful to be able to find a single ordered pair that is a solution to each of two different equations. One means of obtaining such an ordered pair is by graphing the two equations on the same set of axes and determining the coordinates of the point where they intersect. For example, consider the equations $x + y = 5$ and $x - y = 1$. Using the intercept method of graphing, we find that two ordered pairs that are

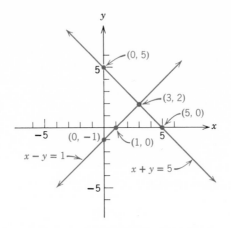

Figure 6.4

solutions of $y = 5 - x$ are

$$(0, 5) \quad \text{and} \quad (5, 0).$$

Two ordered pairs that are solutions of $y = x - 1$ are

$$(0, 1) \quad \text{and} \quad (1, 0).$$

The graphs of the equations are shown in Figure 6.4. The coordinates of the point of intersection are the components of $(3, 2)$.* Hence, $(3, 2)$ should satisfy each equation.

Check.

$y = 5 - x,$	$y = x - 1,$
$(2) = 5 - (3)$	$(2) = (3) - 1,$
$2 = 2;$	$2 = 2.$

Equations considered together in this fashion are said to form a **system of equations** and, in general, the solution of such a system is a single ordered pair. The components of this ordered pair satisfy each of the two equations. If the graphs of the equations do not intersect, that is, the lines are parallel, the equations are said to be **inconsistent,** and there is no ordered pair that will satisfy both equations. If the graphs of the equa-

---

* It should be noted that, in general, graphical solutions are only approximate. We shall develop methods for exact solutions in a later section.

tions are the same line, the equations are said to be **dependent,** and each ordered pair which satisfies one equation will satisfy the other.

EXERCISES 6.5

Find the solution of each system by graphical methods. If no solution exists, so state.

Sample problem : $x + y = 8$
$\qquad\qquad\qquad 5x - 2y = 5$

Using the intercept method of graphing, we find that two solutions of $x + y = 8$ are

$\qquad$ (0, 8) and (8, 0).

Two solutions of $5x - 2y = 5$ are

$$\left(0, -\frac{5}{2}\right) \quad \text{and} \quad (1, 0).$$

The graphs of the two equations intersect at the point corresponding to (3, 5).

Ans. (3, 5)

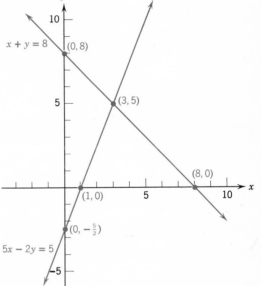

1. $\quad y = 3x$
$\qquad x + y = 8$

2. $\quad x - y = -2$
$\qquad 3x - y = 8$

3. $2x - y = 0$
$\qquad 2x - 3y = -4$

4. $y + 3x = 0$
$\qquad 4x - 3y = 13$

5. $\quad x - 3y = 0$
$\qquad 2x - y = -5$

6. $2y + x = 0$
$\qquad y - x = 6$

7. $y = x$
$\quad\; y = 4 - x$

8. $5y - x = 0$
$\quad\; -y + x = 4$

9. $x + y = 6$
$\quad\; x - y = 2$

10. $\quad y = -x$
$\qquad 2x + y = 3$

11. $y - x = 1$
$\quad\;\; y + x = -5$

12. $\quad x + y = 4$
$\qquad 2x + 2y = 8$

13. $\quad x - 2y = 3$
$\qquad 3x - 6y = 9$

14. $3x = 4y$
$\qquad x = 2 - y$

15. $\qquad y = 2x + 5$
$\qquad x - 3y = -20$

16. $2x + 7y - 12 = 0$
$\qquad x + 5y \quad\;\; = 0$

17. $\quad x + 3y = 5$
$\qquad 2x + 6y = 5$

18. $\quad x = 3y - 4$
$\qquad 6y = 2x + 5$

19. $5x - 2y + 8 = 0$
$\qquad 3x + y + 7 = 0$

20. $7y - 2x + 6 = 0$
$\qquad 8y - 5x - 4 = 0$

6.6 ALGEBRAIC SOLUTION OF SYSTEMS I

Systems of equations can also be solved algebraically. The solutions obtained by such a method will not be approximations.

Let us illustrate the algebraic solution of a simultaneous system by using the example of the preceding section.

$$x + y = 5 \quad (1)$$
$$x - y = 1 \quad (2)$$

Obtain an equation in one variable by adding Equations 1 and 2.

$$2x = 6$$
$$x = 3$$

The solution of this equation yields $x = 3$. Substitute **3** for x in either Equation 1 or 2 to obtain the corresponding value of y. In this case we have selected Equation 1.

$$(3) + y = 5$$
$$y = 2$$

Ans. $x = 3$, $y = 2$; or $(3, 2)$

Check the solution by direct substitution in Equations 1 and 2.

$$x + y = 5 \qquad x - y = 1$$
$$(3) + (2) = 5; \quad (3) - (2) = 1$$

Notice that this method of solution is simply an application of the addition axiom in order to obtain an equation containing a single variable. The equation in one variable in conjunction with either of the original equations then form an equivalent system whose solution is readily obtained.

EXERCISES 6.6

Solve each system.

Sample problem:

$$2x - y = 0 \quad (1)$$
$$\underline{2x + y = 4} \quad (2)$$
$$4x \qquad = 4$$

Obtain an equation in one variable by adding Equations 1 and 2.

Solve the resulting equation for x.

$$x = 1$$

Substitute 1 for x in either Equation 1 or Equation 2, say Equation 1, and solve for y.

$$2(1) - y = 0$$
$$2 = y$$

Ans. $x = 1$, $y = 2$; or $(1, 2)$

1. $x + y = 5$
    $x - y = 1$

2. $x + y = 10$
    $x - y = 4$

3. $x + y = 3$
    $-x + y = 5$

4. $-x + y = 7$
    $x + y = 5$

5. $x + 2y = 10$
    $x - 2y = 2$

6. $2x + y = 3$
    $-2x + y = -1$

7. $3x + 2y = 5$
    $-2x - 2y = -4$

8. $5x - 3y = -1$
    $3x + 3y = 9$

9. $3x + 3y = 15$
    $3x - 3y = 27$

10. $6x - y = 4$
    $2x + y = 4$

11. $7x - 3y = -10$
    $x + 3y = 2$

12. $3x - 2y = 11$
    $3x + 2y = 19$

Sample problem:

$$2a + b = 4 \qquad (1)$$
$$a + b = 3 \qquad (2)$$

Multiply each member of Equation 2 by -1. Add Equations 1 and 2′.* Alternatively, subtract Equation 2 from Equation 1.

$$-a - b = -3 \qquad (2')$$
$$\underline{2a + b = 4 \qquad (1)}$$
$$a = 1$$

Substitute 1 for a in either Equation 1 or Equation 2, say Equation 2.

$$(1) + b = 3$$
$$b = 2$$

Ans. $a = 1$, $b = 2$; or $(1, 2)$ [Where the variables are a and b, the ordered pair is given in the form (a, b).]

13. $2a + b = 3$
    $a + b = 2$

14. $a + b = 6$
    $3a + b = 10$

15. $a + b = 7$
    $a + 3b = 11$

16. $a + 2b = -1$
    $3a + 2b = 1$

17. $3a + 2b = 1$
    $2a + 2b = 0$

18. $6a + 5b = 6$
    $-4a + 5b = -4$

* The symbol ′, called "prime," indicates an equivalent equation; that is, Equation 2′ is equivalent to Equation 2.

19. $4a + 2b = 4$
$3a + 2b = 8$

20. $4a + 2b = 4$
$6a + 2b = 8$

21. $a + 3b = 2$
$2a + 3b = 7$

22. $3a - 4b = 19$
$-2a - 4b = -6$

23. $3a - 4b = 0$
$3a + 2b = 18$

24. $3a - 2b = 5$
$-a - 2b = -15$

25. $x + y = -1$
$2x + y = -5$

26. $2x + 3y = -5$
$2x - 4y = 16$

27. $3x + 4y = -10$
$x + 4y = -6$

28. $4x - 4y = -4$
$4x - 3y = -3$

29. $7x + 6y = 12$
$9x + 6y = 12$

30. $3a + 2b = -12$
$a + 2b = -4$

31. $4a - 6b = 8$
$-2a - 6b = 14$

32. $20x + 10y = 25$
$-10x + 10y = -5$

Sample problem :

$$\frac{x}{6} + \frac{y}{4} = \frac{3}{2} \qquad (1)$$

$$\frac{2x}{3} - \frac{y}{2} = 0 \qquad (2)$$

Remove fractions by multiplying each equation by L.C.D. of fractions in that equation.

$$(\overset{2}{\cancel{12}})\,\frac{x}{\cancel{6}} + (\overset{3}{\cancel{12}})\,\frac{y}{\cancel{4}} = (\overset{6}{\cancel{12}})\,\frac{3}{\cancel{2}}$$

$$(\overset{2}{\cancel{6}})\,\frac{2x}{\cancel{3}} - (\overset{3}{\cancel{6}})\,\frac{y}{\cancel{2}} = (6)0$$

$$2x + 3y = 18 \qquad (1')$$
$$4x - 3y = 0 \qquad (2')$$

Solve resulting system.

$$6x = 18$$
$$x = 3$$

Substitute 3 for x in Equation 2'.

$$4(3) - 3y = 0$$
$$-3y = -12$$
$$y = 4$$

Ans. $x = 3$, $y = 4$; or $(3, 4)$

33. $y + \dfrac{1}{2}x = 0$

$\dfrac{1}{3}y - \dfrac{1}{3}x = 2$

34. $\dfrac{a}{5} + \dfrac{2b}{5} = 2$

$\dfrac{a}{2} - b = 1$

35. $\dfrac{2x}{3} + y = 3$

$\dfrac{x}{2} - \dfrac{y}{4} = \dfrac{5}{4}$

36. $x - \dfrac{2}{3}y = -4$

$\dfrac{x}{4} + \dfrac{y}{2} = -1$

37. $\dfrac{a}{4} - \dfrac{b}{3} = 0$

$\dfrac{a}{2} + \dfrac{b}{3} = 3$

38. $a + \dfrac{2(b+1)}{3} = 1$

$\dfrac{5a}{2} - \dfrac{b+8}{4} = -5$

39. $\dfrac{x-1}{3} + \dfrac{y-1}{3} = 2$

$\dfrac{x-1}{2} + \dfrac{y-1}{6} = \dfrac{5}{3}$

40. $\dfrac{x-1}{2} - \dfrac{y+2}{3} = -2$

$\dfrac{x-1}{4} + \dfrac{y+2}{2} = -1$

6.7 ALGEBRAIC SOLUTION OF SYSTEMS II

The solution of a system of equations by addition depends upon one of the variables having identical coefficients in both of the equations. If such is not the case, we may find equations that are equivalent to the equations in the system and do have identical coefficients on one of the variables. Consider the system:

$$-5x + 3y = 1 \qquad (1)$$
$$-7x - 2y = 3. \qquad (2)$$

If we multiply each member of Equation 1 by 2 and each member of Equation 2 by 3, we obtain an equivalent system

$$-10x + 6y = 2 \qquad (1')$$
$$-21x - 6y = 9 \qquad (2')$$

which may be solved as in the preceding section.

In all our preceding exercises and examples, the terms involving the variables have been in the left-hand member and the constant term in the right-hand member. We shall refer to this arrangement as the **standard form** for systems. It is convenient to arrange equations in such form before proceeding with the solution of a system of equations.

EXERCISES 6.7

Solve.

Sample problem:

$$3x + 2y = 11 \qquad (1)$$
$$5x - 4y = 11 \qquad (2)$$

Multiply each member of Equation 1 by 2. Add Equations 1' and 2.

Solution continued on the next page

$$6x + 4y = 22 \quad (1')$$
$$\underline{5x - 4y = 11} \quad (2)$$
$$11x \qquad = 33$$

Solve for x.

$$x = 3$$

Substitute 3 for x in Equation 1 and solve for y.

$$3(3) + 2y = 11$$
$$2y = 2$$
$$y = 1$$

Ans. $x = 3,\ y = 1$; or $(3,\ 1)$

1. $3x + 2y = 7$ $x + y = 3$	**2.** $2x - 3y = 8$ $x + y = -1$	**3.** $2x - y = 2$ $3x + 2y = 10$
4. $a - 4b = 9$ $3a + 2b = 13$	**5.** $3a - b = -5$ $2a + 3b = -7$	**6.** $-x + 3y = -1$ $-6x + y = -6$
7. $3a - 3b = -3$ $-6a + 2b = 14$	**8.** $3x - 6y = 6$ $x - 2y = 3$	**9.** $5x + 3y = 19$ $2x - y = 12$
10. $5x - 3y = 32$ $2x + 6y = -16$	**11.** $3x - 5y = -1$ $x + 2y = 18$	**12.** $3x + 3y = 0$ $6x + 9y = -6$

Sample problem :

$$2y = 11 - 3x$$
$$5x = 11 + 4y$$

Arrange equations in standard form.

$$3x + 2y = 11$$
$$5x - 4y = 11$$

Solve as described in the previous sample problem.

13. $3x + 2y = 7$ $x = y - 1$	**14.** $3x + 9 = -2y$ $x = -3y + 25$	**15.** $a + 5b = 0$ $-3a + 10 = 10b$
16. $x = 8 - 2y$ $2x = 6 + y$	**17.** $8b - 3a = 5$ $a = b$	**18.** $6x = 22 + 2y$ $8x = 33 - y$
19. $8a = 4b + 4$ $3a = 2b + 3$	**20.** $x + 3y = 35$ $0 = 2x - y$	**21.** $5b = 3a + 8$ $2b = -a + 1$
22. $x - y = 15$ $2x = -3y$	**23.** $3x - 2y = 3$ $2x = y + 2$	**24.** $2x = 2y + 2$ $4x = 5 + 4y$
25. $2x + 3y = -1$ $3x + 5y = -2$	**26.** $3x - 2y = 13$ $7x + 3y = 15$	**27.** $2x = 3y - 1$ $3x + 4y = 24$

28. $5x - 2y = 0$
$2x - 3y = -11$

29. $3b = 9$
$2b + a = 10$

30. $b = 5$
$2b = 4a - 2$

31. $2a + 3b = 0$
$5a - 2b = -19$

32. $8x - 7y = 0$
$7x = 8y + 15$

Sample problem:

$$\frac{x + 1}{2} - \frac{2y - 1}{6} = \frac{7}{6} \qquad (1)$$

$$\frac{2x - 1}{4} - \frac{y - 3}{4} = 1 \qquad (2)$$

Express each equation without fractions by multiplying by L.C.D. of fractions in that equation.

$$(6)\frac{x + 1}{2} - (6)\frac{2y - 1}{6} = (6)\frac{7}{6}$$

$$(4)\frac{2x - 1}{4} - (4)\frac{y - 3}{4} = (4)1$$

$$3(x + 1) - (2y - 1) = 7$$
$$(2x - 1) - (y - 3) = 4$$

Write equations in standard form.

$$3x - 2y = 3 \qquad (1')$$
$$2x - y = 2 \qquad (2')$$

Solve the system 1' and 2'. Multiply Equation 2' by -2, and solve for x.

$$3x - 2y = 3 \qquad (1')$$
$$-4x + 2y = -4 \qquad (2'')$$
$$-x = -1$$
$$x = 1$$

Substitute 1 for x in Equation 1'.

$$3(1) - 2y = 3$$
$$y = 0$$

Ans. $x = 1, y = 0$; or $(1, 0)$

33. $\dfrac{5a}{4} + b = \dfrac{11}{2}$

$a + \dfrac{b}{3} = 3$

34. $2a - \dfrac{5b}{2} = 13$

$\dfrac{a}{3} + \dfrac{b}{5} = \dfrac{14}{15}$

35. $\dfrac{x}{4} + \dfrac{y}{5} = 1$

$\dfrac{2x}{9} - \dfrac{y}{9} = -2$

36. $\dfrac{5x}{8} + y = \dfrac{1}{4}$

$\dfrac{5x}{4} - \dfrac{3y}{2} = 4$

37. $\dfrac{x}{3} - \dfrac{y}{2} = 1$

$\dfrac{2x + 3}{5} - \dfrac{5y + 1}{11} = 2$

38. $\dfrac{2x + 1}{7} + \dfrac{3y + 2}{5} = \dfrac{1}{5}$

$\dfrac{3x - 2}{2} + \dfrac{y + 4}{4} = 4$

39. $\dfrac{y + 4}{3} = \dfrac{x + 3}{7}$

$\dfrac{x}{2} - \dfrac{7y}{6} = \dfrac{19}{6}$

40. $\dfrac{2x}{3} - \dfrac{y - 4}{2} = 5$

$2x - \dfrac{3y}{2} = 9$

6.8 WORD PROBLEMS

If two variables are related by a single first-degree equation, there are infinitely many ordered pairs that are solutions of the equation. If the two variables are also related by another first-degree equation independent of the first, we have observed that there can be only one ordered pair that is a solution of both equations. Therefore, in order to solve problems using two variables, it is necessary to represent two independent relationships using two equations. Many problems can be solved more easily by using a system of equations than by using a single equation involving one variable.

EXERCISES 6.8

In each of the following exercises:

    a. Represent two independent conditions of the problem by a system of equations using two variables.

    b. Solve the system.

Sample problem : A 12-foot board is cut into two parts so that one part is 2 feet longer than the other. How long is each part?

Draw sketch.

Identify the variables both in symbols and in words.

Let $x = $ the longer part;

    $y = $ the shorter part.

Obtain two equations and solve the system.

$$x + y = 12 \qquad (1)$$
$$\underline{x - y = 2} \qquad (2)$$
$$2x \quad\;\; = 14$$
$$x = 7$$

Substitute 7 for x in Equation 1 or 2, say 2.

$$(7) - y = 2$$
$$y = 5$$

Ans. Longer piece is 7 feet; shorter piece is 5 feet.

1. The sum of two numbers is 25 and their difference is 9. What are the numbers?

2. The sum of two numbers is 21 and their difference is 13. What are the numbers?

3. A 20-foot board is cut into two pieces, one of which is 2 feet longer than the other. How long is each piece?

4. A 30-foot board is cut into two pieces, one of which is 6 feet shorter than the other. How long is each piece?

5. The length of a rectangle is 10 inches more than the width, and the perimeter of the rectangle is 28 inches. What are the dimensions of the rectangle?

6. A rectangle has a width 7 inches less than the length, and the perimeter is 46 inches. What are the dimensions of the rectangle?

7. Two packages weighed together total 28 pounds. One of the packages weighs 8 pounds less than twice the other. How much does each weigh?

8. Two packages weighed together total 45 pounds. One of the packages weighs 11 pounds more than the other. How much does each weigh?

9. A house and lot together sold for $12,000. The house was valued at $5000 more than the lot. What was the value of each separately?

10. A washer and a dryer together cost $356. The dryer cost $20 more than two times the washer. What was the price of each?

11. It took 24 working hours to paint the outside walls and trim of a house. If it took 6 more hours to paint the trim than it did the walls, how long did it take to paint each?

Sample problem: Two trains left towns A and B, which are 300 miles apart, at the same time and proceeded toward each other on parallel tracks. At the time they met, the train from A had traveled 12 miles farther than the train from B. How many miles from A were the trains when they met?

Solution continued on the next page

Identify the variables both in symbols and words.

Let x = distance from town A;

y = distance from town B.

Obtain two equations and solve the system.

$$x + y = 300$$
$$x - y = 12$$
$$2x = 312$$
$$x = 156$$

Ans. Distance from A is 156 miles.

12. Two trains left towns A and B, which are 240 miles apart, at the same time and proceeded toward each other on parallel tracks. At the time they met, the train from A had traveled 10 miles farther than the train from B. How many miles from A were the trains when they met?

13. A freight train is made up of 92 cars, not counting the engine and its caboose. These cars are partly flat cars and partly box cars. There are 28 more flat cars than box cars. How many flat cars are there in the train?

14. A certain fishing spot is located 27 miles from town. Part of the distance can be driven in a car, but part of it must be traveled on foot. If it is possible to drive 11 more miles than must be walked, how far must be walked?

15. A loaf of bread and a can of corn together cost 72 cents. The bread cost a dime more than the corn. What was the cost of each?

16. An investor bought some stock in a water company and some stock in a uranium mine. After holding them a month, he sold them. He found he had made $45. "If I don't count the brokerage," he told his wife, "I made four times as much on the water stock as I lost on the uranium stock." How much did he lose on the uranium stock?

17. A man bought a toy train and a doll as presents for his children. He paid a total of $55. If the train cost $1 less than three times the doll, what was the price of each?

18. A mixture of coarse and fine sand weighs 450 pounds. If the fine sand weighs 120 pounds less than twice the weight of the coarse sand, how many pounds of each is in the mixture?

19. The sum of two numbers is 24. One half of one number is 3 more than the other number. What are the numbers?

20. The difference of two numbers is 13. If the smaller number is 2 more than one fourth of the larger, what are the numbers?

21. A collection of 34 coins consists of dimes and quarters. How many coins of each kind are in the collection if the total value is $5.50?

22. The total income from two investments is \$380. One investment yields 4%
and the second investment yields 5%. How much is invested at each rate if
the total investment was \$8000?

23. A sum of \$3600 is invested, part at 4% and the remainder at 6%. Find the
amount of each investment if the interest on each investment is the same.

24. One solution contains 60% alcohol and a second solution contains 30%
alcohol. How much of each solution is needed to make 33 gallons that is
50% alcohol?

CHAPTER REVIEW

1. Given $C = \pi d$. The circumference of a circle π times the diameter.

    a. Which of the symbols are constants?
    b. Which symbols are variables?
    c. If the diameter increases, what happens to the circumference?

2. Solve $2x - y = 4$ explicitly for y.

3. Solve $2y - 3x = 6$ explicitly for y.

4. If $y = 2x + 1$, find the solutions with specified first components.

    a. $(3, ?)$ *b.* $(-2, ?)$ *c.* $(0, ?)$ *d.* $(-\frac{1}{2}, ?)$

5. If $x - y = 5$, find the solutions with specified first components.

    a. $(4, ?)$ *b.* $(-2, ?)$ *c.* $(0, ?)$ *d.* $(-6, ?)$

6. Graph the following ordered pairs on a set of rectangular axes:

    a. $(3, 4)$ *b.* $(-2, 3)$ *c.* $(3, -2)$ *d.* $(0, 4)$

In Exercises 7–10, graph each equation.

7. $x + y = 3$ **8.** $2y - x = 4$ **9.** $x = 3$ **10.** $3x + 2y = 6$

11. Where does the graph of $x - y = 8$ cross the x-axis?

12. Where does the graph of $x - y = 8$ cross the y-axis?

In Exercises 13–16, find the solution of each system by algebraic
methods and check by graphing.

13. $x + y = 3$ **14.** $5x - 2y = -9$
    $-x + y = 5$ $5x + 3y = 26$

15. $16x - 3y = -2$ **16.** $7x = 3y + 1$
    $5x + 4y = 29$ $2x + 4y = 10$

17. Two packages together weigh 84 pounds, and one of the packages
weighs 20 pounds more than the other. How much does each weigh?

18. A rectangle has a perimeter of 150 inches, and its length is 6 inches less than twice its width. What are the dimensions of the rectangle?

19. The sum of two numbers is -40, and their difference is -8. What are the numbers?

20. One number is eight more than four times the other and their sum is -2. What are the numbers?

CUMULATIVE REVIEW

1. Graph all integers between $-\frac{3}{2}$ and $\frac{15}{4}$ on a line graph.

2. If $a = 0$, $b = 1$, $c = -1$, $d = 2$, find the value of $\dfrac{bc + d}{ab + d}$.

3. What is the circumference of a circle with a radius of length 14 inches. (Use $\frac{22}{7}$ for π.)

4. Given $s = \frac{1}{2}gt^2 + c$. Find s, if $c = 2000$, $g = 32$, and $t = 2$.

Simplify.

5. $\dfrac{3x + 6}{2x + 4}$

6. $\dfrac{a^2 - b^2}{a^2 - 2ab + b^2}$

7. $\dfrac{6a - 5}{8} + \dfrac{3a + 5}{12}$

8. $\dfrac{2}{x - 2} - \dfrac{3}{x + 1}$

9. $\dfrac{7a - 14}{5a - 10} \cdot \dfrac{3a - 3}{7a - 7}$

10. $\dfrac{3a + 3}{2a - 6} \div \dfrac{6a + 6}{3a - 9}$

11. $\dfrac{x - \dfrac{x}{y}}{1 - \dfrac{1}{y}}$

12. $(x^2 - 6x + 8) \div (x - 2)$

Solve each equation for x.

13. $\dfrac{3x}{4} - 9 = 0$

14. $x - \dfrac{3x - 2}{2} = \dfrac{1}{2}$

15. $\dfrac{3}{5} = \dfrac{x + 1}{x + 3}$

16. $\dfrac{x + a}{b} = a$

17. Graph: $y = 2x - 6$.

18. By algebraic methods solve the system: $2x - 2y = 10$
$\qquad\qquad x + 2y = 2.$

19. The sum of two numbers is 28. One of them is 6 more than ten times the other. Find the numbers, first by using one equation with one variable and then by using a system of equations with two variables.

20. Find two consecutive integers such that twice the first less half the second is 10. Solve first by using one equation with one variable and then by using a system of equations with two variables.

REVIEW OF FACTORING

The following exercises review processes we studied earlier. The ability to factor will be helpful to you in Chapter 7. If you have difficulty in factoring any of these expressions you should review the appropriate sections in Chapter 4. Factor each polynomial completely.

[4.2]

1. $5x + 10y$

2. $3x^2 + 6x - 3$

3. $-2x^2 - 4$

4. $ab - ac$

5. $abc + ab - ac$

6. $x^2y - xy^2 + xy$

[4.4]

7. $x^2 + 5x + 6$

8. $y^2 - 6y + 9$

9. $y^2 - 7y - 8$

10. $y^2 + 2y - 35$

11. $x^2 - 16$

12. $y^2 - b^2$

[4.6]

13. $2y^2 - y - 3$

14. $6y^2 + y - 1$

15. $6x^2 - 13x + 6$

16. $3x^2 - 8x - 35$

17. $4x^2 - 25$

18. $9y^2 - 4c^2$

[4.7]

19. $4y^2 + 6y + 2$

20. $6x^2 + 21x + 9$

21. $18x^2 - 42x - 16$

22. $80x^2 - 10x - 25$

23. $12y^2 - 48$

24. $50x^2 - 32$

25. $x^2 + 2ax + a^2$

26. $x^2 - 2ax + a^2$

27. $y^2 + 6by + 9b^2$

28. $y^2 - 4by + 4b^2$

29. $x^2 + 8ax + 16a^2$

30. $y^2 - 10by + 25b^2$

CHAPTER 7

QUADRATIC EQUATIONS

A **quadratic equation** is an equation which, in simplest form, contains the second but no higher power of the variable. To facilitate working with quadratic equations, we shall designate as standard form for such equations

$$ax^2 + bx + c = 0.$$

where a, b, and c are constants and $a \neq 0$. Observe that in standard form, the right-hand member is 0 and the terms in the left-hand member are in order of descending powers of the variable. If all three terms are present, for example,

$$2x^2 + 3x - 1 = 0 \quad \text{and} \quad 3x^2 - 2x + 1 = 0,$$

the equation is called a **complete quadratic equation.** If either $b = 0$ or $c = 0$, that is, if one or the other of the last two terms is missing, for example,

$$x^2 - 3 = 0 \quad \text{and} \quad x^2 + 4x = 0,$$

the equation is called an **incomplete quadratic equation.** In this chapter, we shall study one method of finding solutions of quadratic equations.

7.1 SOLUTION OF EQUATIONS IN FACTORED FORM

You know that a solution or root of an equation is a number which, when substituted for the variable, results in a true statement. Now, suppose we have an equation of the form

$$(x - 3)(x - 2) = 0.$$

This equation asserts that the product of two numbers, $(x - 3)$ and $(x - 2)$, is 0. As solutions we seek numbers which, when substituted for x,

162

result in a true statement. To find such numbers, we utilize the following principle:

| *If the product of two or more factors is 0, at least one of the factors is 0.*

Therefore, $(x - 3)(x - 2) = 0$ will be true only if $(x - 3)$ is 0 or if $(x - 2)$ is 0. For what values of x will $x - 3 = 0$? Clearly, if $x = 3$, then $x - 3 = 0$. For what values of x will $x - 2 = 0$? For $x = 2$. Similarly, to solve any equation in factored form for which one member is 0, we can proceed as follows:

1. Set each factor equal to 0.
2. Solve each of the resulting equations.

Sometimes the values of the variable for which one or both factors equal zero can be determined by inspection. This should be done whenever possible.

EXERCISES 7.1

Which of the following products are equal to 0?

1. $(3)(0)$ **2.** $(2 - 4)(2 - 2)$ **3.** $3(4 - 2)$

4. $(7 - 0)(3)$ **5.** $(6)(7 - 7)(5 - 2)$ **6.** $(3)(3 - 7)(5 - 5)$

7. $(2 - 3)(3 - 2)(2 - 1)$ **8.** $(6 - 6)(4 - 3)(5 - 4)$

9. $(2 - 1)(3 - 0)(2 - 0)$ **10.** $(2 - 1)(4 - 4)(6 - 5)$

11. $(-3 + 7)(4 + 2 - 6)7$ **12.** $(8 + 8)(7 - 2)(6 + 2 - 5)$

For what values of x will each of the following factors equal 0?

Sample problem:

$(x - 7)$

           Determine the value by inspection or set $(x - 7)$ equal to 0 and solve the resulting equation.

$x - 7 = 0$

Ans. $x = 7$

13. $(x - 3)$ **14.** $(x + 4)$ **15.** $(x - 5)$ **16.** $(3x - 1)$ **17.** $(4x - 2)$

18. $(3x + 2)$ **19.** $(4x - 1)$ **20.** $(2x + 1)$ **21.** $(5x - 20)$ **22.** $(3x - 3)$

For what values of a will each of the following products equal 0?

Sample problem:

$$(a - 2)(a + 1)$$

Determine values by inspection or set each factor equal to 0 and solve the resulting equations.

$a - 2 = 0 \qquad a + 1 = 0$

Ans. $a = 2, \qquad\qquad a = -1$

23. $(a - 2)(a - 3)$ **24.** $(a + 3)(a + 1)$

25. $3a(a - 5)$ **26.** $2a(2a - 1)$

27. $(2a + 3)(a - 2)$ **28.** $(2a - 3)(a + 2)$

29. $a(a - 1)(a + 1)$ **30.** $a(a - 3)(a + 4)$

31. $(2a - 2)(2a + 3)(a - 7)$ **32.** $(3a - 4)(a + 3)(2a + 1)$

Solve each of the following equations.

Sample problem:

$$(x - 3)(x + 4) = 0$$

Determine values by inspection or set each factor equal to 0 and solve the resulting equations.

$x - 3 = 0 \qquad x + 4 = 0$

Ans. $x = 3, \qquad\qquad x = -4$

Check. $(3 - 3)(3 + 4) = 0$ $[(-4) - 3][(-4 + 4)] = 0$

$\qquad\qquad (0)(7) = 0$ $\qquad\qquad (-7)(0) = 0$

$\qquad\qquad\qquad 0 = 0$ $\qquad\qquad\qquad 0 = 0$

33. $(x - 2)(x - 3) = 0$ **34.** $(x + 2)(x - 4) = 0$

35. $y(y - 4) = 0$ **36.** $p(p - 7) = 0$

37. $(r + 3)(r) = 0$ **38.** $(x + 6)(2x) = 0$

39. $(x - 2)(x + 3) = 0$ **40.** $(x + 5)(x - 5) = 0$

41. $(x - 1)(x + 8) = 0$ **42.** $(x + 3)(x + 7) = 0$

43. $(t + 2)(t - 3) = 0$ **44.** $(x + 1)(x - 3) = 0$

45. $u(u - 4) = 0$ **46.** $x(x + 3) = 0$

47. $(b + 4)(b - 3) = 0$ **48.** $(b - 7)(b - 1) = 0$

49. $(2x - 3)(4x + 3) = 0$ **50.** $(3u - 1)(u + 1) = 0$

51. $(3y - 2)(3y + 2) = 0$ **52.** $(x + 8)(3x - 8) = 0$

53. $2z(2z + 3) = 0$

54. $r(3r + 7) = 0$

55. $(x - 3)(x - 2)(x - 1) = 0$

56. $(x + 6)(x + 5)(x + 4) = 0$

57. $x(x + 2)(x - 1) = 0$

58. $x(x - 3)(x + 2) = 0$

59. $2x(x + 4)(x - 3) = 0$

60. $(x)(x + 1)(x - 1) = 0$

61. $(x)(2x + 1)(2x - 1) = 0$

62. $(2x - 3)(3x + 2)(2x + 2) = 0$

Solve for x, y, or z.

Sample problem:

$$x(3x + a)(x - a) = 0$$

Determine solutions by inspection or set each factor equal to 0 and solve the resulting equations.

$$x = 0 \qquad 3x + a = 0 \qquad x - a = 0$$

Ans. $x = 0,$ $\qquad x = -\dfrac{a}{3},$ $\qquad x = a$

63. $(x - a)(x + a) = 0$

64. $(y - b)(y - 3b) = 0$

65. $(2x + a)(x - a) = 0$

66. $(2x + a)(2x - a) = 0$

67. $x(4x - b) = 0$

68. $ax(bx + c) = 0$

69. $y(2y + 3b)(3y - 2b) = 0$

70. $z(z - a)(2z + 3a) = 0$

71. $bz(z - b)(8z + b) = 0$

72. $bz(2z + 3b)(3z + 2b) = 0$

7.2 SOLUTION OF INCOMPLETE QUADRATIC EQUATIONS BY FACTORING

We observe from the preceding section that if we can write an equation so that one member is in the form of a product of linear factors and the other member is zero, we can find solutions for the equation. In general, there is one solution for each linear factor.

We begin our study of solving quadratic equations by first solving incomplete quadratic equations, that is, quadratic equations such as $y^2 - 2y = 0$, $x^2 = 4$, etc. To solve such a quadratic equation by factoring:

1. Write the equation in standard form.
2. Factor the left-hand member.
3. Set each factor equal to 0.
4. Solve each of the resulting equations.

If the equation is not factorable, other methods of solution must be used. These methods are discussed in Chapter 9.

We can check solutions for quadratic equations in the same manner in which we check solutions for linear equations—by direct substitution in the original equation.

EXERCISES 7.2

Solve by factoring.

Sample problem:
$$x^2 = 5x$$

Write in standard form.

$$x^2 - 5x = 0$$

Factor left-hand member.

$$x(x - 5) = 0$$

Determine solutions by inspection or set each factor equal to 0 and solve the resulting equations.

$$x = 0 \qquad x - 5 = 0$$

Ans. $x = 0,$ $\qquad x = 5$

Check. $(0)^2 = 5(0)$ $\qquad (5)^2 = 5(5)$
$$0 = 0 \qquad\qquad 25 = 25$$

1. $x^2 + 2x = 0$ 2. $z^2 = 2z$ 3. $2y^2 = 5y$ 4. $3x^2 - 6x = 0$
5. $4x^2 = 18x$ 6. $5x^2 = 25x$ 7. $y^2 - y = 0$ 8. $y^2 + y = 0$

Sample problem:
$$x^2 = 25$$

Write in standard form.

$$x^2 - 25 = 0$$

Factor left-hand member.

$$(x - 5)(x + 5) = 0$$

Determine solutions by inspection or set each factor equal to 0 and solve.

$$x - 5 = 0 \qquad x + 5 = 0$$

Ans. $x = 5,$ $\qquad x = -5$

9. $x^2 - 1 = 0$ **10.** $x^2 = 36$ **11.** $x^2 - 4 = 0$

12. $x^2 = 9$ **13.** $x^2 - 16 = 0$ **14.** $x^2 - 100 = 0$

15. $x^2 = 64$ **16.** $x^2 = 49$ **17.** $3x^2 - 27 = 0$

18. $2x^2 = 32$ **19.** $5x^2 = 45$ **20.** $7x^2 = 63$

Sample problem:

$$\frac{15}{2} x^2 - \frac{10}{3} = 0$$

Multiply each term by the L.C.D. 6.

$$(6) \overset{3}{\underset{}{\frac{15}{\cancel{2}}}} x^2 - (6) \overset{2}{\underset{}{\frac{10}{\cancel{3}}}} = (6)0$$

$$45x^2 - 20 = 0$$

Factor left-hand completely.

$$5(9x^2 - 4) = 0$$

$$5(3x - 2)(3x + 2) = 0$$

Determine solutions by inspection or set each factor containing a variable equal to 0 and solve the resulting equations. The constant 5 has no effect on the solution.

$$3x - 2 = 0 \qquad 3x + 2 = 0$$
$$\quad 3x = 2 \qquad \quad 3x = -2$$

Ans. $x = \dfrac{2}{3}, \qquad x = -\dfrac{2}{3}$

21. $x^2 - \dfrac{1}{9} = 0$ **22.** $\dfrac{1}{3} x^2 - \dfrac{4}{3} = 0$ **23.** $\dfrac{2}{3} x^2 - \dfrac{3}{2} = 0$

24. $\dfrac{5}{2} y^2 - 10 = 0$ **25.** $\dfrac{x^2}{2} = 8$ **26.** $3x^2 = \dfrac{75}{4}$

27. $\dfrac{x^2}{2} + x = 0$ **28.** $\dfrac{x^2}{3} - 2x = 0$ **29.** $\dfrac{x^2}{4} + \dfrac{x}{2} = 0$

30. $\dfrac{x^2}{18} + \dfrac{x}{3} = 0$ **31.** $\dfrac{x^2}{5} = x$ **32.** $\dfrac{x^2}{6} = \dfrac{x}{2}$

Solve for x, y, or z.

Sample problems:

a. $\qquad x^2 = -ax$ $\qquad$ *b.* $a^2x^2 = b^2$

Write in standard form.

$$x^2 + ax = 0 \qquad \qquad a^2x^2 - b^2 = 0$$

Factor left-hand member.

Solution continued on the next page

$$x(x + a) = 0 \qquad\qquad (ax - b)(ax + b) = 0$$

Determine solutions by inspection
or set each factor equal to 0 and
solve the resulting equations.

$$x = 0; \quad x + a = 0 \qquad ax - b = 0; \quad ax + b = 0$$
$$ax = b \qquad\qquad ax = -b$$

Ans. $x = 0,$ $\qquad\qquad x = -a,$ $\qquad\qquad x = \dfrac{b}{a},$ $\qquad\qquad x = \dfrac{-b}{a}$

33. $x^2 - a^2 = 0$ $\qquad$ **34.** $z^2 = bz$ $\qquad$ **35.** $ax^2 - ac^2 = 0$

36. $d^2y^2 - a^2 = 0$ $\qquad$ **37.** $ab^2x^2 = ab^2x$ $\qquad$ **38.** $4x^2 - c^2 = 0$

39. $cy - 3y^2 = 0$ $\qquad$ **40.** $ay = y^2$ $\qquad$ **41.** $bx - b^2x^2 = 0$

42. $ax + a^3x^2 = 0$ $\qquad$ **43.** $\dfrac{x^2}{a^2} - 4 = 0$ $\qquad$ **44.** $\dfrac{y^2}{2} + cy = 0$

45. $\dfrac{a^2x^2}{b^2} - 9 = 0$ $\qquad$ **46.** $\dfrac{y^2}{c} + by = 0$

7.3 SOLUTION OF COMPLETE QUADRATIC EQUATIONS BY FACTORING

The methods developed in Section 7.2 are also applicable to the solution
of complete quadratic equations. As before, if the equation is not factorable, other methods must be used.

EXERCISES 7.3

Solve by factoring.

Sample problem:

$$x^2 - 4x - 5 = 0$$

Factor left-hand member.

$$(x - 5)(x + 1) = 0$$

Determine the solutions by inspection
or set each factor equal to 0 and solve
the resulting equations.

$$x - 5 = 0 \qquad x + 1 = 0$$

Ans. $x = 5,$ $\qquad\qquad x = -1$

Check. $\quad (5)^2 - 4(5) - 5 = 0 \qquad (-1)^2 - 4(-1) - 5 = 0$

$\qquad\qquad\quad 25 - 20 - 5 = 0 \qquad\qquad 1 + 4 - 5 = 0$

$\qquad\qquad\qquad\qquad\quad 0 = 0 \qquad\qquad\qquad\qquad 0 = 0$

1. $z^2 - 2z + 1 = 0$ $\qquad$ **2.** $x^2 + 2x + 1 = 0$ $\qquad$ **3.** $r^2 - 3r - 4 = 0$

4. $x^2 - 4x + 4 = 0$ $\qquad$ **5.** $t^2 + 8t + 12 = 0$ $\qquad$ **6.** $a^2 - 8a + 15 = 0$

7. $x^2 + 7x + 6 = 0$ $\qquad$ **8.** $y^2 - 7y - 8 = 0$ $\qquad$ **9.** $x^2 - x - 12 = 0$

10. $w^2 - 23w - 24 = 0$ $\qquad$ **11.** $x^2 - 10x + 24 = 0$ $\qquad$ **12.** $u^2 + u - 42 = 0$

13. $x^2 + 5x - 14 = 0$ $\qquad$ **14.** $x^2 + 8x + 15 = 0$ $\qquad$ **15.** $x^2 + 12x + 36 = 0$

16. $x^2 + 14x + 49 = 0$ $\qquad$ **17.** $x^2 - 16x + 15 = 0$ $\qquad$ **18.** $x^2 + 14x - 15 = 0$

Sample problem:

$$2x^2 - 6x = 8$$

Write equation in standard form.

$$2x^2 - 6x - 8 = 0$$

Factor left-hand member completely.

$$2(x^2 - 3x - 4) = 0$$
$$2(x - 4)(x + 1) = 0$$

Determine solutions by inspection or set each factor containing variable equal to 0 and solve the resulting equations.

$$x - 4 = 0 \qquad x + 1 = 0$$

Ans. $x = 4, \qquad x = -1$

19. $2x^2 - 10x = 12$ $\qquad$ **20.** $3t^2 - 6t = -3$ $\qquad$ **21.** $4s^2 - 12s = 16$

22. $4x^2 - 24x = 28$ $\qquad$ **23.** $2x^2 + 2x = 60$ $\qquad$ **24.** $3x^2 + 6x = 45$

25. $3x^2 - x = 4$ $\qquad$ **26.** $4x^2 + 4x = 3$ $\qquad$ **27.** $6x^2 = 11x - 3$

28. $4x^2 = 4x + 3$ $\qquad$ **29.** $4x^2 = 4x - 1$ $\qquad$ **30.** $12x^2 = 8x + 15$

31. $7 = x^2 - 6x$ $\qquad$ **32.** $3s + 40 = s^2$ $\qquad$ **33.** $12x - 9 = 4x^2$

34. $x + 15 = 2x^2$ $\qquad$ **35.** $-1 = 9x^2 - 6x$ $\qquad$ **36.** $-1 = 16x^2 + 8x$

37. $x^2 + x = 2x + 2$ $\qquad$ **38.** $2x^2 + 8x - 2 = 3x - x^2$

39. $x^2 + 3x - 5 = 2 - 2x - x^2$ $\qquad$ **40.** $2x^2 + 4x - 10 = 2x + 2$

41. $3y^2 = 2y + 60 + y$ $\qquad$ **42.** $8x^2 = 6 - 2x$

Sample problem:

$$y^2 = \frac{13}{6}y - 1$$

Multiply each member by L.C.D. 6.

Solution continued on the next page

$$(6)y^2 = (\not{6}) \frac{13}{\not{6}} y - (6)1$$
$$6y^2 = 13y - 6$$

Write in standard form; factor left-hand member.

$$6y^2 - 13y + 6 = 0$$
$$(2y - 3)(3y - 2) = 0$$

Determine solutions by inspection or set each factor equal to 0 and solve the resulting equations.

$$2y - 3 = 0 \qquad 3y - 2 = 0$$
$$2y = 3 \qquad\qquad 3y = 2$$

Ans. $y = \dfrac{3}{2} \qquad\qquad y = \dfrac{2}{3}$

43. $\dfrac{2}{3}x^2 + \dfrac{1}{3}x - 2 = 0$ **44.** $\dfrac{3}{4}x^2 + \dfrac{5}{2}x - 2 = 0$ **45.** $x^2 + 3x + \dfrac{9}{4} = 0$

46. $\dfrac{3}{2}x^2 - \dfrac{1}{4}x - \dfrac{1}{2} = 0$ **47.** $4x^2 + 13x + \dfrac{15}{2} = 0$ **48.** $\dfrac{1}{3}x^2 - \dfrac{5}{2}x + 3 = 0$

49. $\dfrac{x^2}{2} + x = \dfrac{15}{2}$ **50.** $x - 1 = \dfrac{x^2}{4}$ **51.** $\dfrac{x^2}{3} + x = \dfrac{-2}{3}$

52. $\dfrac{21}{2} + 2y = \dfrac{y^2}{2}$ **53.** $\dfrac{x^2}{6} + \dfrac{x}{3} = \dfrac{1}{2}$ **54.** $\dfrac{x^2}{15} = \dfrac{x}{5} + \dfrac{2}{3}$

Sample problem:

$$x(x + 2) = 8$$

Remove parentheses.

$$x^2 + 2x = 8$$

Write in standard form.

$$x^2 + 2x - 8 = 0$$

Factor left-hand member.

$$(x + 4)(x - 2) = 0$$

Determine solutions by inspection or set each factor equal to 0 and solve the resulting equations.

$$x + 4 = 0 \qquad x - 2 = 0$$

Ans. $x = -4, \qquad\quad x = 2$

55. $y(2y - 3) = -1$ **56.** $x(x + 2) = 3$ **57.** $2(x^2 - 1) = 3x$

58. $r(r - 2) = 6 - r$ **59.** $x(x + 2) - 3x - 2 = 0$ **60.** $2p(p - 2) = p + 3$

Solve for x, y, or z.

Sample problem:

$$x^2 + ax - 2a^2 = 0$$

Factor left-hand member.

$$(x - a)(x + 2a) = 0$$

Determine solutions by inspection or set each factor equal to 0 and solve the resulting equations for x.

$$x - a = 0 \qquad x + 2a = 0$$

Ans. $x = a, \qquad\quad x = -2a$

61. $x^2 + 2ax + a^2 = 0$ **62.** $y^2 - 4by + 4b^2 = 0$ **63.** $z^2 - 3bz = 4b^2$

64. $a^2y^2 + 2aby = -b^2$ **65.** $x^2 - cx = 20c^2$ **66.** $x^2 = 2cx + 8c^2$

Sample problem:

$$(x - 4)(x + 3) = -10$$

Multiply the factors in the left-hand member.

$$x^2 - x - 12 = -10$$

Write in standard form.

$$x^2 - x - 2 = 0$$

Factor left-hand member.

$$(x - 2)(x + 1) = 0$$

Determine solutions by inspection or set each factor equal to 0 and solve the resulting equations.

$$x - 2 = 0 \qquad x + 1 = 0$$

Ans. $x = 2, \qquad\quad x = -1$

67. $(x - 2)(x + 1) = 4$ **68.** $(x - 5)(x + 1) = -8$

69. $(x - 5)(x + 2) = -12$ **70.** $(x - 2)(x + 3) = 24$

71. $(x - 2)(x - 1) = 1 - x$ **72.** $(x + 3)^2 = 2x + 14$

73. $(2x + 5)(x - 4) = -18$ **74.** $(2x - 1)(x - 2) = -1$

75. $(6x + 1)(x + 1) = 4$ **76.** $(x - 2)(x + 1) = x(2 - x)$

77. $x(3x + 2) = (x + 2)^2$ **78.** $(x + 1)(3x + 7) = (x + 3)(6x - 1)$

Sample problem:

$$\frac{1}{8x^2} - \frac{13}{24x} = -\frac{1}{2}$$

Multiply each term by L.C.D. $24x^2$.

$$\overset{3}{(24x^2)} \frac{1}{8x^2} - \overset{x}{(24x^2)} \frac{13}{24x} = -\overset{12}{(24x^2)} \frac{1}{2}$$

$$3 - 13x = -12x^2$$

Write in standard form.

$$12x^2 - 13x + 3 = 0$$

Factor left-hand member.

$$(4x - 3)(3x - 1) = 0$$

Determine solutions by inspection or set each factor equal to 0 and solve the resulting equations.

$$4x - 3 = 0 \qquad 3x - 1 = 0$$
$$4x = 3 \qquad\quad 3x = 1$$

Ans. $x = \dfrac{3}{4}, \qquad x = \dfrac{1}{3}$

Note. Answer should be checked to insure that no denominator in original equation is zero.

79. $x + \dfrac{1}{x} = 2$ **80.** $\dfrac{x}{4} - \dfrac{3}{4} = \dfrac{1}{x}$ **81.** $1 - \dfrac{2}{x} = \dfrac{15}{x^2}$

82. $\dfrac{1}{2} + \dfrac{1}{2x} = \dfrac{1}{x^2}$ **83.** $1 - \dfrac{3}{2x} - \dfrac{1}{x^2} = 0$ **84.** $3 = \dfrac{10}{x^2} - \dfrac{7}{x}$

85. $\dfrac{1}{x} - \dfrac{1}{6} = \dfrac{1}{x+1}$ **86.** $1 + \dfrac{2}{x-1} = \dfrac{2}{x(x-1)}$ **87.** $1 + \dfrac{1}{x(x-1)} = \dfrac{3}{x}$

88. $\dfrac{4}{x} - 3 = \dfrac{5}{2x+3}$ **89.** $x - \dfrac{10}{x-3} = 0$ **90.** $\dfrac{4}{3x} + \dfrac{3}{3x+1} + 2 = 0$

Sample problem:

$$\frac{7}{x-3} - \frac{3}{x-4} = \frac{1}{2}$$

Multiply each term by L.C.D. $2(x-3)(x-4)$.

$$2(x-3)(x-4) \frac{7}{(x-3)} - 2(x-3)(x-4) \frac{3}{(x-4)} = 2(x-3)(x-4) \frac{1}{2}$$

$$14(x-4) - 6(x-3) = (x-3)(x-4)$$

Remove parentheses.

$$14x - 56 - 6x + 18 = x^2 - 7x + 12$$
$$8x - 38 = x^2 - 7x + 12$$

Write in standard form.

$$x^2 - 15x + 50 = 0$$

Factor left-hand member.

$$(x - 10)(x - 5) = 0$$

Determine solutions by inspection or set each factor equal to 0 and solve the equations.

$$x - 10 = 0 \qquad x - 5 = 0$$

Ans. $x = 10,$ $\qquad x = 5$

Note. Answer should be checked to insure that no denominator in original problem is zero.

91. $\dfrac{14}{x - 6} - \dfrac{6}{x - 8} = \dfrac{1}{2}$

92. $\dfrac{12}{x - 3} + \dfrac{12}{x + 4} = 1$

93. $\dfrac{2}{x - 3} - \dfrac{6}{x - 8} = -1$

94. $\dfrac{4}{x - 2} - \dfrac{7}{x - 3} = \dfrac{2}{15}$

95. $\dfrac{4}{x - 1} - \dfrac{4}{x + 2} = \dfrac{3}{7}$

96. $\dfrac{3}{x + 6} - \dfrac{2}{x - 5} = \dfrac{5}{4}$

97. $\dfrac{x}{x - 1} - \dfrac{x}{x + 1} = \dfrac{4}{3}$

98. $\dfrac{2x}{2x - 3} - \dfrac{3x}{2x + 3} = \dfrac{15 - 32x^2}{4x^2 - 9}$

7.4 WORD PROBLEMS

A variety of word problems lead to quadratic equations. Upon solution, both results should be checked against the original word problem to insure that they fulfill the physical conditions set forth in the problem.

EXERCISES 7.4

Sample problem: The square of an integer is 7 less than eight times the integer. Find the integer.

Let $x =$ the integer

Write an equation expressing the conditions of the problem.

$$x^2 = 8x - 7$$

Solve equation.

Solution continued on the next page

$$x^2 - 8x + 7 = 0$$
$$(x - 7)(x - 1) = 0$$

$$x - 7 = 0 \qquad x - 1 = 0$$
$$x = 7 \qquad\quad x = 1$$

Since 1 and 7 both meet the conditions of the problem, both are valid solutions.

Ans. 1, 7

1. The square of an integer is equal to five times the integer. Find the integer.

2. If three times the square of a certain integer is increased by the integer itself, the sum is 10. What is the integer?

3. Find two consecutive positive integers whose product is 72.

4. Find two consecutive positive integers whose product is 132.

5. The product of two consecutive positive even integers is 168. Find the integers.

6. The product of two consecutive negative odd integers is 143. Find the integers.

7. The sum of the squares of two consecutive positive integers is 61. Find the integers.

8. The sum of the squares of two consecutive positive odd integers is 130. Find the integers.

9. The square of a positive integer increased by twice the square of the next consecutive integer, gives 66. Find the integer.

10. The square of a positive integer is 79 less than twice the square of the next consecutive integer. Find the integers.

Sample problem : The sum of a certain number and twice its reciprocal is $\frac{19}{3}$. Find the number.

Let $x =$ the number

then $\dfrac{1}{x} =$ the reciprocal of the number

Write an equation expressing the conditions of the problem.

$$x + 2 \left(\frac{1}{x}\right) = \frac{19}{3}$$

Multiply by L.C.D. $3x$ to remove fractions.

$$(3x)x + (3x)2\left(\frac{1}{x}\right) = (3x)\frac{19}{3}$$

$$3x^2 + 6 = 19x$$

Write in standard form.

$$3x^2 - 19x + 6 = 0$$

Solve equation.

$$(3x - 1)(x - 6) = 0$$

$$3x - 1 = 0 \qquad x - 6 = 0$$

$$3x = 1$$

$$x = \frac{1}{3} \qquad\qquad x = 6$$

Since both numbers meet the conditions of the problem, both are valid solutions.

Ans. $\frac{1}{3}$, 6

11. The sum of a certain number and its reciprocal is $\frac{2\,5}{1\,2}$. What is the number?

12. The sum of a certain number and its reciprocal is $\frac{5\,3}{1\,4}$. What is the number?

13. The sum of the reciprocals of two consecutive odd integers is $\frac{1\,2}{3\,5}$. What are the integers?

14. The sum of the reciprocals of two consecutive even integers is $\frac{9}{4\,0}$. Find the integers.

15. The reciprocal of a positive integer is added to twice the reciprocal of the next consecutive integer and the sum is $\frac{2\,5}{7\,2}$. What are the integers?

16. Twice the reciprocal of a positive integer is subtracted from three times the reciprocal of the next successive integer and the difference is $\frac{2}{2\,1}$. What are the integers?

Sample problem : The length of a rectangle is 3 inches less than twice its width, and the area of the rectangle is 54 square inches. Find the dimensions of the rectangle.

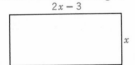

Sketch figure.

Represent unknown quantities symbolically.

Let x = width
then $2x - 3$ = length

Write an equation relating the known and the unknown quantities.

Solution continued on the next page

[(width)(length) = area]
$$x(2x - 3) = 54$$

Remove parentheses.

$$2x^2 - 3x = 54$$

Solve equation.

$$2x^2 - 3x - 54 = 0$$
$$(2x + 9)(x - 6) = 0$$
$$2x + 9 = 0 \qquad x - 6 = 0$$
$$x = -\frac{9}{2} \qquad x = 6$$

Since $-\frac{9}{2}$ does not meet the physical conditions for the problem, 6 is the only meaningful solution.

Ans. Width = 6 inches
length = 9 inches

17. Find the dimensions of a rectangle whose area is 12 square feet if the length is 4 feet greater than the width.

18. Find the dimensions of a rectangle whose area is 28 square feet if the length is 3 feet greater than the width.

19. If the sum of the length and the width of a rectangle is 13 inches, and its area is 42 square inches, what are the dimensions of the rectangle?

20. If the sum of the length and the width of a rectangle is 21 inches, and its area is 108 square inches, what are the dimensions of the rectangle?

21. If the perimeter of a rectangle is 40 inches, and its area is 96 square inches, what are the dimensions of the rectangle?

22. If the perimeter of a rectangle is 52 inches, and its area is 168 square inches, what are the dimensions of the rectangle?

23. The side of one square is 4 inches greater than the side of another, and the sum of their areas is 106 square inches. How long is the side of each square?

24. The side of one square is 5 inches greater than the side of another, and the sum of their areas is 73 square inches. How long is the side of each square?

25. A motor boat travels 24 miles downstream on a river and returns to its starting place. If the speed of the current is 2 miles per hour, and the round trip takes 5 hours, what is the speed of the boat in still water?

26. A crew rows a boat 6 miles downstream and then rows back to their starting place. If the speed of the current is 2 miles per hour, and the total trip takes 4 hours, how fast would the crew row in still water?

27. A man drove 180 miles from town A to town B and returned to town A. If he drove 15 miles per hour faster on the return trip than he did on the initial trip, and the initial trip took one hour longer, what was the man's speed on each trip?

28. A plane flew 480 miles at a certain speed, then increased its speed by 20 miles per hour and continued on the same course. After having flown a total distance of 840 miles in a total of 5 hours, it landed. What was its original speed?

CHAPTER REVIEW

1. For what values of x will $x(x - 2)(x + 5)$ equal 0?

In Exercises 2–17, solve for x, y or z.

2. $x^2 - 2x = 0$　　　　　**3.** $x^2 = 49$

4. $3y^2 = 27$　　　　　　**5.** $11z^2 = 44z$

6. $\dfrac{x^2}{4} - 9 = 0$　　　　**7.** $a^2x^2 - b^4 = 0$

8. $\dfrac{x^2}{c} = a^2x$　　　　　**9.** $y^2 - 4y = 5$

10. $y^2 = 7y + 18$　　　　**11.** $\dfrac{z^2}{6} + \dfrac{z}{6} = 2$

12. $\dfrac{x}{2} - 1 = \dfrac{x^2}{16}$　　　**13.** $y(y - 6) = 16$

14. $8x^2 - 20x = 12$　　　**15.** $(x + 5)(x - 8) = -36$

16. $\dfrac{2}{x} - \dfrac{1}{6} = \dfrac{2}{x + 2}$　　　**17.** $\dfrac{4}{x - 6} - \dfrac{12}{x - 16} = -1$

18. The sum of two numbers is 11 and their product is 30. Find the numbers.

19. The length of a rectangle is 2 inches less than four times the width, and its area is 12 square inches. Find the dimensions of the rectangle.

20. The sum of the reciprocals of two consecutive integers is $\frac{11}{30}$. Find the integers.

CUMULATIVE REVIEW

1. Simplify: $\dfrac{4^2 - 2^2}{3} - \dfrac{4^2 + 2^2}{4}$.

2. If $a = 0$, $b = -1$, and $c = 2$, find the value of $a(b^2 + c^2)$.

3. Arrange the numbers -3, $\dfrac{3}{8}$, $\dfrac{3}{7}$, 3, 0, $\dfrac{-5}{2}$, and $\dfrac{-5}{3}$ in order from smallest to largest.

4. Factor: $x^3 - 3x^2 + 2x$.

5. Multiply: $(2x - 3)(x + 4)$.

6. Write $-\dfrac{x + 2}{-3}$ in standard form.

7. Simplify: $(x - 3)(x + 2) - (x^2 - 3x)$.

8. Represent $\dfrac{3}{x^2 + x} - \dfrac{2}{x + 1}$ as a single fraction.

9. Express $\dfrac{3}{x - 1}$ as an equivalent fraction with a denominator of $x^2 + 2x - 3$.

10. Simplify: $\dfrac{3x^2 - x - 2}{2x^2 + x - 3}$.

11. Solve the system $2x - 3 = y$ by algebraic methods.
$$3x + 2y = 15$$

12. Graph the equation: $x + 2y = 4$.

13. Solve: $\dfrac{7}{8} = \dfrac{42}{y + 4}$.

14. What is the ratio of 7 inches to 1 foot 9 inches.

15. The numerator of a certain fraction is five more than the denominator, and the fraction is equivalent to $\frac{4}{3}$. Find the fraction.

16. Two packages together weigh 140 pounds. If one package weighs 30 pounds more than the other, what is the weight of each?

In Exercises 17–19, solve each equation.

17. $3y^2 - 2y = y$ **18.** $25x^2 - 4 = 5$ **19.** $x(x + 3) = 5x + 3$

20. The sum of the reciprocals of two successive even integers is $\frac{5}{12}$. Find the integers.

8

RADICAL EXPRESSIONS

8.1 RADICALS

Many quadratic equations, such as

$$x^2 - 3 = 0 \quad \text{and} \quad x^2 + 4x - 1 = 0,$$

are not factorable by using any of the numbers we have studied. In this chapter we propose to investigate a new kind of number—one which will enable us to find solutions to some nonfactorable quadratic equations.

First, let us define a new representation for numbers with which you are already familiar. For all nonnegative numbers, a, we define $\sqrt{a}$ (read "the **square root** of a") to be the nonnegative number such that

$$\sqrt{a} \cdot \sqrt{a} = a.$$

For example

$$\sqrt{4} = 2 \quad \text{because} \quad 2 \cdot 2 = 4,$$

$$\sqrt{9} = 3 \quad \text{because} \quad 3 \cdot 3 = 9,$$

and

$$\sqrt{16} = 4 \quad \text{because} \quad 4 \cdot 4 = 16.$$

The symbol $\sqrt{}$ is called a **radical**.* The numbers 4, 9, and 16 as used above are called **radicands**.

Each positive number has two square roots, since we have $(a)(a) = a^2$ and $(-a)(-a) = a^2$. The symbol $\sqrt{a}$ is always used to represent the positive square root; to represent the negative square root of a, the symbol $-\sqrt{a}$ is used. For example, 3 has two square roots; $\sqrt{3}$ represents the positive root, and $-\sqrt{3}$ represents the negative root. The symbol $\pm\sqrt{a}$ is sometimes used to denote both the positive and negative square roots

---

* The radical symbol is also used to represent other roots of a number. By attaching an index to the radical, we may indicate the order of the root under discussion. Thus, $\sqrt[3]{a}$ indicates the cube root of a, $\sqrt[7]{a}$ indicates the seventh root of a, and $\sqrt[n]{a}$ indicates the nth root of a. Where no index is indicated the square root is to be understood

179

of a. Variables in all radicands in this book are assumed to represent positive numbers.

EXERCISES 8.1

Find each square root.

Sample problems:

    a. $\sqrt{49}$ *b.* $-\sqrt{\dfrac{4}{81}}$ *c.* $\pm\sqrt{\dfrac{4}{25}}$ *d.* $\sqrt{0}$

    Ans. 7   *Ans.* $-\dfrac{2}{9}$ *Ans.* $\pm\dfrac{2}{5}$ *Ans.* 0

1. $\sqrt{16}$ **2.** $\sqrt{36}$ **3.** $-\sqrt{81}$ **4.** $-\sqrt{121}$

5. $\pm\sqrt{144}$ **6.** $\pm\sqrt{225}$ **7.** $\sqrt{9}$ **8.** $\sqrt{1}$

9. $\sqrt{\dfrac{1}{36}}$ **10.** $-\sqrt{\dfrac{1}{4}}$ **11.** $\pm\sqrt{\dfrac{4}{9}}$ **12.** $\pm\sqrt{\dfrac{9}{25}}$

Write each of the following as an equivalent radical expression.

Sample problems:

    a. 5   *b.* -10 *c.* $\dfrac{2}{3}$

    Ans. $\sqrt{25}$ *Ans.* $-\sqrt{100}$ *Ans.* $\sqrt{\dfrac{4}{9}}$

13. 3   **14.** 8   **15.** -7 **16.** -6

17. 13   **18.** 12   **19.** -5 **20.** -4

21. $\dfrac{1}{2}$ **22.** $\dfrac{8}{9}$ **23.** $-\dfrac{7}{8}$ **24.** $-\dfrac{2}{7}$

Find each square root.

Sample problems:

    a. $\sqrt{y^6}$ *b.* $\sqrt{49x^2y^6}$ *c.* $\pm\sqrt{(c+d)^2}$

    Ans. y^3 *Ans.* $7xy^3$ *Ans.* $\pm(c+d)$

25. $\sqrt{x^2}$ **26.** $\sqrt{y^4}$ **27.** $\sqrt{4x^2}$ **28.** $\sqrt{a^2b^2}$

29. $-\sqrt{a^2c^4}$ **30.** $-\sqrt{9x^6y^6}$ **31.** $\pm\sqrt{36a^6}$ **32.** $\pm\sqrt{100x^{10}}$

33. $\sqrt{121a^2b^2}$ **34.** $\sqrt{(x+y)^2}$ **35.** $-\sqrt{(a+b)^2}$ **36.** $-\sqrt{4(x+y)^2}$

37. $\sqrt{\dfrac{a^2}{b^2}}$ **38.** $-\sqrt{\dfrac{b^4}{100}}$ **39.** $\pm\sqrt{\dfrac{9}{x^2y^2}}$ **40.** $\pm\sqrt{\dfrac{4x^2}{y^2}}$

Write each of the following as equivalent radical expressions.

Sample problems:

    a. $3x^3y$ *b.* $-(x+y)$ *c.* $\pm\dfrac{3x}{4}$

    Ans. $\sqrt{9x^6y^2}$ *Ans.* $-\sqrt{(x+y)^2}$ *Ans.* $\pm\sqrt{\dfrac{9x^2}{16}}$

41. x **42.** y^2 **43.** xy^2 **44.** $3x$

45. $4y^2$ **46.** $7xy$ **47.** $-8x^2y^2$ **48.** $-7x^7$

49. $-10x^{10}y^{10}$ **50.** $-(x+y)$ **51.** $\pm(2x+y)$ **52.** $\pm(3x+2y)$

53. $\dfrac{1}{2}$ **54.** $\dfrac{1}{3}$ **55.** $\dfrac{3}{4}$ **56.** $\dfrac{2}{3}a$

57. $\pm\dfrac{4}{5}b^2$ **58.** $\pm\dfrac{3}{2}ab$ **59.** $\dfrac{1}{a}$ **60.** $-\dfrac{1}{ab}$

61. $-\dfrac{3x}{y}$ **62.** $-\dfrac{y}{4x}$ **63.** $\dfrac{a+b}{a}$ **64.** $\dfrac{b+1}{b}$

8.2 IRRATIONAL NUMBERS

In Chapter 5, we discussed fractions. If the numerator of an arithmetic fraction is an integer and the denominator is a nonzero integer, the fraction represents a **rational number.** A number that cannot be expressed as the quotient of two integers is an **irrational number.** The study of irrational numbers in any detail is beyond the scope of this book. We shall content ourselves with observing that any radical with a radicand which is not, itself, the square of a rational number represents an irrational number. Thus,

$$\sqrt{2},\ \sqrt{3},\ \sqrt{5},\ \text{ and }\ \sqrt{\frac{5}{7}},$$

are irrational numbers, whereas

$$\sqrt{4},\ \sqrt{\frac{9}{25}},\ \text{ and }\ \sqrt{16},$$

are rational numbers.

Irrational numbers cannot be exactly represented by decimal fractions. However, we can approximate irrational numbers to any desired degree of accuracy. For example, correct to two decimal places, $\sqrt{2} = 1.41$. That line segments equal to $\sqrt{2}$ in length exist (the diagonal of a square whose side is one unit in length) will be shown when we study the Pythagorean theorem in Chapter 9. Thus, $\sqrt{2}$ can be associated with a point on a line graph. In fact, any irrational number can be associated with a point on a line graph.

We can obtain approximations to the irrational square roots of positive integers by various means. In this book, we shall use a prepared table of square roots which can be found on page 246. In studying operations with radicals in this and the following sections, we assume that all laws valid for the fundamental operations with rational numbers hold for irrational numbers and that the symbols for the fundamental operations are unchanged. For example, the expression $2\sqrt{3}$, represents the product of 2 and $\sqrt{3}$. The expression $4 + \sqrt{7}$ represents the sum of 4 and $\sqrt{7}$.

EXERCISES 8.2

Which of the following numbers are rational and which are irrational?

Sample problems:

$a.\ \sqrt{\dfrac{4}{9}}$ $b.\ \sqrt{3}$ $c.\ 5 + \sqrt{3}$

Ans. rational, since $\sqrt{\dfrac{4}{9}} = \dfrac{2}{3}$ *Ans.* irrational   *Ans.* irrational

1. 6 2. 8.61 3. $\sqrt{2}$ 4. $\sqrt{4}$ 5. $\sqrt{6}$

6. $\sqrt{9}$ 7. $\sqrt{25}$ 8. $\sqrt{100}$ 9. $3\sqrt{16}$ 10. $\sqrt{7}$

11. $-\sqrt{13}$ 12. $-2\sqrt{100}$ 13. $\sqrt{\dfrac{4}{9}}$ 14. $-\sqrt{\dfrac{16}{25}}$ 15. $-\sqrt{\dfrac{2}{3}}$

16. $\sqrt{\dfrac{4}{5}}$ 17. $1 + \sqrt{4}$ 18. $3.1 + \sqrt{4}$ 19. $2 + \sqrt{5}$ 20. $1 + \sqrt{3}$

Using the table of square roots on page 246, find a decimal approximation for each of the following. Round off answers to two decimal places. For the sake of uniformity, if the digit in the third decimal place is 5, round to the next higher digit in the second decimal place.

Sample problems:

a. $\sqrt{23}$　　　　b. $-2\sqrt{46}$　　　　c. $\frac{1}{2}\sqrt{62}$

　　　4.796　　　　　　$-2(6.782)$　　　　　$\frac{7.874}{2}$

　　　　　　　　　　　$-1\ .564$　　　　　　3.937

　　Ans. 4.80　　　*Ans.*　·13.56　　　*Ans.* 3.94

21. $\sqrt{57}$　　　　**22.** $\sqrt{83}$　　　　**23.** $\sqrt{3}$　　　　**24.** $\sqrt{17}$

25. $\sqrt{5}$　　　　**26.** $\sqrt{92}$　　　　**27.** $-\sqrt{26}$　　　　**28.** $-\sqrt{54}$

29. $2\sqrt{3}$　　　　**30.** $3\sqrt{2}$　　　　**31.** $-5\sqrt{3}$　　　　**32.** $-6\sqrt{5}$

33. $\frac{1}{3}\sqrt{18}$　　　**34.** $\frac{1}{4}\sqrt{48}$　　　**35.** $-\frac{1}{5}\sqrt{75}$　　　**36.** $-\frac{2}{3}\sqrt{21}$

Sample problems:

a. $3 + 2\sqrt{2}$　　　b. $\frac{3 + \sqrt{3}}{2}$　　　c. $1 - 2\sqrt{3}$

　$3 + 2(1.414)$　　　$\frac{3 + 1.732}{2}$　　　$1 - 2(1.732)$

　$3 + 2.828$　　　　$\frac{4.732}{2}$　　　　$1 - 3.464$

　　5.828　　　　　　2.366　　　　　　-2.464

　Ans. 5.83　　　　*Ans.* 2.37　　　　*Ans.* -2.46

37. $1 + \sqrt{3}$　　**38.** $2 - \sqrt{5}$　　**39.** $3 - \sqrt{2}$　　**40.** $5 + \sqrt{5}$

41. $5 + 3\sqrt{7}$　　**42.** $-3 + 2\sqrt{6}$　**43.** $-7 - 3\sqrt{28}$　**44.** $-6 + 2\sqrt{35}$

45. $\frac{3 + 2\sqrt{2}}{2}$　　**46.** $\frac{7 - 5\sqrt{5}}{3}$　　**47.** $\frac{6 - 2\sqrt{3}}{5}$　　**48.** $\frac{7 + 3\sqrt{3}}{2}$

49. $\sqrt{3} - \sqrt{2}$　　**50.** $\sqrt{5} - \sqrt{7}$　　**51.** $3\sqrt{3} - 2\sqrt{5}$　　**52.** $2\sqrt{2} - 5\sqrt{5}$

Graph each set of numbers on a separate line graph. Estimate the location of graphs of numbers between integers.

Sample problem: $\sqrt{13}$, 4, $\sqrt{7}$

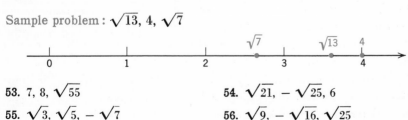

53. 7, 8, $\sqrt{55}$　　　　　　　　**54.** $\sqrt{21}$, $-\sqrt{25}$, 6

55. $\sqrt{3}$, $\sqrt{5}$, $-\sqrt{7}$　　　　　　**56.** $\sqrt{9}$, $-\sqrt{16}$, $\sqrt{25}$

57. $\sqrt{1}, -\sqrt{2}, \sqrt{3}$ **58.** $-\sqrt{6}, \sqrt{8}, \sqrt{10}$

59. $-\sqrt{4}, \sqrt{3}, -\sqrt{2}$ **60.** $\sqrt{2}, 0, -\sqrt{2}$

61. $-\sqrt{40}, \sqrt{30}, -\sqrt{20}$ **62.** $-\sqrt{1}, 0, \sqrt{1}$

63. $\sqrt{35}, -\sqrt{16}, -\sqrt{37}$ **64.** $\sqrt{21}, \sqrt{27}, \sqrt{30}$

8.3 SIMPLIFICATION OF RADICAL EXPRESSIONS—MONOMIALS

A radical expression is considered to be in simplest form if no prime factor of the radicand occurs more than once. We may determine whether a radical is in simplest form by examining the prime factors of the radicand; e.g., $\sqrt{78}$ is in simplest form because none of the factors in its completely factored form, $\sqrt{13 \cdot 3 \cdot 2}$, are repeated. The radical expression $\sqrt{20}$ is not in simplest form because the factor 2 occurs more than once when the radicand is in completely factored form, $\sqrt{2 \cdot 2 \cdot 5}$.

To find a means of simplifying a radical which has a repeated factor in the radicand, note that

$$\sqrt{4 \cdot 9} = \sqrt{36}$$
$$= 6,$$

and

$$\sqrt{4}\,\sqrt{9} = 2 \cdot 3$$
$$= 6.$$

If we generalize, we have

$$\sqrt{ab} = \sqrt{a}\,\sqrt{b}.$$

Stated in words, this equation asserts that:

> *The square root of a product is equal to the product of the square roots of its factors.*

In simplifying radicals, we first express the radicand as two factors, one of which is a perfect square. We can then write the latter without using radical notation. For example, $\sqrt{216}$ may be expressed as $\sqrt{36}\,\sqrt{6}$ from which we obtain the simpler form $6\,\sqrt{6}$. If perfect square factors are difficult to determine, it is frequently helpful to write a radicand in completely factored form and examine this form for repeated factors. These factors determine perfect squares. Thus, by writing $\sqrt{216}$ in completely factored form, we observe that

$$\sqrt{216} = \sqrt{2 \cdot 2 \cdot 2 \cdot 3 \cdot 3 \cdot 3}$$
$$= \sqrt{2^2}\,\sqrt{3^2}\,\sqrt{2 \cdot 3}$$
$$= 2 \cdot 3 \sqrt{6}$$
$$= 6\sqrt{6}.$$

By simplifying radical expressions, we can extend the scope of the table of square roots. For example, $\sqrt{216}$, which is not available in the tables, may be approximated by observing that

$$\sqrt{216} = \sqrt{36}\,\sqrt{6}$$
$$= 6\sqrt{6},$$

from which we have

$$6\sqrt{6} \approx 6(2.449) = 14.694.$$

(The symbol $\approx$ is read "approximately equal to.")

In simplifying radicals whose radicands contain variables we observe that any variable possessing an exponent that is an even natural number is a perfect square, and its square root is obtained by dividing the exponent by 2. For example,

$$\sqrt{x^6} = x^3$$

and

$$\sqrt{x^{10}} = x^5.$$

A radical expression whose radicand has a variable as a factor with an odd natural number for an exponent can be simplified by factoring the variable factor into two factors, one factor having an exponent of 1 and the other having an exponent which is an even number. For example,

$$\sqrt{x^7} = \sqrt{x^6}\,\sqrt{x} = x^3\sqrt{x}.$$

EXERCISES 8.3

Simplify.

Sample problems:

a. $\sqrt{24}$ b. $\sqrt{1575}$

Factor radicand completely.

$\sqrt{4 \cdot 6}$ $\sqrt{5 \cdot 5 \cdot 3 \cdot 3 \cdot 7}$

Simplify.

Solution continued on the next page

$$\sqrt{4}\,\sqrt{6} \qquad\qquad \sqrt{5^2}\,\sqrt{3^2}\,\sqrt{7}$$
$$5 \cdot 3\,\sqrt{7}$$

Ans. $2\sqrt{6}$ *Ans.* $15\sqrt{7}$

1. $\sqrt{8}$ **2.** $\sqrt{12}$ **3.** $\sqrt{18}$ **4.** $\sqrt{49}$

5. $-\sqrt{20}$ **6.** $-\sqrt{27}$ **7.** $-\sqrt{72}$ **8.** $-\sqrt{24}$

9. $\sqrt{64}$ **10.** $\sqrt{162}$ **11.** $\sqrt{288}$ **12.** $\sqrt{84}$

13. $\sqrt{125}$ **14.** $\sqrt{450}$ **15.** $-\sqrt{1080}$ **16.** $-\sqrt{450}$

17. $\pm\sqrt{720}$ **18.** $\pm\sqrt{588}$ **19.** $\pm\sqrt{1944}$ **20.** $\pm\sqrt{1125}$

Sample problems:

    a. $\sqrt{x^2}$ *b.* $\sqrt{y^3}$ *c.* $-\sqrt{x^9}$
                 $\sqrt{y^2}\,\sqrt{y}$ $-\sqrt{x^8}\,\sqrt{x}$

   Ans. x *Ans.* $y\sqrt{y}$ *Ans.* $-x^4\sqrt{x}$

21. $\sqrt{x^3}$ **22.** $\sqrt{y^5}$ **23.** $\sqrt{y^7}$ **24.** $\sqrt{x^{10}}$

25. $-\sqrt{x^{11}}$ **26.** $-\sqrt{x^{13}}$ **27.** $\sqrt{x^6}$ **28.** $-\sqrt{x^4}$

29. $\pm\sqrt{x^8}$ **30.** $\pm\sqrt{x^{15}}$ **31.** $\sqrt{x^{12}}$ **32.** $\sqrt{x^{14}}$

Sample problems:

    a. $\sqrt{12y^3}$ *b.* $\sqrt{48x^2y^3}$ *c.* $-\sqrt{20y^3}$
     $\sqrt{4y^2}\,\sqrt{3y}$ $\sqrt{16x^2y^2}\,\sqrt{3y}$ $-\sqrt{4y^2}\,\sqrt{5y}$

Ans. $2y\sqrt{3y}$ *Ans.* $4xy\sqrt{3y}$ *Ans.* $-2y\sqrt{5y}$

33. $\sqrt{4x^2}$ **34.** $\sqrt{8x^2}$ **35.** $\sqrt{9x^3}$ **36.** $\sqrt{12x^3}$

37. $-\sqrt{24y^5}$ **38.** $-\sqrt{121x^5}$ **39.** $\sqrt{64y^4}$ **40.** $\sqrt{36x^5}$

41. $\sqrt{49x^7}$ **42.** $\sqrt{16x^2}$ **43.** $\pm\sqrt{32x^3}$ **44.** $\pm\sqrt{72y^3}$

45. $\sqrt{80x^2}$ **46.** $\sqrt{98y^3}$ **47.** $-\sqrt{64x}$ **48.** $-\sqrt{3x^2}$

49. $\pm\sqrt{5y^3}$ **50.** $\pm\sqrt{7x^2}$ **51.** $\sqrt{48x^2y}$ **52.** $\sqrt{20x^2y^2}$

53. $\sqrt{25x^3y^2}$ **54.** $\sqrt{50xy^2}$ **55.** $-\sqrt{45a^4b}$ **56.** $-\sqrt{40x^5y^2}$

57. $\sqrt{3^2x^2}$ **58.** $\sqrt{2^2y^3}$ **59.** $\sqrt{8^2x^2y^2}$ **60.** $\sqrt{4b^3c^4}$

61. $-\sqrt{9cd}$ **62.** $-\sqrt{10x^3y^2}$ **63.** $\sqrt{7y^2z^2}$ **64.** $\sqrt{6y^3z^2}$

65. $\sqrt{\dfrac{9}{16}x^2y^2}$ **66.** $\sqrt{\dfrac{4}{9}x^3y}$ **67.** $\pm\sqrt{\dfrac{25}{36}y^2}$ **68.** $\pm\sqrt{\dfrac{1}{4}ab^2c^3}$

Sample problems:

$$a.\ 3\sqrt{4x^3}$$

$$3\sqrt{4x^2}\sqrt{x}$$

$$3(2x)\sqrt{x}$$

Ans. $6x\sqrt{x}$

$$b.\ \pm\dfrac{3x}{y}\sqrt{18x^3y^3}$$

$$\pm\dfrac{3x}{y}\sqrt{9x^2y^2}\sqrt{2xy}$$

$$\pm\dfrac{3x}{y}(3xy)\sqrt{2xy}$$

Ans. $\pm9x^2\sqrt{2xy}$

69. $2\sqrt{x^2}$ **70.** $3\sqrt{x^2y}$ **71.** $3\sqrt{4x}$ **72.** $4\sqrt{5x^2}$

73. $7\sqrt{49y^3}$ **74.** $-4\sqrt{16x^2}$ **75.** $2x\sqrt{x^2y}$ **76.** $3x\sqrt{9x^3}$

77. $-\dfrac{1}{3}\sqrt{9a^3}$ **78.** $\dfrac{1}{5}\sqrt{25y^3}$ **79.** $\pm\dfrac{1}{2}x\sqrt{16x^4}$ **80.** $\pm\dfrac{2a}{3}\sqrt{36a^3b^3}$

81. $\dfrac{1}{xy}\sqrt{x^3y^2}$ **82.** $\dfrac{x^2}{y}\sqrt{xy^3}$ **83.** $\dfrac{bc}{a}\sqrt{a^3b^2c}$ **84.** $\dfrac{a^2c}{b}\sqrt{b^4c}$

Use the table of square roots, page 246, to approximate each expression. Round off answers to two decimal places.

Sample problems:

$$a.\ \sqrt{243}$$

$$\sqrt{81}\sqrt{3}$$

$$9\sqrt{3}$$

$$9(1.732)$$

$$15.588$$

Ans. 15.59

$$b.\ 3+2\sqrt{200}$$

$$3+2\sqrt{100}\sqrt{2}$$

$$3+2(10)\sqrt{2}$$

$$3+20(1.414)$$

$$3+28.28$$

Ans. 31.28

85. $\sqrt{108}$ **86.** $\sqrt{162}$ **87.** $\sqrt{275}$

88. $\sqrt{207}$ **89.** $3+\sqrt{125}$ **90.** $24-\sqrt{176}$

91. $5-\sqrt{300}$ **92.** $11-\sqrt{242}$ **93.** $-2\sqrt{243}$

94. $-5\sqrt{120}$ **95.** $6+3\sqrt{104}$ **96.** $1+2\sqrt{128}$

8.4 SIMPLIFICATION OF RADICAL EXPRESSIONS—POLYNOMIALS

You should recall from Section 1.8 that like terms of algebraic expressions are added by adding the numerical coefficients of the terms, e.g.,

$$2r+3r=5r,$$

where r represents any number. In particular, if r represents an irrational number, say $\sqrt{2}$, we have

$$2\sqrt{2} + 3\sqrt{2} = 5\sqrt{2}.$$

Thus, we may add radical expressions, by adding their numerical coefficients, provided the radicands involved are identical. If the radicands differ, we can only indicate addition, e.g., $3\sqrt{2} + 4\sqrt{3}$. As before, if no numerical coefficient is written before a radical, it is understood that the coefficient is 1. Thus, $\sqrt{3}$ means $1\sqrt{3}$. Radicals should be written in simplest form before attempting to combine like terms.

From the distributive law

$$a(\sqrt{3} + \sqrt{2}) = a\sqrt{3} + a\sqrt{2},$$

where a may be either rational or irrational. By the symmetric property of equality, we may reverse the multiplication to assert that

$$a\sqrt{3} + a\sqrt{2} = a(\sqrt{3} + \sqrt{2}),$$

where the right-hand member is in factored form.

EXERCISES 8.4

Simplify.

Sample problems:

$$a.\ \sqrt{5} + 3\sqrt{5} \qquad\qquad b.\ \sqrt{5} - 3\sqrt{5}$$
$$Ans.\ 4\sqrt{5} \qquad\qquad Ans.\ -2\sqrt{5}$$

1. $\sqrt{3} + 2\sqrt{3}$ **2.** $\sqrt{7} - 3\sqrt{7}$

3. $3\sqrt{5} - 2\sqrt{5}$ **4.** $8\sqrt{5} - 2\sqrt{5} + 3\sqrt{5}$

5. $2\sqrt{3} - 4\sqrt{3} + 2\sqrt{3}$ **6.** $\sqrt{5} - 3\sqrt{5} + 7\sqrt{5}$

Sample problems:

$$a.\ 5\sqrt{2} - \sqrt{8} + \sqrt{12} \qquad\qquad b.\ 2\sqrt{3a} + \sqrt{27a} - 2\sqrt{12a}$$
$$5\sqrt{2} - 2\sqrt{2} + 2\sqrt{3} \qquad\qquad 2\sqrt{3a} + 3\sqrt{3a} - 4\sqrt{3a}$$
$$Ans.\ 3\sqrt{2} + 2\sqrt{3} \qquad\qquad Ans.\ \sqrt{3a}$$

7. $2\sqrt{3} + \sqrt{27}$ **8.** $\sqrt{8} + \sqrt{18}$

9. $\sqrt{50} - 2\sqrt{32}$ **10.** $2\sqrt{6} - 2\sqrt{24} + \sqrt{54}$

11. $\sqrt{12} + 2\sqrt{27} - 3\sqrt{48}$

12. $\sqrt{20} + \sqrt{45} - 2\sqrt{80}$

13. $3\sqrt{2} - 4\sqrt{3} + \sqrt{2}$

14. $2\sqrt{3} - \sqrt{4} + 3\sqrt{3}$

15. $\sqrt{3} + 2\sqrt{12} + \sqrt{18}$

16. $\sqrt{36} - 2\sqrt{32} + \sqrt{49}$

17. $3\sqrt{144} - 4\sqrt{49} + 3\sqrt{24}$

18. $\sqrt{12} - \sqrt{27} + 2\sqrt{8}$

19. $\sqrt{8} - \sqrt{4} + \sqrt{2}$

20. $\sqrt{75} - 2\sqrt{3} + \sqrt{27}$

21. $\sqrt{12} + \sqrt{18} - 3\sqrt{2}$

22. $2\sqrt{128} + \sqrt{24} - \sqrt{54}$

23. $\sqrt{4a} + \sqrt{9a}$

24. $\sqrt{12a} - \sqrt{3a}$

25. $2\sqrt{x} + 2\sqrt{25x}$

26. $3\sqrt{2x} - \sqrt{8x}$

27. $\sqrt{16b^3} - b\sqrt{25b} + 3b\sqrt{b}$

28. $\sqrt{xy^2} + 2\sqrt{xy^2} - \sqrt{4xy^2}$

29. $\sqrt{4xy^3} + 2\sqrt{xy^3} - 9\sqrt{xy^3}$

30. $3\sqrt{ab^4} + \sqrt{4ab^4} + \sqrt{36ab^4}$

Express without parentheses.

Sample problems:

$$a.\ 2(3 + 4\sqrt{2})$$
$$Ans.\ 6 + 8\sqrt{2}$$

$$b.\ a(4\sqrt{3} - 6\sqrt{a})$$
$$Ans.\ 4a\sqrt{3} - 6a\sqrt{a}$$

31. $4(\sqrt{3} + 1)$

32. $2(3 - \sqrt{2})$

33. $-5(6 + \sqrt{7})$

34. $-2(\sqrt{6} - 3)$

35. $4(\sqrt{2} - \sqrt{3})$

36. $3(\sqrt{3} + \sqrt{7})$

37. $3(1 + 3\sqrt{a})$

38. $2(4\sqrt{a} - 5)$

39. $-4(\sqrt{a} - \sqrt{b})$

40. $-6(\sqrt{x} + 2\sqrt{y})$

41. $2(\sqrt{2} - 3\sqrt{3} - 5)$

42. $-3(6 + \sqrt{5} - 2\sqrt{3})$

43. $-(\sqrt{a} + \sqrt{b} - \sqrt{c})$

44. $-(2\sqrt{a} - \sqrt{b} + 2\sqrt{c})$

45. $x(\sqrt{x} + 3)$

46. $x(4 - \sqrt{y})$

47. $x(\sqrt{x} + 2\sqrt{y})$

48. $y(\sqrt{xy} - \sqrt{y})$

49. $xy(y\sqrt{x} + 2)$

50. $xy(4 - x\sqrt{x})$

Simplify radical expressions where possible and factor.

Sample problems:

$$a.\ 8\sqrt{3} - 10$$

$$b.\ \sqrt{12} + 4$$
$$2\sqrt{3} + 4$$

$$c.\ y\sqrt{x} - y^2\sqrt{y}$$

$$Ans.\ 2(4\sqrt{3} - 5)$$

$$Ans.\ 2(\sqrt{3} + 2)$$

$$Ans.\ y(\sqrt{x} - y\sqrt{y})$$

51. $2 + 2\sqrt{3}$

52. $6 - 3\sqrt{2}$

53. $4\sqrt{2} - 12$

54. $3\sqrt{7} - 3$

55. $4\sqrt{5} + 8$

56. $8 + 32\sqrt{5}$

57. $8 - 32\sqrt{5}$

58. $4 + 2\sqrt{3}$

59. $6 + 24\sqrt{2}$

60. $5\sqrt{5} - 10$

61. $3 + \sqrt{18}$

62. $2 - \sqrt{32}$

63. $4 - 2\sqrt{8}$

64. $6 + 2\sqrt{27}$

65. $21 + \sqrt{18}$

66. $6 + \sqrt{72}$

67. $4 + \sqrt{16y}$

68. $3 - 2\sqrt{9y}$

69. $6y - \sqrt{8y^2}$

70. $8y + \sqrt{20y^2}$

Simplify fractions.

Sample problems:

   a. $\dfrac{6 - 3\sqrt{7}}{3}$ *b.* $\dfrac{-2 - \sqrt{72}}{4}$

                                 Simplify radicals.

                $\dfrac{-2 - 6\sqrt{2}}{4}$

                             Factor numerator and simplify.

    $\dfrac{\cancel{3}(2 - \sqrt{7})}{\cancel{3}}$ $\dfrac{\cancel{2}(-1 - 3\sqrt{2})}{\underset{2}{\cancel{4}}}$

   Ans. $2 - \sqrt{7}$ *Ans.* $\dfrac{-1 - 3\sqrt{2}}{2}$

71. $\dfrac{4 + 6\sqrt{3}}{2}$

72. $\dfrac{3 - 3\sqrt{2}}{3}$

73. $\dfrac{6 - 2\sqrt{5}}{2}$

74. $\dfrac{9 - 3\sqrt{5}}{3}$

75. $\dfrac{-2 + \sqrt{8}}{2}$

76. $\dfrac{-6 + \sqrt{54}}{3}$

77. $\dfrac{4 + 3\sqrt{12}}{2}$

78. $\dfrac{2 - \sqrt{8}}{4}$

79. $\dfrac{3 + \sqrt{18}}{6}$

80. $\dfrac{8 + \sqrt{32}}{16}$

81. $\dfrac{5 - \sqrt{75}}{10}$

82. $\dfrac{16 - 2\sqrt{48}}{16}$

Write each sum or difference as a single fraction.

Sample problems:

    a. $\dfrac{2}{3} - \dfrac{\sqrt{7}}{3}$ *b.* $\dfrac{2}{3} + \dfrac{5}{6}\sqrt{7}$

                       In problem *b*, build $\frac{2}{3}$ to a fraction with denominator 6.

$$\frac{(2)2}{(2)3} + \frac{5}{6}\sqrt{7}$$

Add numerators.

Ans. $\dfrac{2 - \sqrt{7}}{3}$ *Ans.* $\dfrac{4 + 5\sqrt{7}}{6}$

83. $\dfrac{2}{3} + \dfrac{\sqrt{2}}{3}$ 84. $\dfrac{5}{2} - \dfrac{\sqrt{3}}{2}$ 85. $\dfrac{\sqrt{3}}{5} - \dfrac{1}{5}$

86. $\dfrac{\sqrt{2}}{7} + \dfrac{1}{7}$ 87. $\dfrac{2\sqrt{10}}{3} - \dfrac{\sqrt{3}}{3}$ 88. $\dfrac{\sqrt{17}}{5} - \dfrac{3\sqrt{7}}{5}$

89. $\dfrac{\sqrt{11}}{a} + \dfrac{1}{a}$ 90. $\dfrac{\sqrt{5}}{b} - \dfrac{3}{b}$ 91. $\dfrac{5}{b} + \dfrac{3\sqrt{2}}{b}$

92. $\dfrac{1}{b} - \dfrac{2\sqrt{3}}{b}$ 93. $\dfrac{1}{2} + \dfrac{\sqrt{3}}{6}$ 94. $\dfrac{\sqrt{5}}{3} - \dfrac{5}{6}$

95. $\dfrac{2\sqrt{5}}{5} - \dfrac{1}{10}$ 96. $\dfrac{1}{4} + \dfrac{3\sqrt{3}}{8}$

Sample problems:

a. $\dfrac{1}{2} - \dfrac{\sqrt{3}}{3}$

$\dfrac{(3)1}{(3)2} - \dfrac{\sqrt{3}\,(2)}{3(2)}$

Ans. $\dfrac{3 - 2\sqrt{3}}{6}$

b. $4 - \dfrac{2\sqrt{3}}{5}$

$\dfrac{(5)4}{(5)1} - \dfrac{2\sqrt{3}}{5}$

Ans. $\dfrac{20 - 2\sqrt{3}}{5}$

97. $\dfrac{2}{5} + \dfrac{\sqrt{3}}{3}$ 98. $\dfrac{3}{7} - \dfrac{\sqrt{2}}{2}$ 99. $\dfrac{\sqrt{3}}{4} - \dfrac{1}{3}$

100. $\dfrac{\sqrt{5}}{2} - \dfrac{2}{3}$ 101. $\dfrac{2\sqrt{3}}{3} - \dfrac{\sqrt{2}}{2}$ 102. $\dfrac{3\sqrt{5}}{4} + \dfrac{\sqrt{3}}{5}$

103. $4 + \dfrac{3\sqrt{2}}{2}$ 104. $2 - \dfrac{\sqrt{2}}{3}$ 105. $\dfrac{\sqrt{3}}{5} + 1$

106. $\dfrac{2\sqrt{2}}{3} - 1$ 107. $\dfrac{6\sqrt{3}}{4} + 3$ 108. $\dfrac{12\sqrt{7}}{8} - 3$

8.5 MULTIPLICATION OF RADICAL EXPRESSIONS

In Section 8.3, we observed that

$$\sqrt{ab} = \sqrt{a}\,\sqrt{b}.$$

By the symmetric property of equality,

$$\sqrt{a}\,\sqrt{b} = \sqrt{ab}.$$

Stated in words, we have:

The product of two square roots is equal to the square root of the product of the radicands.

EXERCISES 8.5

Simplify.

Sample problems:

$a.$ $\sqrt{2}\,\sqrt{3}$ $b.$ $\sqrt{2x}\,\sqrt{6xy}$ or $\sqrt{2x}\,\sqrt{6xy}$

  $\sqrt{2\cdot 3}$ $\sqrt{2x\cdot 6xy}$ $\sqrt{2x}\,\sqrt{2x}\,\sqrt{3y}$

                    $\sqrt{12x^2 y}$

                    $\sqrt{4x^2}\,\sqrt{3y}$

  Ans. $\sqrt{6}$ *Ans.* $2x\sqrt{3y}$ $2x\sqrt{3y}$

1. $\sqrt{3}\,\sqrt{5}$ **2.** $\sqrt{2}\,\sqrt{7}$ **3.** $\sqrt{3}\,\sqrt{10}$ **4.** $\sqrt{5}\,\sqrt{13}$

5. $\sqrt{3}\,\sqrt{6}$ **6.** $\sqrt{2}\,\sqrt{10}$ **7.** $\sqrt{8}\,\sqrt{2}$ **8.** $\sqrt{27}\,\sqrt{3}$

9. $\sqrt{2x}\,\sqrt{3x}$ **10.** $\sqrt{5a}\,\sqrt{3a}$ **11.** $\sqrt{2xy}\,\sqrt{6xy^2}$ **12.** $\sqrt{6x^2}\,\sqrt{3x^2 y}$

13. $\sqrt{8a}\,\sqrt{18a}$ **14.** $\sqrt{12b}\,\sqrt{32b}$ **15.** $\sqrt{10x^2}\,\sqrt{15y}$ **16.** $\sqrt{18a^2}\,\sqrt{6b}$

Sample problem:

$2\sqrt{6}\,\sqrt{8}$ or $2\sqrt{6}\,\sqrt{8}$

$2\sqrt{48}$ $2\sqrt{3}\,\sqrt{2}\,\sqrt{2}\,\sqrt{4}$

$2\sqrt{16}\,\sqrt{3}$ $2\sqrt{3}\,(2)(2)$

$2\cdot 4\sqrt{3}$

Ans. $8\sqrt{3}$ $8\sqrt{3}$

17. $\sqrt{2}\,\sqrt{5}\,\sqrt{3}$

18. $\sqrt{5}\,\sqrt{3}\,\sqrt{7}$

19. $\sqrt{5}\,\sqrt{10}\,\sqrt{2}$

20. $\sqrt{6}\,\sqrt{3}\,\sqrt{2}$

21. $(2\,\sqrt{3})(\sqrt{2})(\sqrt{9})$

22. $(5\,\sqrt{5})(3\,\sqrt{10})(\sqrt{4})$

23. $(2\,\sqrt{x})(3\,\sqrt{x})(\sqrt{x})$

24. $(x\,\sqrt{2})(x\,\sqrt{3})(\sqrt{6})$

25. $(a\,\sqrt{b})(b\,\sqrt{c})(c\,\sqrt{a})$

26. $(b\,\sqrt{a})(a\,\sqrt{b})(a\,\sqrt{ab})$

27. $(x\,\sqrt{x})(\sqrt{x^2})(\sqrt{x^3})$

28. $(a^2\,\sqrt{a})(2a\,\sqrt{a})(a\,\sqrt{a^2})$

Sample problems:

a. $\sqrt{3}(2 + \sqrt{2})$

$\quad (\sqrt{3})(2) + (\sqrt{3})(\sqrt{2})$

Ans. $2\,\sqrt{3} + \sqrt{6}$

b. $\sqrt{3}\,(\sqrt{6} - \sqrt{15})$

$\quad (\sqrt{3})(\sqrt{6}) - (\sqrt{3})(\sqrt{15})$

$\quad \sqrt{18} - \sqrt{45}$

Ans. $3\,\sqrt{2} - 3\,\sqrt{5}$

29. $\sqrt{2}\,(3 + \sqrt{3})$

30. $\sqrt{3}\,(5 + \sqrt{5})$

31. $\sqrt{3}\,(\sqrt{6} + 2)$

32. $\sqrt{2}\,(\sqrt{6} + 3)$

33. $\sqrt{5}\,(4 + \sqrt{10})$

34. $\sqrt{3}\,(2 - \sqrt{15})$

35. $\sqrt{3}\,(\sqrt{2} + \sqrt{6})$

36. $\sqrt{5}\,(\sqrt{3} - \sqrt{10})$

37. $\sqrt{3}\,(\sqrt{3} + \sqrt{2})$

38. $\sqrt{5}\,(\sqrt{5} + \sqrt{3})$

39. $\sqrt{2}\,(\sqrt{10} - \sqrt{2})$

40. $\sqrt{3}\,(\sqrt{3} + \sqrt{15})$

Sample problem:

$(2 + \sqrt{3})(1 - 2\,\sqrt{3})$

Apply distributive law.

$2 - 4\,\sqrt{3} + \sqrt{3} - 2\,\sqrt{3}\,\sqrt{3}$

Simplify.

$2 - 3\,\sqrt{3} - 6$

Ans. $-4 - 3\,\sqrt{3}$

41. $(3 + \sqrt{2})(1 - \sqrt{2})$

42. $(2 - \sqrt{2})(3 + \sqrt{2})$

43. $(\sqrt{5} - 1)(\sqrt{5} + 3)$

44. $(\sqrt{7} + 3)(\sqrt{7} - 5)$

45. $(2 + \sqrt{3})(2 - \sqrt{3})$

46. $(3 + \sqrt{2})(3 - \sqrt{2})$

47. $(3 - 2\,\sqrt{5})(3 + 2\,\sqrt{5})$

48. $(4 - 3\,\sqrt{6})(4 + 3\,\sqrt{6})$

49. $(2\,\sqrt{3} + 3\,\sqrt{5})(\sqrt{3} - 2\,\sqrt{5})$

50. $(2\,\sqrt{5} - 3\,\sqrt{2})(\sqrt{5} + \sqrt{2})$

51. $(3\,\sqrt{7} - 2\,\sqrt{5})(2\,\sqrt{7} + 3\,\sqrt{5})$

52. $(5\,\sqrt{6} - 2\,\sqrt{3})(\sqrt{6} - \sqrt{3})$

8.6 QUOTIENTS OF RADICAL EXPRESSIONS

In order to simplify a fraction that contains a radical in the denominator or in both the numerator and the denominator, we observe that

$$\sqrt{\frac{36}{9}} = \sqrt{4} = 2,$$

and

$$\frac{\sqrt{36}}{\sqrt{9}} = \frac{6}{3} = 2.$$

Generalizing, we have

$$\frac{\sqrt{a}}{\sqrt{b}} = \sqrt{\frac{a}{b}}, \qquad b \neq 0.$$

Stated in words:

> *The quotient of two square roots is equal to the square root of the quotient of the radicands.*

For example,

$$\frac{\sqrt{6}}{\sqrt{3}} = \sqrt{\frac{6}{3}} = \sqrt{2}.$$

It is often convenient, particularly in simple numerical computations, to express a fraction whose denominator contains a radical as an equivalent fraction with a denominator free of radicals. This process is called **rationalizing the denominator.** This can be done by building to a fraction with a perfect square in the denominator and then extracting the indicated root. For example, we can rationalize the denominator of the fraction $\frac{\sqrt{2}}{\sqrt{3}}$ by multiplying the numerator and the denominator by $\sqrt{3}$ to obtain

$$\frac{\sqrt{2}\,\sqrt{3}}{\sqrt{3}\,\sqrt{3}} = \frac{\sqrt{6}}{\sqrt{9}} = \frac{\sqrt{6}}{3}.$$

Alternatively, we may represent the fraction $\frac{\sqrt{2}}{\sqrt{3}}$ in the form $\sqrt{\frac{2}{3}}$ and then multiply the numerator and the denominator of the radicand by 3 to obtain

$$\sqrt{\frac{2 \cdot 3}{3 \cdot 3}} = \sqrt{\frac{6}{9}} = \frac{\sqrt{6}}{\sqrt{9}} = \frac{\sqrt{6}}{3}.$$

The result is the same and you should use the approach you find the simplest.

To illustrate one advantage of the rationalized form, consider the numerical computation of a decimal approximation for $\dfrac{\sqrt{2}}{\sqrt{3}}$. If we approach this problem directly, we obtain $\dfrac{\sqrt{2}}{\sqrt{3}} \approx \dfrac{1.414}{1.732}$ and arrive at a problem in long division. If we first rationalize the denominator, we obtain $\dfrac{\sqrt{2}}{\sqrt{3}} = \dfrac{\sqrt{6}}{3} \approx \dfrac{2.449}{3}$ and arrive at a simple division process, in fact, one which can be done mentally.

EXERCISES 8.6

Simplify.

Sample problems:

$$a. \quad \frac{\sqrt{12}}{\sqrt{3}} \qquad\qquad b. \quad \frac{2\sqrt{30}}{\sqrt{6}} \qquad\qquad c. \quad \frac{3\sqrt{6a}}{\sqrt{2a}}$$

$$\sqrt{\frac{12}{3}} \qquad\qquad 2\sqrt{\frac{30}{6}} \qquad\qquad 3\sqrt{\frac{6a}{2a}}$$

$$\sqrt{4}$$

$$\textit{Ans. } 2 \qquad\qquad \textit{Ans. } 2\sqrt{5} \qquad\qquad \textit{Ans. } 3\sqrt{3}$$

1. $\dfrac{\sqrt{18}}{\sqrt{2}}$ 2. $\dfrac{\sqrt{8}}{\sqrt{2}}$ 3. $\dfrac{\sqrt{75}}{\sqrt{3}}$ 4. $\dfrac{\sqrt{80}}{\sqrt{5}}$

5. $\dfrac{\sqrt{27a}}{\sqrt{3a}}$ 6. $\dfrac{\sqrt{28a}}{\sqrt{7a}}$ 7. $\dfrac{\sqrt{8a}}{\sqrt{2}}$ 8. $\dfrac{\sqrt{12a}}{\sqrt{3}}$

9. $\dfrac{\sqrt{15b}}{\sqrt{5}}$ 10. $\dfrac{\sqrt{21b}}{\sqrt{7b}}$ 11. $\dfrac{\sqrt{ab}}{\sqrt{a}}$ 12. $\dfrac{\sqrt{7abc}}{\sqrt{bc}}$

13. $\dfrac{2\sqrt{14bc}}{\sqrt{2c}}$ 14. $\dfrac{3\sqrt{8a}}{\sqrt{2}}$ 15. $\dfrac{\sqrt{2}\sqrt{3}}{\sqrt{6}}$ 16. $\dfrac{\sqrt{6}\sqrt{8}}{\sqrt{3}}$

17. $\dfrac{\sqrt{a}\sqrt{ab}}{\sqrt{b}}$ 18. $\dfrac{\sqrt{3a}\sqrt{6a}}{\sqrt{2}}$ 19. $\dfrac{\sqrt{ab}\sqrt{3b}}{\sqrt{a}}$ 20. $\dfrac{\sqrt{3}\sqrt{10}}{\sqrt{6}}$

Rationalize each denominator.

Sample problems:

$a.$ $\dfrac{\sqrt{3}}{\sqrt{a}}$ or $\dfrac{\sqrt{3}}{\sqrt{a}}$

$\dfrac{\sqrt{3}\ \sqrt{a}}{\sqrt{a}\ \sqrt{a}}$ $\sqrt{\dfrac{3 \cdot a}{a \cdot a}}$

$\dfrac{\sqrt{3a}}{\sqrt{a^2}}$ $\dfrac{\sqrt{3a}}{\sqrt{a^2}}$

Ans. $\dfrac{\sqrt{3a}}{a}$ *Ans.* $\dfrac{\sqrt{3a}}{a}$

$b.$ $\sqrt{\dfrac{1}{2}}$ or $\sqrt{\dfrac{1}{2}}$

$\sqrt{\dfrac{1 \cdot 2}{2 \cdot 2}}$ $\dfrac{\sqrt{1}\ \sqrt{2}}{\sqrt{2}\ \sqrt{2}}$

$\dfrac{\sqrt{2}}{\sqrt{4}}$ $\dfrac{\sqrt{2}}{\sqrt{4}}$

Ans. $\dfrac{\sqrt{2}}{2}$ *Ans.* $\dfrac{\sqrt{2}}{2}$

21. $\dfrac{5}{\sqrt{2}}$ **22.** $\dfrac{5}{\sqrt{3}}$ **23.** $\dfrac{2}{\sqrt{x}}$ **24.** $\dfrac{5}{\sqrt{x}}$

25. $\dfrac{a}{\sqrt{b}}$ **26.** $\dfrac{x}{\sqrt{y}}$ **27.** $\sqrt{\dfrac{1}{3}}$ **28.** $\sqrt{\dfrac{1}{5}}$

29. $\sqrt{\dfrac{2}{a}}$ **30.** $\sqrt{\dfrac{2a}{b}}$ **31.** $\sqrt{\dfrac{3a}{b}}$ **32.** $\sqrt{\dfrac{5b}{a}}$

Sample problems:

$a.$ $\dfrac{\sqrt{12}}{\sqrt{3x}}$ or $\dfrac{\sqrt{12}}{\sqrt{3x}}$

$\sqrt{\dfrac{12}{3x}}$ $\dfrac{\sqrt{12}\ \sqrt{3x}}{\sqrt{3x}\ \sqrt{3x}}$

$\sqrt{\dfrac{4 \cdot x}{x \cdot x}}$ $\dfrac{\sqrt{36x}}{\sqrt{9x^2}}$

$\dfrac{\sqrt{4}\ \sqrt{x}}{\sqrt{x^2}}$ $\dfrac{6\sqrt{x}}{3x}$

Ans. $\dfrac{2\sqrt{x}}{x}$ *Ans.* $\dfrac{2\sqrt{x}}{x}$

$b.$ $\dfrac{2\sqrt{5}}{\sqrt{8}}$ or $\dfrac{2\sqrt{5}}{\sqrt{8}}$

$2\sqrt{\dfrac{5 \cdot 2}{8 \cdot 2}}$ $\dfrac{2\sqrt{5}\ \sqrt{2}}{\sqrt{8}\ \sqrt{2}}$

$2\sqrt{\dfrac{10}{16}}$ $\dfrac{2\sqrt{10}}{\sqrt{16}}$

$\dfrac{2\sqrt{10}}{4}$ $\dfrac{2\sqrt{10}}{4}$

Ans. $\dfrac{\sqrt{10}}{2}$ *Ans.* $\dfrac{\sqrt{10}}{2}$

33. $\dfrac{\sqrt{18}}{\sqrt{2x}}$ **34.** $\dfrac{\sqrt{8}}{\sqrt{2y}}$ **35.** $\dfrac{\sqrt{75}}{\sqrt{3y}}$ **36.** $\dfrac{\sqrt{80}}{\sqrt{5x}}$

37. $\dfrac{a\sqrt{2}}{\sqrt{a}}$ **38.** $\dfrac{b\sqrt{3}}{\sqrt{b}}$ **39.** $\dfrac{4\sqrt{3x}}{\sqrt{8}}$ **40.** $\dfrac{9\sqrt{5x}}{\sqrt{27}}$

41. $\dfrac{a\sqrt{32}}{\sqrt{2a}}$ **42.** $\dfrac{b\sqrt{21}}{\sqrt{3b}}$ **43.** $\dfrac{4y\sqrt{3x}}{\sqrt{4y}}$ **44.** $\dfrac{9x\sqrt{2y}}{\sqrt{27x}}$

Sample problems:

a. $\sqrt{\dfrac{20}{3}}$ or $\sqrt{\dfrac{20}{3}}$ b. $\sqrt{\dfrac{4}{3x}}$ or $\sqrt{\dfrac{4}{3x}}$

$\dfrac{\sqrt{4}\,\sqrt{5}}{\sqrt{3}}$ $\sqrt{\dfrac{4\cdot 5\cdot 3}{3\cdot 3}}$ $\dfrac{2}{\sqrt{3x}}$ $\sqrt{\dfrac{4\cdot 3x}{3x\cdot 3x}}$

$\dfrac{2\sqrt{5}\,\sqrt{3}}{\sqrt{3}\,\sqrt{3}}$ $\dfrac{\sqrt{4}\,\sqrt{15}}{\sqrt{9}}$ $\dfrac{2\sqrt{3x}}{\sqrt{3x}\,\sqrt{3x}}$ $\dfrac{\sqrt{4}\,\sqrt{3x}}{\sqrt{9x^2}}$

Ans. $\dfrac{2\sqrt{15}}{3}$ *Ans.* $\dfrac{2\sqrt{15}}{3}$ *Ans.* $\dfrac{2\sqrt{3x}}{3x}$ *Ans.* $\dfrac{2\sqrt{3x}}{3x}$

45. $\sqrt{\dfrac{8}{3}}$ 46. $\sqrt{\dfrac{18}{5}}$ 47. $\sqrt{\dfrac{9}{2}}$ 48. $\sqrt{\dfrac{12}{7}}$

49. $\sqrt{\dfrac{72}{5}}$ 50. $\sqrt{\dfrac{98}{3}}$ 51. $\sqrt{\dfrac{50}{2x}}$ 52. $\sqrt{\dfrac{75}{3y}}$

53. $\sqrt{\dfrac{24}{3x}}$ 54. $\sqrt{\dfrac{32}{4y}}$ 55. $\sqrt{\dfrac{x^3}{xy}}$ 56. $\sqrt{\dfrac{y^5}{xy^2}}$

Rationalize each denominator and find a decimal approximation (round off answers to two decimal places).

Sample problems:

a. $\sqrt{\dfrac{5}{3}}$ b. $4\sqrt{\dfrac{1}{3}}$

$\dfrac{\sqrt{5}\,\sqrt{3}}{\sqrt{3}\,\sqrt{3}}$ $4\sqrt{\dfrac{1\cdot 3}{3\cdot 3}}$

$\dfrac{\sqrt{15}}{3}\ (\sqrt{15}\approx 3.873)$ $\dfrac{4}{3}\sqrt{3}\ (\sqrt{3}\approx 1.732)$

$\dfrac{\sqrt{15}}{3}\approx \dfrac{3.873}{3}=1.291$ $\dfrac{4}{3}\sqrt{3}\approx \dfrac{4}{3}(1.732)=2.309$

Ans. 1.29   *Ans.* 2.31

57. $\sqrt{\dfrac{1}{7}}$ 58. $\sqrt{\dfrac{3}{5}}$ 59. $\dfrac{3}{\sqrt{2}}$ 60. $\dfrac{2}{\sqrt{3}}$ 61. $\dfrac{3}{\sqrt{5}}$

62. $\dfrac{2}{\sqrt{6}}$ 63. $3\sqrt{\dfrac{1}{3}}$ 64. $5\sqrt{\dfrac{1}{5}}$ 65. $\sqrt{\dfrac{32}{3}}$ 66. $\sqrt{\dfrac{48}{5}}$

CHAPTER REVIEW

1. Which of the following are irrational numbers?

$$\sqrt{6}, \ -\sqrt{9}, \ \sqrt{4}, \ \sqrt{\frac{9}{25}}, \ -\sqrt{\frac{2}{3}}$$

2. Using the table of square roots, find a decimal approximation for:

    a. $\sqrt{93}$.   *b.* $2\sqrt{47}$.   *c.* $\frac{1}{4}\sqrt{32}$.

3. Locate the numbers 8, $\sqrt{80}$, and $\frac{19}{2}$ on a line graph.

Simplify each expression in Exercises 4–8.

4. *a.* $\sqrt{72}$ *b.* $-\sqrt{90}$ *c.* $\sqrt{175}$

5. *a.* $\sqrt{y^4}$ *b.* $\sqrt{x^{15}}$ *c.* $\sqrt{x^3 y^7}$

6. *a.* $x\sqrt{27}$ *b.* $3\sqrt{3x^2}$ *c.* $\frac{1}{3}\sqrt{27x^2}$

7. *a.* $\sqrt{7} + 3\sqrt{7}$ *b.* $2\sqrt{6} - 3\sqrt{6} + 2\sqrt{6}$
    c. $7\sqrt{11} - 3\sqrt{11} + \sqrt{11}$

8. *a.* $2\sqrt{12} - 4\sqrt{27}$ *b.* $\sqrt{9x} - \sqrt{4x}$
    c. $2\sqrt{x^2 y} - 3\sqrt{4x^2 y} + 5x\sqrt{y}$

9. Express without parentheses.

    a. $3(\sqrt{y} - 6)$ *b.* $y(\sqrt{xy} - 2y)$ *c.* $\sqrt{3}\,(\sqrt{2} - \sqrt{6})$

10. Simplify radicals where possible and factor.

    a. $2 - \sqrt{8}$ *b.* $\sqrt{27} - 3\sqrt{5}$ *c.* $3x^2 - \sqrt{5x^4}$

Simplify each expression in Exercises 11–20.

11. *a.* $\dfrac{3 - 2\sqrt{27}}{3}$ *b.* $\dfrac{6 - 3\sqrt{12}}{2}$ *c.* $\dfrac{4 - \sqrt{32}}{4}$

12. *a.* $\dfrac{3}{2} - \dfrac{\sqrt{3}}{2}$ *b.* $\dfrac{\sqrt{15}}{5} + \dfrac{2\sqrt{15}}{5}$ *c.* $\dfrac{2}{3} - \dfrac{\sqrt{3}}{6}$

13. *a.* $\dfrac{\sqrt{5}}{3} - \dfrac{3}{2}$ *b.* $\dfrac{2\sqrt{3}}{5} - 1$ *c.* $\dfrac{3\sqrt{6}}{4} + 2$

14. *a.* $\sqrt{5} \cdot \sqrt{3}$ *b.* $\sqrt{16} \cdot \sqrt{32}$ *c.* $\sqrt{3x^2} \cdot \sqrt{6x}$

15. *a.* $\sqrt{5} \cdot \sqrt{2} \cdot \sqrt{15}$ *b.* $(2\sqrt{6})(\sqrt{3})(\sqrt{2})$ *c.* $(x\sqrt{3})(\sqrt{4x})$

16. *a.* $\sqrt{3}(2 - \sqrt{2})$ *b.* $\sqrt{7}(\sqrt{2} - \sqrt{14})$ *c.* $\sqrt{8}(\sqrt{2} - \sqrt{3})$

17. *a.* $(2 - \sqrt{3})(2 + \sqrt{3})$ *b.* $(\sqrt{5} - \sqrt{7})(\sqrt{5} + \sqrt{7})$
  c. $(2 - \sqrt{3})(3 - 2\sqrt{3})$

18. *a.* $\dfrac{\sqrt{27}}{\sqrt{3}}$ *b.* $\dfrac{\sqrt{12a}}{\sqrt{2}}$ *c.* $\dfrac{\sqrt{3a} \cdot \sqrt{ab}}{\sqrt{b}}$

19. *a.* $\sqrt{\dfrac{3}{5}}$ *b.* $\sqrt{\dfrac{12}{5}}$ *c.* $\sqrt{\dfrac{3}{2x}}$

20. *a.* $\dfrac{\sqrt{85}}{\sqrt{5x}}$ *b.* $\dfrac{\sqrt{3y}}{\sqrt{2x^2}}$ *c.* $\dfrac{4\sqrt{7x}}{\sqrt{2x}}$

CUMULATIVE REVIEW

1. A positive number has __?__ square roots.

2. If $a = -4$, $b = 2$, and $c = 0$, find the value of $\dfrac{2a - 4}{3 - bc}$.

3. Multiply: $(-3ab)(2c)(b^2)$.

4. Represent $\dfrac{a - b}{2} + \dfrac{a - 3b}{3}$ as a single fraction.

5. Reduce to lowest terms: $\dfrac{3a^2x - 3ax}{24a^2x^2 + 60ax^2}$.

6. Divide: $(x^4 + 3x^3 - x^2)$ by (x^2).

7. Factor: $4x^2 - 12x + 9$.

8. Solve: $3(x - 2) - 7 = 5(2x + 5) - 3$.

9. Solve: $\dfrac{y - 6}{5} = \dfrac{12y + 3}{5} - 3y + 3$.

10. The sum of two numbers is 146. If n represents the smaller of the two numbers, represent the larger number in terms of n.

11. Write in terms of x, the number of cents in x quarters.

12. Solve the system: $\dfrac{x}{2} - \dfrac{y}{3} = 1$

  $x - \dfrac{2y}{3} = 2.$

13. Solve for y: $2by = 9d - 5by$.

14. Solve: $2x^2 = 5x + 3$.

15. The sum of two numbers is 154. If the larger number is eight less than twice the smaller, what are the numbers?

16. Write an equivalent radical representation for -4.

17. Simplify: $\sqrt{63x^7}$.

18. What is the altitude of a triangle whose base is 10 inches and whose area is 70 square inches?

19. Simplify: $\sqrt{18} - 2\sqrt{5} - \sqrt{20} + \sqrt{50}$.

20. The product of two consecutive integers is equal to two more than twice their sum. What are the integers?

CHAPTER 9

SOLUTION OF
QUADRATIC EQUATIONS
BY OTHER METHODS

In Chapter 7 you learned to solve, by factoring methods, quadratic equations whose solutions are rational numbers. Having studied irrational numbers in Chapter 8, you are now ready to examine additional methods of solving quadratic equations.

9.1 EXTRACTION OF ROOTS

We can solve an equation of the form

$$x^2 - a = 0$$

by writing it in the form

$$x^2 = a$$

and observing that for a greater than or equal to zero, x is a number which, when multiplied by itself, yields a. Therefore, by the definition of a square root, x must be a square root of a. Since a has two square roots, we have $\sqrt{a}$ and $-\sqrt{a}$ as solutions for the equation. We sometimes use the double sign notation to represent both roots, that is, $x = \pm \sqrt{a}$. For example, if

$$x^2 - 5 = 0,$$

we have

$$x^2 = 5,$$

from which

$$x = \pm \sqrt{5}.$$

This method of solving equations is sometimes referred to as solving by **extraction of roots,** since in a sense, we have simply equated the square roots of the members of the equation.

Quadratic equations of the form

$$(x + k)^2 = d$$

can also be solved by extraction of roots. For example, from

$$(x - 2)^2 = 9$$

we obtain

$$x - 2 = \pm 3,$$
$$x = \pm 3 + 2,$$

from which

$$x = +3 + 2 = 5$$

or

$$x = -3 + 2 = -1.$$

EXERCISES 9.1

Solve.

Sample problem:

$$3y^2 = 48$$

Write with y^2 as left-hand member.

$$y^2 = 16$$

Extract square root of each member.

$$y = \pm \sqrt{16}$$

Simplify.

$$y = \pm 4$$

Ans. $y = 4;$ $y = -4$

Check. $3(4)^2 = 48$ $3(-4)^2 = 48$
$3(16) = 48$ $3(16) = 48$
$48 = 48$ $48 = 48$

1. $x^2 = 4$ **2.** $y^2 = 9$ **3.** $x^2 - 16 = 0$

4. $x^2 - 25 = 0$ **5.** $98 = 2x^2$ **6.** $12 = 3x^2$

7. $x^2 - 3 = 0$ **8.** $7 - z^2 = 0$ **9.** $y^2 - 10 = 0$

10. $3x^2 - 15 = 0$ **11.** $4x^2 - 24 = 0$ **12.** $7x^2 = 42$

13. $12 = z^2$ **14.** $24 = b^2$ **15.** $x^2 - 18 = 0$

16. $3x^2 - 24 = 0$ **17.** $3x^2 - 54 = 0$ **18.** $5x^2 - 100 = 0$

Sample problem:

$$5x^2 - 3 = x^2 + 9$$

Write with x^2 as left-hand member.

$$4x^2 = 12$$
$$x^2 = 3$$

Extract square root of each member.

$$x = \pm \sqrt{3}$$

Ans. $x = \sqrt{3}$; $x = -\sqrt{3}$

19. $2x^2 - 4 = x^2$ **20.** $6x^2 + 3 = 4x^2 + 11$ **21.** $3 = x^2 - 2$

22. $4t^2 - 16 = 16$ **23.** $4y^2 - 10 = y^2 - 10$ **24.** $s^2 - 2 = 4 - s^2$

Sample problem:

$$\frac{1}{3}x^2 - \frac{3}{4} = 0$$

Multiply each member by L.C.D. 12.

$$(\overset{4}{\cancel{12}})\frac{1}{\cancel{3}}x^2 - (\overset{3}{\cancel{12}})\frac{3}{\cancel{4}} = (12)0$$

Write with x^2 as left-hand member.

$$4x^2 - 9 = 0$$
$$4x^2 = 9$$
$$x^2 = \frac{9}{4}$$

Extract square root of each member.

$$x = \pm \frac{3}{2}$$

Ans. $x = \frac{3}{2}$; $x = \frac{-3}{2}$

25. $\frac{1}{4}x^2 = 5$ **26.** $\frac{2}{3}y^2 - 4 = 0$ **27.** $\frac{2}{3}x^2 = 6$

28. $\frac{2x^2}{3} - 4 = \frac{x^2}{3}$ **29.** $\frac{5x^2}{2} - 4 = 2x^2$ **30.** $\frac{1}{2}x^2 - 4 = \frac{3}{2}$

Solve each of the following equations for the indicated variable.

Sample problem:

$$K = \frac{wv^2}{64}, \quad \text{for } v$$

Multiply each member by L.C.D. 64.

$$(64)K = (\cancel{64})\left(\frac{wv^2}{\cancel{64}}\right)$$
$$64K = wv^2$$

Write with v^2 as left-hand member.

$$\frac{64K}{w} = v^2$$
$$v^2 = \frac{64K}{w}$$

Extract square root of each member.

Solution continued on the next page

$$v = \pm \sqrt{\frac{64K}{w}}$$

Simplify.

$$v = \frac{\pm \sqrt{64} \sqrt{K}}{\sqrt{w}}$$

Rationalize denominator.

$$v = \frac{\pm 8 \sqrt{K} \sqrt{w}}{\sqrt{w} \sqrt{w}}$$

$$v = \frac{\pm 8 \sqrt{Kw}}{w}$$

Ans. $v = \dfrac{8 \sqrt{Kw}}{w}; \quad v = \dfrac{-8 \sqrt{Kw}}{w}$

31. $x^2 - a = 0$, for x

32. $b = x^2$, for x

33. $\dfrac{x^2}{3} - b^2 a^3 = 0$, for x

34. $\dfrac{ax^2}{2} - b = 0$, for x

35. $\dfrac{2y^2}{5} = \dfrac{b}{3}$, for y

36. $\dfrac{y^2}{2} + a = \dfrac{2a}{3} + 2y^2$, for y

37. $s = \dfrac{1}{2} gt^2$, for t

38. $V = \dfrac{1}{3} \pi r^2 h$, for r

39. $A = 4\pi r^2$, for r

40. $C = bh^2 r$, for h

41. $I = \dfrac{3k}{d^2}$, for d

42. $F = \dfrac{k}{d^2}$, for d

Given $x^2 + y^2 = z^2$ and values for two of the variables. Find values for the third variable.

Sample problem : $y = 4$, $z = 5$

Substitute 4 for y and 5 for z in $x^2 + y^2 = z^2$.

$$x^2 + (4)^2 = (5)^2$$

Simplify.

$$x^2 + 16 = 25$$

Write with x^2 as left-hand member.

$$x^2 = 9$$

Extract square root of each member.

$$x = \pm 3$$

Ans. $x = 3; \quad x = -3$

43. $x = 15, y = 20$ **44.** $x = 10, y = 24$

45. $x = 6, z = 10$ **46.** $y = 9, z = 41$

47. $x = 5, y = 5$ **48.** $x = 11, z = 61$

Solve for x.

Sample problem :

$(x + 3)^2 = 25$

Extract square root of each member.

$x + 3 = \pm 5$

Solve resulting first-degree equations.

$$x = \pm 5 - 3$$
$$x = +5 - 3; \quad x = -5 - 3$$

Ans. $x = 2; \quad x = -8$

49. $(x - 1)^2 = 4$ **50.** $(x + 3)^2 = 9$ **51.** $(x - 2)^2 = 25$

52. $(x + 1)^2 = 36$ **53.** $(x - 5)^2 = 1$ **54.** $(x + 7)^2 = 1$

55. $(x - a)^2 = 25$ **56.** $(x + b)^2 = 4$ **57.** $(x - 3)^2 = a^2$

58. $(x + 5)^2 = b^2$ **59.** $(x - a)^2 = b^2$ **60.** $(x + a)^2 = b^2$

Sample problem :

$(x - 2)^2 = 20$

Extract square root of each member.

$x - 2 = \pm \sqrt{20}$

Solve resulting first-degree equations.

$$x - 2 = \pm 2 \sqrt{5}$$
$$x = 2 \pm 2 \sqrt{5}$$

Ans. $x = 2 + 2 \sqrt{5}; \quad x = 2 - 2 \sqrt{5}$

61. $(x + 3)^2 = 2$ **62.** $(x - 2)^2 = 3$ **63.** $(x + 5)^2 = 5$

64. $(x - 6)^2 = 7$ **65.** $(x + 10)^2 = 8$ **66.** $(x - 1)^2 = 12$

67. $(x - 5)^2 = a$ **68.** $(x + 2)^2 = a$ **69.** $(x + 1)^2 = b$

70. $(x - 7)^2 = b$ **71.** $(x - b)^2 = a$ **72.** $(x + b)^2 = a$

9.2 COMPLETING THE SQUARE

Thus far, the methods we have used to solve quadratic equations apply to special cases only. Let us now develop a method which is applicable to any quadratic equation.

First you should recall that

$$(x + q)^2 = x^2 + 2qx + q^2,$$

from which you can see that in the square of a binomial expressed as a trinomial, the last term q^2 must be the square of one half the coefficient of x; i.e., q^2 is the square of one half of $2q$. For example, the value for k^2, such that the expression

$$x^2 + 6x + k^2$$

is equivalent to the square of the binomial

$$(x + k)^2,$$

is 9, the square of one half of 6, the coefficient of x. Thus,

$$x^2 + 6x + 9 = (x + 3)^2.$$

Using this procedure, any quadratic equation can be written in the form $(x + k)^2 = d$, which we learned to solve in the preceding section. As an example of this procedure, consider

$$x^2 - 6x - 7 = 0.$$

We first write the equation equivalently in the form

$$x^2 - 6x \qquad = 7.$$

Now, by adding 9 [the square of $\frac{1}{2}(-6)$] to each member, we have

$$x^2 - 6x + 9 = 7 + 9$$

or, equivalently,

$$(x - 3)^2 = 16,$$

which we can solve by extraction of roots. In the event the coefficient on the second-degree term is not 1, we must divide each term in the equation by that coefficient before proceeding. Thus,

$$2x^2 - 3x - 9 = 0$$

should be written

$$x^2 - \frac{3}{2}x - \frac{9}{2} = 0$$

before proceeding further. The solution of this equation is completed in the sample problem on page 208. The foregoing method of solution is referred to as solving an equation by **completing the square**. We can summarize the procedure as follows:

1. Write the equation in standard form.

2. If the coefficient of the second-degree term is different from 1, divide each term in the equation by this coefficient.

3. Write the equation with the constant term in the right-hand member.

4. Add to each member the square of one half the coefficient of the first-degree term.

5. Rewrite the equation with the left-hand member expressed as a perfect square.

6. Solve by extraction of roots.

EXERCISES 9.2

Solve by completing the square.

Sample problem:
$$x^2 - x - 2 = 0$$

Rewrite equation with constant term in the right-hand member.

$$x^2 - x \qquad = 2$$

Square one half the coefficient of x and add to each member.

$$x^2 - x + \frac{1}{4} = 2 + \frac{1}{4}$$

Rewrite left-hand member as a perfect square.

$$\left(x - \frac{1}{2}\right)^2 = \frac{9}{4}$$

Extract square root of each member.

$$x - \frac{1}{2} = \pm \frac{3}{2}$$

Solve resulting first-degree equations.

$$x = \frac{1}{2} \pm \frac{3}{2}$$

$$x = \frac{1}{2} + \frac{3}{2}; \quad x = \frac{1}{2} - \frac{3}{2}$$

Ans. $x = 2; \quad x = -1$

Solution continued on the next page

Check. $(2)^2 - (2) - 2 = 0$ $\qquad$ $(-1)^2 - (-1) - 2 = 0$
$$4 - 2 - 2 = 0 \qquad\qquad 1 + 1 - 2 = 0$$
$$0 = 0 \qquad\qquad\qquad 0 = 0$$

1. $x^2 + 4x - 12 = 0$ $\qquad$ **2.** $x^2 - 2x - 15 = 0$ $\qquad$ **3.** $z^2 - 2z + 1 = 0$

4. $y^2 - y - 6 = 0$ $\qquad$ **5.** $y^2 + y - 20 = 0$ $\qquad$ **6.** $x^2 - x - 20 = 0$

7. $x^2 + 3x + 2 = 0$ $\qquad$ **8.** $u^2 + 5u + 6 = 0$ $\qquad$ **9.** $z^2 - 3z - 4 = 0$

10. $y^2 + 9y + 20 = 0$ $\qquad$ **11.** $r^2 - 3r - 10 = 0$ $\qquad$ **12.** $p^2 - 5p + 4 = 0$

13. $x^2 - 2x - 1 = 0$ $\qquad$ **14.** $y^2 + 4y = 4$ $\qquad$ **15.** $z^2 = 3z + 3$

16. $s^2 + 1 = -3s$ $\qquad$ **17.** $t^2 = 3 - t$ $\qquad$ **18.** $-x^2 - 6x = 1$

Sample problem:

$$2x^2 - 3x - 9 = 0$$

Divide each term by coefficient of x^2 and rewrite with constant in right-hand member.

$$x^2 - \frac{3}{2}x \qquad = \frac{9}{2}$$

Square one half the coefficient of x and add to each member.

$$x^2 - \frac{3}{2}x + \frac{9}{16} = \frac{9}{2} + \frac{9}{16}$$

Rewrite left-hand member as a perfect square.

$$\left(x - \frac{3}{4}\right)^2 = \frac{81}{16}$$

Extract square root of each member.

$$x - \frac{3}{4} = \pm \frac{9}{4}$$

Solve resulting first-degree equations.

$$x = \frac{3}{4} \pm \frac{9}{4}$$

$$x = \frac{3}{4} + \frac{9}{4}; \quad x = \frac{3}{4} - \frac{9}{4}$$

Ans. $x = 3; \quad x = -\frac{3}{2}$

19. $4x^2 + 4x - 3 = 0$ $\qquad$ **20.** $4y^2 - 4y = 3$ $\qquad$ **21.** $2x^2 = 2 - 3x$

22. $6z^2 + 6 = 13z$ $\qquad$ **23.** $2t^2 - t - 15 = 0$ $\qquad$ **24.** $1 - r = 6r^2$

9.3 QUADRATIC FORMULA

Solving the general quadratic equation

$$ax^2 + bx + c = 0, \qquad a \neq 0$$

by completing the square, we can obtain a formula expressing the solutions of the equation in terms of the coefficients a, b, and c. We can then solve any quadratic equation by simply substituting the numerical coefficients of the terms in the formula and evaluate the result.

Completing the square in the general quadratic equation is accomplished as follows:

$$ax^2 + bx + c = 0$$

$$ax^2 + bx = -c$$

$$x^2 + \frac{b}{a}x = \frac{-c}{a}$$

$$x^2 + \frac{b}{a}x + \frac{b^2}{4a^2} = \frac{-c}{a} + \frac{b^2}{4a^2}$$

$$\left(x + \frac{b}{2a}\right)^2 = \frac{-c(4a)}{a(4a)} + \frac{b^2}{4a^2}$$

$$\left(x + \frac{b}{2a}\right)^2 = \frac{b^2 - 4ac}{4a^2}$$

$$x + \frac{b}{2a} = \pm\sqrt{\frac{b^2 - 4ac}{4a^2}}$$

$$x = \frac{-b}{2a} \pm \frac{\sqrt{b^2 - 4ac}}{2a}$$

$$x = \frac{-b \pm \sqrt{b^2 - 4ac}}{2a}$$

The last equation is called the **quadratic formula.** Since this formula was developed from the quadratic equation in standard form, any quadratic equation should be written in standard form before attempting to determine values for a, b, and c to substitute in the formula. Furthermore, the sign on the coefficient must be substituted with the coefficient. For example, the equation

$$-x + 3x^2 = 4,$$

is first written as

$$3x^2 - x - 4 = 0,$$

from which

$$a = 3, b = -1, \text{ and } c = -4.$$

In the event that a quadratic equation has fractional coefficients, it is generally advantageous to clear the equation of fractions before proceeding further. For example, if

$$\frac{2}{3} - \frac{1}{2}x = -6x^2,$$

we have

$$(6)\frac{2}{3} - (6)\frac{1}{2}x = (6)(-6x^2),$$

or

$$4 - 3x = -36x^2,$$

from which

$$36x^2 - 3x + 4 = 0,$$

and

$$a = 36, \ b = -3, \text{ and } c = 4.$$

In actual practice, the quadratic formula should be used only when easier methods (factoring or extraction of roots) fail. Many of the following exercises are easier to solve by other methods, but they are included to indicate the complete generality of the quadratic formula. These exercises should be solved by use of the formula.

EXERCISES 9.3

In Exercises 1–20, indicate the values for a, b, and c to be substituted in the quadratic formula.

Sample problems:

    a. $x^2 = x + 2$ *b.* $2x^2 = x$

                                       Write in standard form.

       $x^2 - x - 2 = 0$ $2x^2 - x = 0$

     Ans. $a = 1, \ b = -1, \ c = -2$ *Ans.* $a = 2, \ b = -1, \ c = 0$

1. $x^2 - 3x + 2 = 0$ 2. $y^2 + 5y + 4 = 0$ 3. $x^2 - x - 30 = 0$

4. $y^2 + 3y - 4 = 0$ 5. $x^2 - 2x = 0$ 6. $y^2 = 5y$

7. $4y^2 - 3 = 0$ 8. $2y^2 - 1 = 0$ 9. $2x^2 = 7x - 6$

10. $6x^2 + x = 1$ 11. $6x^2 = 5x - 1$ 12. $3x^2 - 5 = 0$

13. $y^2 + 4 = 8y$ 14. $x^2 = 7x$

Sample problem:

$$\frac{x}{3} = 4 - \frac{x^2}{2}$$

                                     Multiply each term by L.C.D. 6.

$$(\cancel{6})\,\frac{2}{\cancel{3}}\,\frac{x}{\cancel{3}} = (6)4 - (\cancel{6})\,\frac{3}{\cancel{7}}\,\frac{x^2}{\cancel{7}}$$

$$2x = 24 - 3x^2$$

Write in standard form.

$$3x^2 + 2x - 24 = 0$$

Ans. $a = 3,\ b = 2,\ c = -24$

15. $x^2 = x + \dfrac{1}{2}$ **16.** $x^2 = \dfrac{15}{4} - x$ **17.** $2x^2 - 1 + \dfrac{7}{3}x = 0$

18. $y^2 + 1 = \dfrac{13}{6}y$ **19.** $\dfrac{9}{4}y^2 + \dfrac{3}{2}y - 2 = 0$ **20.** $\dfrac{x^2}{3} = \dfrac{x}{2} + \dfrac{3}{2}$

Solve by use of the quadratic formula.

Sample problem :

$$x^2 - x - 6 = 0$$

$$x = \frac{-b \pm \sqrt{b^2 - 4ac}}{2a}$$

Substitute 1 for a, -1 for b, and -6 for c.

$$x = \frac{-(-1) \pm \sqrt{(-1)^2 - 4(1)(-6)}}{2(1)}$$

Perform indicated operations.

$$x = \frac{1 \pm \sqrt{1 + 24}}{2}$$

Simplify.

$$x = \frac{1 \pm \sqrt{25}}{2}$$

$$x = \frac{1 + 5}{2}; \quad x = \frac{1 - 5}{2}$$

Ans. $x = 3; \quad x = -2$

Check. $(3)^2 - (3) - 6 = 0$ $(-2)^2 - (-2) - 6 = 0$

           $9 - 3 - 6 = 0$ $4 + 2 - 6 = 0$

              $0 = 0$ $0 = 0$

21. $x^2 - 3x + 2 = 0$ **22.** $y^2 + 5y + 4 = 0$

23. $z^2 - 4z - 12 = 0$ **24.** $x^2 - x - 30 = 0$

25. $x^2 + 2x - 15 = 0$ **26.** $y^2 + 3y - 4 = 0$

27. $x^2 + 3x - 1 = 0$ **28.** $y^2 + 5y + 5 = 0$

29. $y^2 - 3y - 2 = 0$ **30.** $x^2 + x - 1 = 0$

Sample problem:

$x^2 - 9 = 0$

$$x = \frac{-b \pm \sqrt{b^2 - 4ac}}{2a}$$

Substitute 1 for a, 0 for b, and -9 for c.

$$x = \frac{-(0) \pm \sqrt{(0)^2 - 4(1)(-9)}}{2(1)}$$

Perform indicated operations.

$$x = \frac{\pm \sqrt{36}}{2}$$

Simplify.

$$x = \frac{+6}{2}; \qquad x = \frac{-6}{2}$$

Ans. $x = 3; \quad x = -3$

31. $x^2 - 2x = 0$ (*Hint. c = 0*)   **32.** $x^2 - 4 = 0$ (*Hint. b = 0*)

33. $y^2 = 5y$ **34.** $z^2 = 9$ **35.** $7x = x^2$ **36.** $16 = y^2$

37. $z^2 - 3z = 0$ **38.** $x^2 = 1$ **39.** $4y^2 - 3 = 0$ **40.** $2y^2 - 1 = 0$

Sample problem:

$2x^2 = 2 - 3x$

Write in standard form.

$2x^2 + 3x - 2 = 0$

$$x = \frac{-b \pm \sqrt{b^2 - 4ac}}{2a}$$

Substitute 2 for a, 3 for b, and -2 for c.

$$x = \frac{-(3) \pm \sqrt{(3)^2 - 4(2)(-2)}}{2(2)}$$

Perform indicated operations.

$$x = \frac{-3 \pm \sqrt{9 + 16}}{4}$$

$$x = \frac{-3 \pm \sqrt{25}}{4}$$

Simplify.

$$x = \frac{-3 + 5}{4}; \quad x = \frac{-3 - 5}{4}$$

Ans. $x = \frac{1}{2}; \quad x = -2$

41. $2x^2 = 7x - 6$ **42.** $5 = 6y - y^2$ **43.** $6x^2 + x = 1$

44. $-z = 3 - 2z^2$ **45.** $6x^2 - 13x - 5 = 0$ **46.** $6x^2 = 5x - 1$

47. $x^2 = 2x + 1$ **48.** $x^2 = 2x + 4$ **49.** $y^2 - 4y - 2 = 0$

50. $z^2 + 4 = 8z$ **51.** $2x^2 - x - 1 = 0$ **52.** $3x^2 - 5 = 0$

Sample problem:

$$\frac{x^2}{3} = \frac{1}{3} - \frac{x}{2}$$

Multiply by L.C.D. 6.

$$(\cancel{6}) \frac{x^2}{\cancel{3}} = (\cancel{6}) \frac{1}{\cancel{3}} - (\cancel{6}) \frac{x}{\cancel{2}}$$

$$2x^2 = 2 - 3x$$

Write in standard form.

$$2x^2 + 3x - 2 = 0$$

Solve as shown in preceding sample problem.

53. $x^2 = \frac{15}{4} - x$ **54.** $2x^2 - 1 + \frac{7}{3}x = 0$ **55.** $y^2 + 1 = \frac{13}{6}y$

56. $\frac{9}{4}y^2 + \frac{3}{2}y - 2 = 0$ **57.** $\frac{1}{3}x^2 = \frac{1}{2}x + \frac{3}{2}$ **58.** $\frac{3}{5}x^2 - x - \frac{2}{5} = 0$

9.4 GRAPHING QUADRATIC EQUATIONS IN TWO VARIABLES

In Chapter 6, you learned how to graph first-degree equations in two variables. The same procedure can be used to graph second-degree equations of the form

$$y = ax^2 + bx + c.$$

Since the graph of a second-degree equation of this form is not a straight line but a curve, called a **parabola** (see examples in Figure 9.1), we have to plot more than two points to determine the graph. The significant

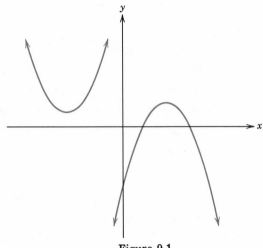

Figure 9.1

features of a parabola include the maximum or minimum point of the curve and the points, if any, where the curve intersects the axes. We shall therefore choose first components for the ordered pairs used to graph the equation so that these features are displayed. The ability to determine the number of ordered pairs necessary and to choose the proper first components is acquired through experience.

EXERCISES 9.4

In Exercises 1–6, find a second component such that each of the ordered pairs satisfies the equation $y = x^2 - 2x - 3$.

$(-3, ?)$

Substitute -3 for x in $y = x^2 - 2x - 3$.

$y = (-3)^2 - 2(-3) - 3$

Simplify.

$y = 9 + 6 - 3$
$y = 12$

Ans. $(-3, 12)$

1. $(0, ?)$ **2.** $(1, ?)$ **3.** $(-1, ?)$ **4.** $(2, ?)$ **5.** $(-2, ?)$ **6.** $(3, ?)$

In Exercises 7–12, find a second component such that each of the ordered pairs satisfies the equation $y = x^2 + x - 2$.

7. (0, ?)   **8.** (−1, ?)   **9.** (1, ?)   **10.** (2, ?)   **11.** (−2, ?)   **12.** (−3, ?)

In Exercises 13–18, find a second component such that each of the ordered pairs satisfies the equation $y = x^2 - 7x + 12$.

13. (0, ?)   **14.** (1, ?)   **15.** (2, ?)   **16.** (3, ?)   **17.** (4, ?)   **18.** (5, ?)

19. Graph the ordered pairs obtained in Exercises 1–6 and connect the points with a smooth curve.

20. Graph the ordered pairs obtained in Exercises 7–12 and connect the points with a smooth curve.

In Exercises 21–28, graph each equation. For x components, use all integers between the given numbers.

Sample problem : $y = x^2 - 3x + 1$, (−2 and 5)

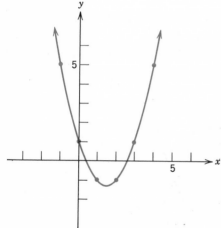

Determine ordered pairs which are solutions to the equation.

(−1, 5), (2, −1), (0, 1), (3, 1), (1, −1), and (4, 5)

Graph these ordered pairs and connect them with a smooth curve.

21. $y = x^2 - 2x$, (−3 and 5)   **22.** $y = x^2 - 4$, (−4 and 4)

23. $y = x^2 + 2x$, (−5 and 3)   **24.** $y = x^2 + 1$, (−4 and 4)

25. $9 - x^2 = y$, (−4 and 4)   **26.** $3x - x^2 = y$, (−3 and 6)

27. $y = x^2 - 5x - 4$, (−2 and 6)   **28.** $y = x^2 + x - 6$, (−4 and 4)

29. In each Exercise 21–24, estimate from the graph the values of x for which y is 0.

30. In each Exercise 25–28, estimate from the graph the values of x for which y is 0.

Graph each equation.

31. $y = x^2$ **32.** $y = x^2 + 3$ **33.** $y = x^2 - 3$

34. $y = 4 - x^2$ **35.** $x^2 - 2x - 3 = y$ **36.** $x^2 + 2x - 3 = y$

9.5   SOLUTION OF QUADRATIC EQUATIONS BY GRAPHING

If we seek solutions to

$$ax^2 + bx + c = 0, \qquad (1)$$

we are looking for values of x that will satisfy the equation. If we graph

$$ax^2 + bx + c = y, \qquad (2)$$

we are representing all ordered pairs (x, y) which satisfy the equation. The values of x for which y is 0 in Equation (2) are the x components of the points where the graph intersects the x-axis as shown in Figure 9.2.

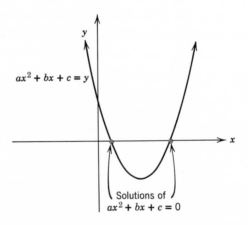

Figure 9.2

These values of x are also solutions to Equation (1), since the two equations are identical for $y = 0$. Therefore, we may solve a quadratic equation of the form (1) by graphing the quadratic equation in two variables of the form (2), and observing where it crosses the x-axis, i.e., where $y = 0$.

In the exercises that follow, the first components should be selected so as to include all intersections of the graph with the x-axis.

EXERCISES 9.5

Solve by graphing. Estimate answers to nearest one-half unit.

Sample problem : $x^2 - 2x - 3 = 0$

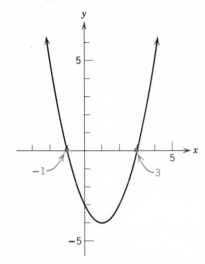

Write the equation in two variables $x^2 - 2x - 3 = y$ or $y = x^2 - 2x - 3$. Find appropriate ordered pairs which satisfy the equation.

$(-2, 5)$, $(1, -4)$, $(-1, 0)$, $(2, -3)$, $(0, -3)$, and $(3, 0)$

Complete the graph. The points at which the curve crosses the x-axis correspond to values for x which satisfy $x^2 - 2x - 3 = 0$.

Ans. $-1; 3$

1. $x^2 - 4 = 0$	**2.** $x^2 + 3x - 4 = 0$	**3.** $x^2 + x - 12 = 0$
4. $x^2 - 2x = 0$	**5.** $x^2 - 2x + 1 = 0$	**6.** $x^2 - x - 6 = 0$
7. $2x^2 + 3x - 2 = 0$	**8.** $2x^2 - 5x + 3 = 0$	**9.** $2x^2 + x - 3 = 0$
10. $2x^2 = 3x$	**11.** $5x^2 + 3x = 2$	**12.** $5x^2 - x = 6$
13. $x^2 - 5x + 6 = 0$	**14.** $x^2 - 3x + 2 = 0$	**15.** $x^2 = 3x$
16. $x^2 = 6x - 9$	**17.** $4x^2 + 4x + 1 = 0$	**18.** $4x^2 = 9$

9.6   THE PYTHAGOREAN THEOREM

A particularly useful application of quadratic equations is illustrated in the solution of problems involving the sides of a right triangle. The early Greeks proved that in any right triangle the sum of the squares of the lengths of the shorter sides, called **legs,** of a right triangle, is equal to the square of the length of the longest side, called the **hypotenuse.** Thus, in Figure 9.3 on page 218,

$$a^2 + b^2 = c^2.$$

This relationship is known as the Pythagorean theorem, in honor of the Greek mathematician Pythagoras.

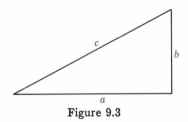

Figure 9.3

If we apply this theorem to compute the length of the diagonal of a square with sides of length one unit, shown in Figure 9.4, we have the following:

$$c^2 = a^2 + b^2,$$

$$c^2 = (1)^2 + (1)^2,$$

$$c^2 = 2,$$

$$c = \pm \sqrt{2}.$$

Figure 9.4

The number $-\sqrt{2}$, does not meet the physical conditions of length. Hence, the length of the diagonal is $\sqrt{2}$ units.

EXERCISES 9.6

Sample problem: Find the length of the diagonal of a rectangle whose length is 6 feet and whose width is 4 feet.

Sketch the rectangle.

Use the Pythegorean theorem.

$$c^2 = a^2 + b^2$$

Substitute 4 for a and 6 for b.

$$c^2 = (4)^2 + (6)^2$$
$$c^2 = 16 + 36$$
$$c = \pm \sqrt{52}$$
$$c = \pm 2 \sqrt{13} \qquad 2\sqrt{13} \text{ is the only meaningful answer.}$$

Ans. Length of diagonal is $2\sqrt{13}$ feet.

1. Find the length of the diagonal of a rectangle whose length is 4 feet and whose width is 3 feet.

2. Find the length of the diagonal of a rectangle whose length is 12 feet and whose width is 5 feet.

3. Find the length of the diagonal of a square whose side is 3 feet in length.

4. Find the length of the diagonal of a square whose side is 2 feet in length.

5. A baseball diamond is a square whose sides are 90 feet in length. Find the straight line distance from home plate to second base. (Use the table of square roots and find the length to the nearest foot.)

6. Find the length of the diagonal of a square whose side is a inches in length.

Sample problem : Find the width of a rectangle whose length is 8 inches and whose diagonal is 10 inches long.

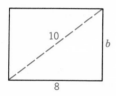

Sketch the rectangle.

Substitute 8 for a and 10 for c in $a^2 + b^2 = c^2$.

$$(8)^2 + b^2 = (10)^2$$
$$64 + b^2 = 100$$
$$b^2 = 100 - 64$$
$$b^2 = 36$$
$$b = \pm 6 \qquad \text{6 is the only meaningful answer.}$$

Ans. Width is 6 inches.

7. Find the length of a rectangle whose width is 5 inches and whose diagonal is 13 inches long.

8. Find the length of a rectangle whose diagonal is 20 inches long and whose width is 12 inches.

9. Find the width of a rectangle whose diagonal is 11 inches long and whose length is 9 inches.

10. Find the width of a rectangle whose length is 5 inches and whose diagonal is 6 inches long.

Sample problem : The length of a rectangle is 2 inches greater than the width. The diagonal is 10 inches long. Find dimensions of the rectangle.

Solution continued on the next page

Sketch the rectangle.

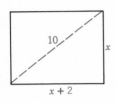

Substitute x for a, $x + 2$ for b, and 10 for c in $a^2 + b^2 = c^2$.

$$(x)^2 + (x + 2)^2 = (10)^2$$

Solve resulting equation.

$$x^2 + x^2 + 4x + 4 = 100$$
$$2x^2 + 4x - 96 = 0$$
$$2(x - 6)(x + 8) = 0$$

$$x - 6 = 0 \qquad x + 8 = 0$$
$$x = 6 \qquad\quad x = -8 \qquad \text{6 is the only meaningful solution.}$$

Ans. Width = 6 inches,
length = 8 inches.

11. The length of a rectangle is 3 inches greater than the width, and the diagonal is 15 inches in length. Find the dimensions of the rectangle.

12. The width of a rectangle is 7 inches less than the length, and the diagonal is 13 inches in length. Find the dimensions of the rectangle.

13. The width of a rectangle is 3 inches less than the length, and the square of the length of the diagonal is 29 inches. Find the dimensions of the rectangle.

14. The length of a rectangle is 5 inches greater than the width, and the square of the length of the diagonal is 73 inches. Find the dimensions of the rectangle.

15. The length of a rectangle is twice the width, and the diagonal is $3\sqrt{5}$ inches in length. Find the dimensions of the rectangle.

16. The length of a rectangle is three times the width, and the diagonal is $2\sqrt{10}$ inches in length. Find the dimensions of the rectangle.

Sample problem: A 25-foot ladder is placed against a wall so that its foot is 7 feet from the foot of the wall. How far up does the ladder extend?

Sketch figure.

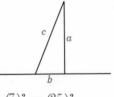

Substitute 7 for b and 25 for c in $a^2 + b^2 = c^2$.

$$a^2 + (7)^2 = (25)^2$$

Simplify.

$$a^2 + 49 = 625$$
$$a^2 = 576$$

Solve by extraction of roots.

$$a = \pm \sqrt{576}$$
$$a = \pm 24 \qquad 24 \text{ is the only meaningful solution.}$$

Ans. 24 feet

17. How long must a wire be to stretch from the top of a 40-foot telephone pole to a point on the ground 30 feet from the foot of the pole?

18. How high on a building will a 25-foot ladder reach if its foot is 15 feet from the wall against which the ladder is to be placed?

19. If a 30-foot pine tree casts a shadow of 30 feet, how far is it from the tip of the shadow to the top of the tree?

20. One leg of a right triangle is 6 inches longer than the other, and the hypotenuse has a length 6 inches less than twice that of the shorter leg. Find the dimensions of the right triangle.

CHAPTER REVIEW

Solve for x, y, or z by any method.

1. *a.* $x^2 - 25 = 0$ *b.* $3x^2 - 27 = 0$

2. *a.* $6x^2 - 42 = 0$ *b.* $\dfrac{2y^2}{3} = 4$

3. *a.* $(z - 2)^2 = 9$ *b.* $(z + 3)^2 = 1$

4. *a.* $(x - 7)^2 = 16$ *b.* $(x - a)^2 = c^2$

5. *a.* $(x + 3)^2 = a$ *b.* $(y + a)^2 = 4$

6. *a.* $x^2 + 3x - 4 = 0$ *b.* $y^2 = 3y + 3$

7. *a.* $2x^2 + 4x + 2 = 0$ *b.* $y^2 - y = 2$

8. Solve by completing the square: $y^2 - 4y = 5$.

In Exercises 9–11, solve each equation using the quadratic formula.

9. $\dfrac{x^2}{4} = \dfrac{15}{4} - \dfrac{x}{2}$ **10.** $x^2 + 3x + 1 = 0$ **11.** $\dfrac{x^2}{4} + 1 = \dfrac{13}{12} x$

12. Graph: $y = x^2 + 3x$.

13. Graph: $y = x^2 + 3x - 4$.

14. Solve by graphing: $x^2 - x - 6 = 0$.

15. If $x^2 + y^2 = z^2$, and $x = 12$, $z = 20$, find y.

16. If $a^2 + b^2 = c^2$, and $a = 6$, $b = 6$, find c.

17. Find the length of the diagonal of a rectangle whose width is 7 inches and whose length is 9 inches.

18. Find the length of the diagonal of a square with sides 8 inches long.

19. A cable is to be stretched from a point 18 feet up a telephone pole to a point on the ground 24 feet from the base of the pole. If the pole is mounted on level ground, what is the length of the stretched cable?

20. Water flows down a river at a rate of 2 miles per hour. A motor boat runs upstream for 9 miles and immediately returns downstream 4 miles. If the total trip takes one hour, what is the speed of the boat in still water?

CUMULATIVE REVIEW

1. Write $24x^3y^2$ in completely factored form.

2. If $x = -2$ and $y = -4$, find the value of $\dfrac{x^2 + 2x - 4}{y}$.

3. For what value of x is $\dfrac{3x - 2}{x - 1}$ meaningless?

4. Simplify: $\dfrac{6a^3b^2}{3ab^2}$.

5. Solve for x: $3x - a = \dfrac{2ax - a^2}{a}$.

6. Solve the system: $3x + 4y = 11$
$2x - y = 0$.

7. Represent $\dfrac{3}{x + y} + \dfrac{4}{x^2 + xy}$ as a single fraction.

8. Find three ordered pairs that are solutions of $2x - y = 4$.

9. Simplify: $3x\sqrt{x^2y} + 2\sqrt{x^4y}$.

10. The sum of two numbers is a. If one of the numbers is x, the other is ? .

11. How many solutions has the equation $2x^2 - 8 = 0$?

12. What conclusions can be drawn concerning a and b if $ab = 0$?

13. The sum of two numbers is 18. If one of the numbers is -9, the other is __?__ .

14. One number is four times another. If their sum is 40, find the numbers.

15. The perimeter of a triangle is 30 inches. If the second side is 2 inches longer than the first, and the first is two thirds of the third, find the length of each side.

16. The first angle of a triangle is one-half of the second, and the third is equal to the sum of the other two, find the size of each angle.

17. The area of a triangle is 18 square inches. If the length of the base is four times the length of the altitude, find the base and altitude of the triangle.

18. The sum of two numbers is 16, and their product is 63. Find the numbers.

19. The length of a rectangle is twice the width, and its area is 242 square inches. Find its dimensions.

20. The base of a triangle is three times its altitude. If the triangle contains the same area as a rectangle whose length and width are 4 inches and 6 inches respectively, find the base and altitude of the triangle.

CHAPTER 10

NUMBER SYSTEMS

In this chapter, we shall retrace briefly the mathematical ideas investigated in the preceding chapters. As we studied various sets of numbers and operations performed on these numbers, together with certain assumptions pertaining to them, we were, in effect, studying some properties of a **number system**. As a distinguishing feature of algebra, we used variables to assist us in analyzing some of the properties of such a system.

THE REAL NUMBERS

In this book, we began our studies with a consideration of the natural numbers. By including 0 and the negatives of the natural numbers, we obtained the integers. We discussed the rational numbers, that is, numbers that can be represented by fractions of the form $\frac{a}{b}$ where a and b are integers and b is not equal to 0. The set of rational numbers necessarily includes the integers. We then considered irrational numbers such as $\sqrt{2}$, $-\sqrt{3}$, $\sqrt{5}$, etc., numbers which could not be represented as the quotient of two integers. There are other irrational numbers, which we have not investigated in this book, but with which you will become acquainted if you continue your study of mathematics. The number π

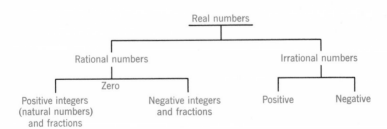

Figure 10.1

is one example. The set of numbers made up of all rational and all irrational numbers is called the set of **real numbers**. A schematic outline of the real numbers appears in Figure 10.1.

PROPERTIES OF THE REAL NUMBERS

Throughout this book, we have assumed that you were familiar with the fundamental operations of arithmetic. The meanings attached to the operations of addition, subtraction, multiplication, and division retained the same significance in algebra; however, a number of formal statements describing some of the properties we assumed were associated with these operations were introduced. These properties are summarized below, together with a reference to the section in which they were introduced.

1. Commutative law of addition: $a + b = b + a$.   [Sect. 1.8]
2. Associative law of addition:
$$(a + b) + c = a + (b + c).$$ [Sect. 1.8]
3. Commutative law of multiplication: $ab = ba$.   [Sect. 1.10]
4. Associative law of multiplication: $(ab)c = a(bc)$.   [Sect. 1.10]
5. Distributive law: $a(b + c) = ab + ac$.   [Sect. 4.1]
6. Symmetric law: if $a = b$, then $b = a$.   [Sect. 3.3]
7. Addition property: if $a = b$, then $a + c = b + c$.   [Sect. 3.3]
8. Multiplication property: if $a = b$, then $ac = bc$.   [Sect. 3.5]
9. Division property: if $a = b$, then $\dfrac{a}{c} = \dfrac{b}{c}$ $(c \neq 0)$.   [Sect. 3.4]
10. Multiplication property of fractions:
$$\frac{a}{b} = \frac{ac}{bc} \quad (b \neq 0, c \neq 0).$$ [Sect. 5.5]
11. Division property of fractions: $\dfrac{a}{b} = \dfrac{\dfrac{a}{c}}{\dfrac{b}{c}}$ $(b \neq 0, c \neq 0)$ [Sect. 5.2]

We use these properties to simplify expressions, to solve equations, and, in general, to guide us in the use of arithmetic and algebraic operations in the real number system.

CORRESPONDENCE BETWEEN THE REAL NUMBERS AND POINTS ON A LINE

The line graph has been useful in indicating the relative order of numbers. We first observed that we could represent all of the natural numbers 1, 2, 3, . . . by points on a line graph with 0 as the origin. By extending the line to the left of the origin, we could then represent all of the integers. By subdividing the line segments between the integers, we could locate points representing each rational number, and finally we mentioned the existence of a point on the line corresponding to each irrational number.

We refer to the relationship between the real numbers and points on a line as a **one-to-one correspondence.**

> *To each point in a line, there corresponds one and only one real number and to each real number, there corresponds one and only one point in the line.*

This correspondence is the basis for all graphing.

IMAGINARY AND COMPLEX NUMBERS

The real numbers are not the only kind of numbers with which mathematics is concerned. To see the need for other numbers, let us consider the solutions to a number of simple equations.

To solve certain types of equations, for example,

$$x + 3 = 5,$$

$$x = 2,$$

we need only the natural numbers. When we solve equations such as

$$x + 5 = 3,$$

$$x = -2,$$

we need the integers, since the natural numbers do not provide a solution. When we solve an equation such as

$$3x = 2,$$

$$x = \frac{2}{3},$$

we need the rational numbers, since no integer will satisfy the equation. When we solve an equation such as

$$x^2 - 2 = 0,$$

$$x = \pm \sqrt{2},$$

we need the irrational numbers, since there is no rational solution.

In this sequence of simple equations, notice how new numbers became necessary in order to obtain solutions. Now if we seek a solution to

$$x^2 + 2 = 0,$$

we have

$$x^2 = -2,$$

$$x = \pm \sqrt{-2}.$$

Since there exists no real number whose square is -2, we must have a number other than a real number if we are to have a solution. We call numbers such as $\sqrt{-2}$, $\sqrt{-3}$, etc., **imaginary numbers.** Numbers of the form $3 + 2\sqrt{-1}$ also occur as solutions of quadratic equations and are called **complex numbers.** Imaginary numbers and real numbers are thus special cases of complex numbers. For example, $\sqrt{-1}$ may be written $0 + \sqrt{-1}$, and 7 may be written $7 + 0\sqrt{-1}$.

Complex numbers have very important practical uses in the physical sciences. You will probably be introduced to their properties in your next course in mathematics.

EXERCISES 10

1. Which of the following are natural numbers?

$$3, \quad -2, \quad \frac{3}{4}, \quad 7, \quad -8, \quad \frac{1}{2}, \quad \frac{-2}{3}, \quad 1, \quad -20, \quad 4$$

2. Which of the following numbers are integers?

$$-1, \quad 3, \quad -\sqrt{3}, \quad 6, \quad \sqrt{9}, \quad -2, \quad \sqrt{-4}, \quad \frac{1}{2}, \quad \frac{-5}{6}, \quad -\sqrt{4}$$

3. Which of the following numbers are rational?

$$\sqrt{1}, \quad \sqrt{2}, \quad -\sqrt{3}, \quad -\sqrt{\frac{4}{9}}, \quad \frac{1}{100}, \quad \frac{-3}{5}, \quad \sqrt{8}, \quad \frac{1}{2}, \quad \sqrt{-9}, \quad \sqrt{100}$$

4. Which of the following numbers are irrational?

$$\sqrt{1}, \quad \sqrt{-2}, \quad -\sqrt{3}, \quad \sqrt{\frac{3}{4}}, \quad \sqrt{-9}, \quad \sqrt{9}, \quad -\sqrt{9}, \quad \sqrt{\frac{4}{9}}, \quad \sqrt{10}, \quad \sqrt{7}$$

5. Which of the following are real numbers?

$$\sqrt{2}, \quad -\sqrt{2}, \quad \sqrt{-2}, \quad \sqrt{\frac{2}{3}}, \quad -\sqrt{\frac{2}{3}}, \quad \sqrt{\frac{-2}{3}}, \quad 2\sqrt{3}, \quad 2\sqrt{-3}$$

6. If n represents a natural number, which of the following represent natural numbers?

$$n + 1, \quad n^2, \quad \sqrt{n}, \quad -n, \quad 10 - n, \quad 3n, \quad \frac{n}{2}, \quad n - 2, \quad n + 3n, \quad n^2 - 2n$$

7. The __?__ law asserts that $7(4 - a) = 28 - 7a$ for all real values of a.

8. The __?__ law of multiplication asserts that $(b)(-a) = (-a)(b)$ for all real values of a and b.

9. The __?__ law of addition asserts that $b + (4 + a) = (b + 4) + a$ for all real values of a and b.

10. The __?__ law of equality asserts that if $-2 = x$, then $x = -2$.

11. Which property would we apply to transform the equation $ax = b$ to an equivalent equation in which the coefficient of x is 1?

12. Which property would we apply to transform the equation $x - 4 = 7$ to an equivalent equation whose left-hand member consists of x alone?

13. What two properties would we apply to transform the equation $2x - 3 = 7$ to an equivalent equation whose left-hand member consists of x alone?

14. In Exercise 13, would it make any difference in which order we applied the properties?

15. Which properties would we apply to transform the equation $\dfrac{x}{a} = b$ to an equivalent equation whose left-hand member consists of x alone?

Which of the following equations have real solutions?

16. $x^2 + 4 = 0$ 17. $-x = -3 + 2$

18. $x^2 - 2x - 7 = 0$ 19. $x^2 - 2x + 7 = 0$

20. The real numbers and the points on a number line are in a __?__ __?__ __?__ correspondence.

FINAL CUMULATIVE REVIEWS

REVIEW I

1. List all prime numbers between 70 and 100.

2. If a and b are natural numbers, which of the following statements are true for all values of a and b?

$$a + b = b + a; \qquad a - b = b - a; \qquad ab = ba; \qquad \frac{a}{b} = \frac{b}{a}.$$

3. Arrange the numbers 6, -2, -4, 5, 3, -1 in order, from smallest to largest.

4. Write an equation expressing the word sentence: "The volume of a cylindrical silo is equal to π times the length of the diameter times the height."

5. If a 30-foot rope is cut into two pieces and x represents one of the pieces, how could the second piece be represented in terms of x?

6. Simplify: $2a(a - 1) + a(a + 2) - a^2$.

7. Divide $(6x^2 + 3x - 1)$ by $3x$.

8. Side b of a triangle is 2 inches longer than a second side a. Side c is twice as long as side a. How long is each side of the triangle if its perimeter is 34 inches?

9. Simplify: $\dfrac{2ab - 4b^2}{a^2 - 4b^2}.$

10. Represent $\dfrac{3}{4} + \dfrac{3}{4a}$ using a single fraction.

11. Simplify: $\dfrac{3xy^2}{4a} \cdot \dfrac{2xa^2}{5y}.$

12. Solve for x: $\dfrac{2a}{b} = \dfrac{6}{4 - x}.$

13. Graph the following ordered pairs on a rectangular coordinate system.

$(2, 6)$; $(3, -4)$; $(-5, -5)$; $(-5, 0)$.

14. Solve the system: $y = x$
$$3x + 2y = 5.$$

15. Where does the graph of $3x + 4y = 12$ cross the x-axis?

16. Simplify: $\dfrac{\sqrt{4^4 y^3}}{8^2 y}.$

17. For what value(s) of y will the fraction $\dfrac{5(y - 2)}{y + 3}$ equal 0?

229

18. An approximate value of $\sqrt{3}$ is 1.73. Find an approximation for $\sqrt{12}$.

19. Simplify: $(\sqrt{2} - \sqrt{5})(\sqrt{2} + \sqrt{5})$.

20. Find two consecutive positive odd integers whose product is 195.

REVIEW II

1. Simplify: $\dfrac{5^2 + 5}{5} - \dfrac{3^2 + 3}{3}$.

2. Division by $\underline{\ ?\ }$ is meaningless.

3. State whether $-2a$ is a solution of $x - a = 4x + 5a$.

4. The product of two numbers is 24. If one of the numbers is b, represent the other number in terms of b.

5. Simplify: $(a + b) - (2a - b) + (a + 3b)$.

6. Solve: $7(a + 3) = a - 9$.

7. One number is 5 less than a second number. The larger plus 5 times the smaller equals 47. Find the numbers.

8. Represent $\dfrac{a}{b} + \dfrac{b}{a}$ using a single fraction.

9. Express $\dfrac{3}{x + 3}$ as an equivalent fraction with denominator $x^2 - 9$.

10. Simplify: $\dfrac{2x}{3y} \div \dfrac{x^2}{y}$.

11. A statement that two ratios are equal is called a $\underline{\ ?\ }$.

12. Graph $2x + 3y = 6$.

13. Which equation has a straight line for a graph?
$$y = x^2 - 1; \qquad x + y = 1; \qquad x = y^2 - 1.$$

14. Solve the system: $2y - x = 7$
$$y + 2x = 1.$$

15. Solve: $(x - 3)^2 = 25$.

16. Which of the following numbers are irrational?
$$\sqrt{4}, \qquad \sqrt{5}, \qquad \sqrt{6}, \qquad \sqrt{7}, \qquad \sqrt{8}, \qquad \sqrt{9}, \qquad \sqrt{10}.$$

17. Simplify: $\sqrt{160x^3y^3z}$.

18. Simplify: $\dfrac{8 - \sqrt{32}}{8}$.

19. Solve: $x^2 + 5x + 2 = 0$.

20. Solve: $(x - 4)(x + 3) = -10$.

REVIEW III

1. Express 360 in completely factored form.

2. If $a = -2$, $b = 1$, $c = 3$, find the value of $a^2bc - abc^2$.

3. Simplify: $a(a + 1) - 2(a^2 + a) - a$.

4. State whether -2 is a solution of $4x + 4 = 2x - 4$.

5. What is the area of a square whose perimeter is 100 inches?

6. Factor completely: $abc - ab$.

7. Factor completely: $6x^2 - 3x - 9$.

8. In a collection of coins, there are 6 more dimes than nickels. If n represents the number of nickels, represent the total value of the collection (in cents) in terms of n.

9. Represent $\dfrac{a - 3b}{5} - \dfrac{a + 3b}{5}$ using a single fraction.

10. Represent $\dfrac{1}{2x} + \dfrac{1}{3x}$ using a single fraction.

11. Divide $(x^2 - 6x - 16)$ by $(x + 2)$.

12. Simplify: $\dfrac{ab}{a^2 - b^2} \div \dfrac{ab}{2a - 2b}$.

13. The denominator of a certain fraction is four more than the numerator and the fraction is equivalent to $\frac{5}{6}$. Find the numerator of the fraction.

14. If 228 bricks are required for 12 linear feet of a wall, how many bricks will be required for 18 linear feet?

15. First-degree equations are called __?__ because their graphs are straight lines.

16. Solve for y in terms of x: $x = \dfrac{3y - 2}{4}$.

17. What value would be substituted for b in the quadratic formula when solving the equation $x^2 + x - 5 = 0$?

18. Simplify: $\sqrt{36a^6b^4c^5}$.

19. Simplify: $4\sqrt{a} + \sqrt{4a} - \sqrt{9a}$.

20. How far from the foot of a vertical pole will a 14-foot wire reach if the other end of the wire is tied to the pole at a height of 6 feet?

REVIEW IV

1. Graph the first ten prime numbers on a line graph.

2. If r and s represent two numbers: (a) What is their sum? (b) What is their product?

3. If $4a$ and $-2b$ are two factors of $24ab$, what is the third factor?

4. If $a = 3$, $b = 2$, $c = -1$, find the value of $\dfrac{ab}{c^2} - \dfrac{a+c}{b}$.

5. Find three consecutive even integers whose sum is -78.

6. Simplify: $(x - b)(x - 2b) - (x^2 + 2b^2)$.

7. Factor completely: $2x^2 - 8$.

8. At a baseball game 260 tickets were sold. Adults paid 80 cents each for their tickets, and children paid 30 cents each. If the total receipts for the game were \$160, how many tickets of each kind were sold?

9. Simplify: $\dfrac{2x - 2}{2}$.

10. Represent $\dfrac{3}{x+2} - \dfrac{1}{(x+2)^2}$ using a single fraction.

11. Divide $12x^2$ by $\dfrac{3x}{4}$.

12. Solve: $\dfrac{13}{x} = 1 + \dfrac{4}{x}$.

13. If $\frac{1}{4}$ inch on a map represents 8 miles, how many miles does 6 inches represent?

14. Only __?__ points are needed to determine the graph of a first degree equation.

15. What is the value of s when r equals 6 if $2r + 6s = 20$?

16. Supply the missing components so that the ordered pairs $(0,\ \ )$, $(2,\ \ )$, and $(-3,\ \ )$ satisfy the equation $3x - y = 6$.

17. Divide $\dfrac{a^2\sqrt{3}}{4}$ by $\dfrac{3a}{\sqrt{3}}$.

18. Solve: $8r(r - 1) = -6r$.

19. Where does the graph of $y = x^2 + x - 30$ intersect the x-axis?

20. If the perimeter of a rectangle is 56 inches and its area is 192 square inches, what are the dimensions of the rectangle?

REVIEW V

1. Simplify: $\dfrac{6 + 2^2}{5} - \dfrac{3^3 - 5^2}{2}$.

2. The signed whole numbers together with zero are called __?__ .

3. Solve: $\dfrac{3x}{2} - 9 = 6$.

4. Factor: $y^2 - 12y + 11$.

5. Simplify: $(x + 3b)(x - 3b) - (x^2 - b^2)$.

6. The length of a rectangle is 8 feet more than its width w. Represent two-thirds of the length in terms of w.

7. Represent $-\dfrac{1-a}{3}$ as a positive fraction with a positive denominator.

8. Divide $(x^3 - 2x^2 + x)$ by x.

9. Divide $\dfrac{2\pi rh}{6+h}$ by $\dfrac{2\pi r}{h}$.

10. A plane travels 875 miles in t hours. Represent the distance the plane can travel in 1 hour in terms of t.

11. Solve: $\dfrac{x-9}{2} = \dfrac{x+12}{9}$.

12. In a proportion, the product of the __?__ equals the product of the __?__ .

13. Graph the set of all points for which $x = 5$ in a rectangular coordinate system.

14. Solve the system: $y = 2x + 5$
$$x - 3y = -20.$$

15. For what value(s) of a will the product $(a+3)(a-7)$ equal zero?

16. Graph $-\sqrt{4}, \sqrt{7}, \sqrt{21}$ and $\sqrt{29}$ on a line graph.

17. Simplify the product of $\sqrt{3}$ and $\sqrt{27}$.

18. Solve: $x^2 + 5x + 2 = 0$.

19. Solve: $x^2 - 2 + \dfrac{7}{3}x = 0$.

20. The sum of a certain natural number and its reciprocal is $\frac{82}{9}$. Find the number.

REVIEW VI

1. If $x = -1$, $y = -2$, $z = -3$, find the value of $x^3 - y^3 + z^3$.

2. Simplify: $\dfrac{3^3 - 2^2 - 1^2}{2}$.

3. Represent $\dfrac{3x^2 - x^2}{x} - \dfrac{x^3}{x^2}$ using a single fraction.

4. The temperature drops 23° from a reading of 6°. What is the new temperature?

5. Simplify: $\dfrac{a^2 - 3a - 4}{a^2 - 1} \cdot \dfrac{a+2}{a-4}$.

6. At a recent election, the winning candidate received 62 votes more than his opponent. If there were 3626 votes cast in all, how many did each candidate receive?

7. Simplify: $3(y + 3)^2 - (18y + 27)$.

8. Factor completely: $a^2 - 25b^2$.

9. One number is eight less than a second number. If n represents the larger number, represent four times the smaller number in terms of n.

10. Find the lowest common denominator of $\dfrac{1}{2}, \dfrac{1}{3}, \dfrac{1}{4}, \dfrac{1}{5},$ and $\dfrac{1}{6}$.

11. Simplify: $\dfrac{3 + \dfrac{2}{3}}{1 - \dfrac{1}{3}}$.

12. Represent $\dfrac{x - 1}{6} - \dfrac{2x + 5}{3}$ using a single fraction.

13. Solve: $\dfrac{7}{8} = \dfrac{21}{y + 2}$.

14. Solve: $\dfrac{3}{5}x + \dfrac{3}{10} = x - \dfrac{1}{2}$.

15. Solve for x: $\dfrac{a + c}{x} = \dfrac{2}{b}$.

16. An approximate value for $\sqrt{2}$ is 1.41, find an approximation for $\sqrt{72}$.

17. Solve the system $5x - 3y = -1$ using graphical methods.
$$3x + 3y = 9$$

18. Solve: $3w(2w + 3) = 0$.

19. Solve: $(x - 1)(x + 3) = 1$.

20. Given $a^2 + b^2 = c^2$. Find b, if $a = 5$ and $c = 13$.

REVIEW VII

1. What is the numerical coefficient of $-x^3$?

2. Solve: $\dfrac{x^2}{2} - x = \dfrac{5}{2}$.

3. Simplify: $(a + b - 2c) - (3a - b + 2c) + (2a + 2b - c)$.

4. Which of the following equations are true for all values of x?
$$x^3 \cdot x^2 = x^5; \qquad x^3 \cdot x^2 = x^6; \qquad 3x^2 = 9x^2$$

5. Factor completely: $4y^2 + 16y + 15$.

6. A 22-foot cable is divided into 2 parts. If y represents the longer piece, represent six times the shorter piece in terms of y.

7. Represent $\dfrac{4}{3y} + \dfrac{7}{3y} - \dfrac{2}{3y}$ using a single fraction.

8. Solve for x: $\dfrac{a}{x} = \dfrac{b}{2c}$.

9. Simplify: $\dfrac{1 - \dfrac{a}{b}}{1 + \dfrac{a}{b}}$.

10. A car travels 90 miles in the same time that a slower car travels 60 miles. If the first car goes 10 miles per hour faster than the second, find the rate of each.

11. Find second components for the ordered pairs $(3, \quad)$, $(-2, \quad)$, $(0, \quad)$, and $(6, \quad)$ so that each ordered pair satisfies $y = 3x + 4$.

12. Solve the system $2x + 3y = -5$ by graphical methods.
$$2y + 8 = x$$

13. Solve the system $x - 2y = 7$ by algebraic methods.
$$2x + y = 4$$

14. Solve: $14x^2 = 28x$.

15. Solve: $\dfrac{4}{x-2} - \dfrac{7}{x-3} = \dfrac{2}{15}$.

16. What term must be added to the expression $x^2 - 8x$ in order to make the expression a perfect square?

17. Simplify: $\dfrac{2 + 2\sqrt{2}}{2}$.

18. Simplify: $\dfrac{\sqrt{12a^2b^3}}{ab}$.

19. Solve for x: $b^2x^2 - c = 0$.

20. A man rowed 9 miles downstream and back again in 6 hours. The rate of the current was 2 miles per hour. Find the rate of the boat in still water.

REVIEW VIII

1. The __?__ law of multiplication asserts that $ab = ba$.

2. For what value of x is the expression $\dfrac{x+2}{x-5}$ meaningless?

3. If n is an odd integer, represent the next three odd integers in terms of n.

4. Factor completely: $a^2 - 6ab + 8b^2$.

5. Simplify: $(x - 2y)^2 - (x^2 + 4y^2)$.

6. Where should a 64-foot cable be cut so that twice the length of the longer piece equals five times that of the shorter?

7. Simplify: $\dfrac{x^2 - x - 20}{x^2 - 7x + 10} \cdot \dfrac{x^2 + 9x + 18}{x^2 + 7x + 12}$.

8. Divide $\dfrac{ab}{a^2 - b^2}$ by $\dfrac{ab}{2a - 2b}$.

9. Simplify: $\dfrac{\dfrac{1}{a} - \dfrac{1}{b}}{\dfrac{1}{ab}}$.

10. Divide $(x^2 + 3x - 7)$ by $(x - 5)$.

11. Solve the system $3y - x - 1 = 0$ algebraically.
$$y + 6x + 6 = 0$$

12. Solve the system $y - 2x - 5 = 0$ by graphical methods.
$$x - 3y + 20 = 0$$

13. Two packages weighed together total 146 pounds One of the packages weighs 12 pounds more than the other. How much does each package weigh?

14. Solve: $x^2 - 5x - 14 = 0$.

15. Simplify: $\sqrt{200x^3y^2}$.

16. Simplify: $\sqrt{125} + 2\sqrt{5}$.

17. Graph: $y = x^2 + x - 6$.

18. Simplify: $5\sqrt{\dfrac{2}{5}}$.

19. Solve: $2x^2 - 2x = 7$.

20. The length of a rectangle is 4 inches less than twice its width, and the area is 240 square inches. Find the dimensions of the rectangle.

REVIEW IX

1. Simplify: $\dfrac{4^2 + 2}{2} - \dfrac{3^3 - 7}{4}$.

2. If $a = 1$, $b = -2$, $c = 2$, find the value of $abc - b^2 + c^2$.

3. Simplify: $2a(a - b) - b(a + b) - (a^2 - b^2)$.

4. Find three consecutive even integers whose sum is 78.

5. Factor completely: $2x^2 - 24x + 22$.

6. The difference of two numbers is 28. If n represents the smaller number, represent the larger in terms of n.

7. Solve: $2(a - 1) = a + 3$.

8. Represent $\dfrac{2}{x} - \dfrac{3}{y}$ using a single fraction.

9. Divide $\dfrac{3b}{4a}$ by $\dfrac{12b^2}{a}$.

10. Divide $(2x^2 + 3x - 1)$ by $(x + 2)$.

11. Solve for x: $\dfrac{2b - 2a}{x} = 2c$.

12. Graph: $x - 3y = 6$.

13. Graph: $y = -2x^2 + 3$.

14. Solve the system $3y - 5x = 1$ by algebraic methods.
$$x + \ \ y = 3$$

15. The value of a collection of coins is \$3.15. There are three more dimes than nickles and two more quarters than dimes. How many of each kind of coin is there in the collection?

16. Simplify the product of $\sqrt{6x}$ and $\sqrt{15x}$.

17. Simplify: $\dfrac{2 + 3\sqrt{12}}{2}$.

18. An approximate value for $\sqrt{2}$ is 1.41. Find an approximation for $\sqrt{18}$.

19. A plane flies directly east for 12 miles, turns and flies south for 16 miles. How far is the plane from its starting point?

20. Where does the graph of $y = 3x^2 + 4x - 1$ intersect the y-axis?

REVIEW X

1. Graph the prime numbers between 20 and 40 on a line graph.

2. Express $240x^2y$ in completely factored form.

3. Arrange the numbers $5, -2, 3, -5, 1, 7, -1$ in order, from smallest to largest.

4. Simplify: $(a - b) - 2(a + b) - (a + 2b)$.

5. Simplify: $(a - b)(a + b) - (a - b)^2$.

6. Factor completely: $3x^2 - 18xy + 24y^2$.

7. Simplify: $\dfrac{2a}{6a^2 + 8a}$.

8. Represent $\dfrac{a + 3b}{7} - \dfrac{a + 2b}{7}$ using a single fraction.

9. Represent $\dfrac{1}{a-3} - \dfrac{2}{(a-3)^2}$ using a single fraction.

10. Solve: $\dfrac{3}{5}x = x - \dfrac{4}{5}$.

11. Graph: $y = x$.

12. Solve the system $5x + 2y - 8 = 0$ by algebraic methods.
$$3x - 7y - 13 = 0$$

13. Simplify: $3\sqrt{3} - \sqrt{12} + \sqrt{75}$.

14. Simplify: $\dfrac{\sqrt{18} - \sqrt{27}}{3}$.

15. Where does the graph of $y = x^2 + 4x + 3$ intersect the x-axis?

16. Find two consecutive integers such that twice the second less one half the first is 14.

17. In a right triangle, if two thirds of one acute angle is added to one half of the second acute angle, the result is 50°. Find each angle.

18. A man gave one third of his money to one son, one fourth to another son, and had $250 left. How much did he have to start with?

19. A furniture dealer sold a desk and a chair for $640. If the desk sold for $40 more than four times the chair, what was the price of each?

20. The hypotenuse of a right triangle is 20 inches long. If one of the remaining sides is 16 inches long, how long is the third side?

GLOSSARY

ABSCISSA

The first component in an ordered pair. The distance of a point from the vertical axis in rectangular coordinates; to the right of the axis if the component is positive; to the left of the axis if the component is negative.

ABSOLUTE VALUE

$$|x| = \begin{array}{l} x, \text{ if } x \text{ is greater than or equal to } 0. \\ -x, \text{ if } x \text{ is less than } 0. \end{array}$$

ALGEBRAIC EXPRESSION

Any variable or numeral or meaningful combination thereof. $3xy - xy^2$, $\dfrac{x+y}{3}$, xyz, etc., are algebraic expressions.

ASSOCIATIVE LAW

a. Addition: $a + (b + c) = (a + b) + c$
b. Multiplication: $(ab)c = a(bc)$

AXIS

A straight line in a plane used as a visual representation of the relative order of the real numbers. A line graph or number line.

BASE (OF A POWER)

The number to which an exponent is attached. In the term x^4, x is the base to which the exponent 4 is attached.

BINOMIAL

An algebraic expression consisting of two terms. $3a + 4b$ is a binomial.

CARTESIAN COORDINATES

See Rectangular coordinates.

COEFFICIENT

Any factor or group of factors in a product is the coefficient of the remaining factors. In $32ab$, 32 is the coefficient of ab; in ax, a is the coefficient of x.

COMMUTATIVE LAW

a. Addition: $a + b = b + a$
b. Multiplication: $ab = ba$

239

COMPLETE QUADRATIC EQUATION

A quadratic equation in one variable containing a second-degree term, a first-degree term, and a nonzero constant term. $2x^2 + 3x - 4 = 0$ is a complete quadratic equation.

COMPLEX FRACTION

A fraction that contains other fractions in its numerator or denominator or both. $\dfrac{3 + \dfrac{1}{a}}{\dfrac{3}{a}}$ is a complex fraction.

COMPLEX NUMBER

Any number of the form $a + b\sqrt{-1}$ where a and b are real numbers.

COMPONENT (OF AN ORDERED PAIR)

Either number of an ordered pair.

CONSECUTIVE INTEGERS

Integers that differ by 1. The numbers -3, -2, -1, 0, 1, 2, and 3 are consecutive integers.

CONSTANT

A symbol representing a single number during a particular discussion.

COORDINATES OF A POINT

A pair of numbers giving the position of the point with respect to an origin.

DEGREE OF A TERM (WITH ONE VARIABLE)

The exponent of the variable. The term $2x^4$ is of degree 4.

DEPENDENT EQUATIONS

A system of equations where every set of values which satisfies one of the equations satisfies them all.

DEPENDENT VARIABLE

A variable whose values are considered determined by the values of another variable.

DESCENDING POWERS

The arrangement of an expression so that each term is of higher degree in one of the variables than the next succeeding term. The algebraic expression $x^4 + x^3 - 2x^2 + x - 1$ is arranged in descending powers of x.

DISTRIBUTIVE LAW

$a(b + c) = ab + ac$

EQUATION

An assertion that two expressions are names for the same number.

EQUIVALENT EQUATIONS

Equations which have the same solutions. The equations $2x + 2 = 6$ and $2x = 4$ are equivalent since 2 is the only solution of each.

EQUIVALENT EXPRESSIONS

Expressions that represent the same number for all values of any variables involved. The expressions, $2c + 3b + c$, $3c + 3b$, and $3(c + b)$ are equivalent because for all values of b and c they represent the same number.

EXPONENT

A number represented by a symbol placed to the right and above another symbol to indicate how many times the number represented by this latter symbol occurs as a factor in a product. In a^3, 3 is the exponent.

FACTOR

Any of a group of numbers that are multiplied together.

FIRST-DEGREE EQUATION

An equation of degree 1; a linear equation.

FORMULA

A relationship between quantities expressed in symbols; an equation.

GRAPH

A geometric representation of a numerical relationship.

INCOMPLETE QUADRATIC EQUATION

A quadratic equation where either the first-degree term or the constant term is missing. $x^2 - 2 = 0$ and $2x^2 + 3x = 0$ are incomplete quadratic equations.

INCONSISTENT EQUATIONS

Equations that have no common solution. Graphically, inconsistent linear equations (in two variables) appear as parallel lines.

INDEPENDENT VARIABLE

A variable considered free to assume any one of a given set of values.

INTEGER

The integers include the natural numbers, the negatives of the natural numbers, and 0.

IRRATIONAL NUMBER

Any real number that is not rational. That is, any real number that is not the quotient of two integers. The numbers $\sqrt{2}$, $\sqrt{7}$, π, etc. are irrational.

LIKE TERMS

Terms whose variable factors are identical. $23xy$ and $2xy$ are like terms.

LINEAR EQUATION

An equation of the first degree. The graph of a linear equation in two variables is a straight line.

LINE GRAPH

A straight line used to represent the relative order of a set of number .

LITERAL EQUATIONS

An equation containing symbols for constants such as a, b, and c in addition to variables such as x, y, and z. The equation $2ax^2 + bx + c = 0$ is a literal equation.

LITERAL NUMBER

A variable. A symbol representing any one of a set of numbers.

LOWEST COMMON DENOMINATOR (L.C.D.)

The smallest natural number or the polynomial of least degree into which each of the denominators of a given set of fractions divide exactly.

MEMBER OF AN EQUATION

The expression to the right of an equal sign constitutes the right-hand member of an equation, and that to the left of an equal sign constitutes the left-hand member. In $2x + 3 = x + 9$, the left-hand member is $2x + 3$ and the right-hand member is $x + 9$.

MONOMIAL

An algebraic expression consisting of one term. The expression $2xy$ is a monomial.

NATURAL NUMBER

A positive whole number, as 1, 2, 3, 4 . . . , etc.

NEGATIVE NUMBER

A number less than 0.

NUMBER LINE

See line graph.

NUMERAL

A symbol representing a number. The symbols "2," "π," and "$\frac{1}{2}$" are numerals.

NUMERICAL EVALUATION

The act of finding the value of an expression. To evaluate $x + 4$ for $x = 3$, means to replace x with 3 and simplify the results (giving 7).

ORDERED PAIR

A pair of numbers in which the order in which the numbers are considered is important. An ordered pair is usually represented (x, y).

ORDINATE

The second component in an ordered pair. The distance of a point from the horizontal axis in rectangular coordinates. The point is above the axis if the component is positive and below the axis if the component is negative.

ORIGIN

The point on a line graph corresponding to 0. The point of intersection of coordinate axes.

PARENTHESES

Symbols, ( ), used to group factors or terms.

POLYNOMIAL

A special kind of algebraic expression. In this book, any term or sum of terms.

POSITIVE NUMBER

A number greater than 0.

PRIME FACTOR

A factor that is a prime number.

PRIME NUMBER

Any natural number that has, as whole number factors, itself and one only. The number 1 is excluded from the set of primes.

QUADRANT

One of the four regions into which a set of rectangular axes divides the plane.

QUADRATIC EQUATION

An equation of degree 2. $x^2 = 2$, $x^2 - 3x = 0$, and $x^2 + 2x = x - 1$ are quadratic equations.

QUADRATIC FORMULA

The formula $x = \dfrac{-b \pm \sqrt{b^2 - 4ac}}{2a}$ used to solve quadratic equations of the form $ax^2 + bx + c = 0$, $a \neq 0$.

RADICAL (OF ORDER 2)

A symbol ($\sqrt{}$) indicating the positive square root of a number. Any expression under a radical sign is called a radicand.

RATIONAL NUMBER

The quotient of two integers, $\dfrac{a}{b}$, where b does not equal zero.

REAL NUMBER

Any number that is either a rational number or an irrational number.

RECIPROCAL

The reciprocal of a number is the quotient obtained by dividing the given number into 1. The reciprocal of 3 is $\frac{1}{3}$; the reciprocal of $\frac{3}{4}$ is $\frac{4}{3}$; etc. The number 0 has no reciprocal.

RECTANGULAR COORDINATES

Numbers specifying the distances of points from two perpendicular number lines.

ROOT OF AN EQUATION

A value for the variable that satisfies the equation; i.e., for which the equation is a true statement. A solution.

SIMPLIFY

To find an equivalent form for an expression that is simpler than the original.

SOLUTION (OF AN EQUATION)

See Root of an equation.

SQUARE ROOT

One of two equal factors of a number. Since $3 \cdot 3 = 9$, the number 3 is a square root of 9. Also, since $(-3)(-3) = 9$, the number -3 is a square root of 9.

STANDARD FORM (FOR A FRACTION)

A positive fraction with positive denominator, such as, $\dfrac{-a}{b}$ or $\dfrac{a}{b}$.

STANDARD FORM (FOR AN EQUATION)

An equation with the left-hand member arranged in descending powers of the variable and the right-hand member 0, such as $3x^2 - 2x + 1 = 0$.

STANDARD FORM (FOR A SYSTEM OF EQUATIONS)

The equations arranged with like terms in order in the left-hand members. For example, $2x + 3y = 7$
$-x + 5y = 3$.

SYMMETRIC PROPERTY OF EQUALITY

If $a = b$, then $b = a$. Thus, if $2x = y + 3$, then $y + 3 = 2x$.

SYSTEMS OF EQUATIONS

A set of two or more equations considered together.

TERM

Any part of an algebraic expression separated from other parts by plus or minus signs.

TRINOMIAL

An algebraic expression consisting of 3 terms. $2x + 3y + 2$ is a trinomial.

UNLIKE TERMS

Terms that differ in their variable factors. $23xy$ and $4x$ are unlike terms; $3x^2$ and $3x^3$ are unlike terms; etc.

VARIABLE

A symbol representing any one of a given set of numbers.

TABLE OF SQUARES, SQUARE ROOTS, AND PRIME FACTORS

No.	Sq.	Sq. Root	Prime Factors	No.	Sq.	Sq. Root	Prime Factors
1	1	1.000		51	2,601	7.141	$3 \cdot 17$
2	4	1.414	2	52	2,704	7.211	$2^2 \cdot 13$
3	9	1.732	3	53	2,809	7.280	53
4	16	2.000	2^2	54	2,916	7.348	$2 \cdot 3^3$
5	25	2.236	5	55	3,025	7.416	$5 \cdot 11$
6	36	2.449	$2 \cdot 3$	56	3,136	7.483	$2^3 \cdot 7$
7	49	2.646	7	57	3,249	7.550	$3 \cdot 19$
8	64	2.828	2^3	58	3,364	7.616	$2 \cdot 29$
9	81	3.000	3^2	59	3,481	7.681	59
10	100	3.162	$2 \cdot 5$	60	3,600	7.746	$2^2 \cdot 3 \cdot 5$
11	121	3.317	11	61	3,721	7.810	61
12	144	3.464	$2^2 \cdot 3$	62	3,844	7.874	$2 \cdot 31$
13	169	3.606	13	63	3,969	7.937	$3^2 \cdot 7$
14	196	3.742	$2 \cdot 7$	64	4,096	8.000	2^6
15	225	3.873	$3 \cdot 5$	65	4,225	8.062	$5 \cdot 13$
16	256	4.000	2^4	66	4,356	8.124	$2 \cdot 3 \cdot 11$
17	289	4.123	17	67	4,489	8.185	67
18	324	4.243	$2 \cdot 3^2$	68	4,624	8.246	$2^2 \cdot 17$
19	361	4.359	19	69	4,761	8.307	$3 \cdot 23$
20	400	4.472	$2^2 \cdot 5$	70	4,900	8.367	$2 \cdot 5 \cdot 7$
21	441	4.583	$3 \cdot 7$	71	5,041	8.426	71
22	484	4.690	$2 \cdot 11$	72	5,184	8.485	$2^3 \cdot 3^2$
23	529	4.796	23	73	5,329	8.544	73
24	576	4.899	$2^3 \cdot 3$	74	5,476	8.602	$2 \cdot 37$
25	625	5.000	5^2	75	5,625	8.660	$3 \cdot 5^2$
26	676	5.099	$2 \cdot 13$	76	5,776	8.718	$2^2 \cdot 19$
27	729	5.196	3^3	77	5,929	8.775	$7 \cdot 11$
28	784	5.292	$2^2 \cdot 7$	78	6,084	8.832	$2 \cdot 3 \cdot 13$
29	841	5.385	29	79	6,241	8.888	79
30	900	5.477	$2 \cdot 3 \cdot 5$	80	6,400	8.944	$2^4 \cdot 5$
31	961	5.568	31	81	6,561	9.000	3^4
32	1,024	5.657	2^5	82	6,724	9.055	$2 \cdot 41$
33	1,089	5.745	$3 \cdot 11$	83	6,889	9.110	83
34	1,156	5.831	$2 \cdot 17$	84	7,056	9.165	$2^2 \cdot 3 \cdot 7$
35	1,225	5.916	$5 \cdot 7$	85	7,225	9.220	$5 \cdot 17$
36	1,296	6.000	$2^2 \cdot 3^2$	86	7,396	9.274	$2 \cdot 43$
37	1,369	6.083	37	87	7,569	9.327	$3 \cdot 29$
38	1,444	6.164	$2 \cdot 19$	88	7,744	9.381	$2^3 \cdot 11$
39	1,521	6.245	$3 \cdot 13$	89	7,921	9.434	89
40	1,600	6.325	$2^3 \cdot 5$	90	8,100	9.487	$2 \cdot 3^2 \cdot 5$
41	1,681	6.403	41	91	8,281	9.539	$7 \cdot 13$
42	1,764	6.481	$2 \cdot 3 \cdot 7$	92	8,464	9.592	$2^2 \cdot 23$
43	1,849	6.557	43	93	8,649	9.644	$3 \cdot 31$
44	1,936	6.633	$2^2 \cdot 11$	94	8,836	9.695	$2 \cdot 47$
45	2,025	6.708	$3^2 \cdot 5$	95	9,025	9.747	$5 \cdot 19$
46	2,116	6.782	$2 \cdot 23$	96	9,216	9.798	$2^5 \cdot 3$
47	2,209	6.856	47	97	9,409	9.849	97
48	2,304	6.928	$2^4 \cdot 3$	98	9,604	9.899	$2 \cdot 7^2$
49	2,401	7.000	7^2	99	9,801	9.950	$3^2 \cdot 11$
50	2,500	7.071	$2 \cdot 5^2$	100	10,000	10.000	$2^2 \cdot 5^2$

ANSWERS

1. 23, 2×3, $\frac{24}{3}$, $6 + 1$

3. 2, 3, 11, 17

5. *a.* 2, 3, 5   *d.* 29, 31

    b. 11, 13, 17   *e.* 37, 41, 43

    c. 23   *f.* 47

7. *a.* 3   *b.* 4   *c.* 25   *d.* 2   *e.* 12   *f.* 25

9.

11.

13.

15.

17.
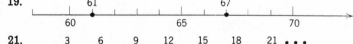

19.

21.
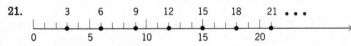

1. *a.* Addition: increased by, add, more than, exceeded by, sum

    b. Subtraction: take away, less than, difference, decreased by, diminished by, subtract

    c. Multiplication: times, multiply, product

    d. Division: divide, quotient

3. $3 + 5$ **5.** $4 + 6$ or $6 + 4$ **7.** $9 \div 4$ **9.** $\dfrac{x}{y}$

11. $b - a$ **13.** $x - y$ **15.** $x + 7$ **17.** $r - 3$

19. $2x$ **21.** Pr **23.** $l + w$ **25.** $c + 5$

27. $3(2 + x)$ **29.** $2 + xy$ **31.** $x - (4 + y)$ **33.** $a(b + c)$

35. $p + q - 3r$ **37.** $\dfrac{r + s}{2y}$

EXERCISES 1.3 (PAGE 7)

1. 2^2 **3.** 3^4 **5.** y^3 **7.** a^2b^3
9. $a^2b^2c^2$ **11.** 5^2x^3 **13.** $2 \cdot 3y^2z$ **15.** $6xyz^2$
17. $(x+2)^2$ **19.** $(2x)^3$ **21.** $2 \cdot 2 \cdot 2$ **23.** $2 \cdot 2 \cdot 2 \cdot 3 \cdot 3$
25. $2 \cdot 2 \cdot 5 \cdot 5$ **27.** xxx **29.** xyy **31.** $abbc$
33. $3xxx$ **35.** $2 \cdot 3x$ **37.** $(3z)(3z)(3z)$ **39.** $3(x+2)(x+2)(x+2)$

EXERCISE 1.4 (PAGE 8)

1. 1   **3.** 19   **5.** 12   **7.** 22   **9.** 48
11. 14   **13.** 3   **15.** 48   **17.** 10   **19.** 8
21. 7   **23.** 2   **25.** 4   **27.** 16   **29.** 9
31. 0   **33.** 1   **35.** 90   **37.** 1000   **39.** 4000

EXERCISES 1.5 (PAGE 10)

1. 6   **3.** 7   **5.** 15   **7.** 27
9. 26   **11.** 21   **13.** 19   **15.** 4
17. 4   **19.** 2   **21.** 6   **23.** 3
25. 1   **27.** 2   **29.** 5   **31.** 1
33. 6   **35.** 18   **37.** 18   **39.** 36
41. 5   **43.** 18   **45.** 36   **47.** 5
49. 10   **51.** 34

EXERCISES 1.6 (PAGE 13)

1. 24   **3.** 15.7   **5.** 14   **7.** 24   **9.** $90°$ **11.** 10
13. 9 square inches   **15.** 120 square feet   **17.** 104 square inches
19. 144 square inches   **21.** 93.76 square inches   **23.** 624.76 square inches

EXERCISES 1.7 (PAGE 15)

1. Binomial; $2x^3$, 2; $3y^2$, 3   **3.** Binomial; x^3, 1; z, 1
5. Binomial; $3x^2$, 3; $6x$, 6   **7.** Monomial; $3x^4$, 3
9. Monomial; $4y^3$, 4   **11.** Binomial; $6x^5$, 6; $2y^4$, 2
13. Monomial; $2x^4$, 2   **15.** Trinomial; $3x^2$, 3; $3y$, 3; $4z$, 4
17. Trinomial; x^3, 1; x^2, 1; $4x$, 4   **19.** Binomial; $3xy^2$, 3; y, 1
21. Monomial   **23.** Binomial; $7xyz$, 7; $3x$, 3

EXERCISES 1.8 (PAGE 17)

1. $7a$ **3.** $6x$
5. $5x^2 + 3x$ **7.** $3a^2 + 3a$
9. $2b^4 + 2b^3 + b^2$ **11.** $5r^4 + r^3$
13. $2a^3 + 3a^2$ **15.** $5x^2y + xy^2$
17. $3x + 3xy + 4y$ **19.** $4x^2y + 4xy^2$
21. $3x + 4y + 2z$ **23.** $x^2y + 2xy + 2xy^2$
25. $3x^3 + 4x^2 + 5x$ **27.** $3z^2 + 2z + 8x + 7y$

29. $5x^2y + x^2 + 2xy + 3x + 2y$ **31.** $3x + 5ax + 3y$
33. $8s^2 + 2t^2 + 2st + r^2$ **35.** $2a + 5b + 2c + 3ab$
37. $2x^2yz + 4xy^2z + 3xyz^2$ **39.** $13x^2yz + 4xyz + 13x^3yz$

EXERCISES 1.9 (PAGE 18)

1. $2x^2$ **3.** $5y^3$ **5.** $4b^2$ **7.** $4r^2$
9. $3x^2$ **11.** 0 **13.** $2ab + 2a$ **15.** $3b^2 + b$
17. $4r^3 + 3s^2$ **19.** $6x^2 + 2y$ **21.** $7h$ **23.** $7x^2y + xy^2$
25. $8x^3yz + 2xyz$ **27.** $17xz^2 + 13x^2z + 2xz$

EXERCISES 1.10 (PAGE 20)

1. x^5 **3.** a^4 **5.** $3y^5$ **7.** $15b^7$ **9.** $4ab^5$
11. $24r^2$ **13.** $24x^3$ **15.** $12x^7$ **17.** $12x^4y^7$
19. x^3y^3 **21.** $3a^4b^4c^2$ **23.** $6ab^4$ **25.** x^3
27. $3x^5$ **29.** $2y^3$ **31.** $3a^2b^2 - b^2$ **33.** $2y^4 - 6y^5$

EXERCISES 1.11 (PAGE 23)

1. 3 **3.** 3 **5.** Meaningless   **7.** x^2 **9.** x^5
11. $5x^4$ **13.** $4xy^2$ **15.** xy **17.** 1 **19.** 1
21. a^3b^4 **23.** $2b^3$ **25.** 0 **27.** ab **29.** $3a^6bc$
31. Meaningless   **33.** $6x$ **35.** $2x$ **37.** $9x^3$ **39.** $3x^2y$
41. $4b^2$ **43.** c **45.** $4x$ **47.** $5 + 8y$ **49.** Meaningless

CHAPTER 1 REVIEW

1. 11, 13, 17, 19, 23

2.

3. *a.* $6x$
    b. $\dfrac{4 + y}{6}$
    c. $y(3 + x)$

4. *a.* $2^2a^2b^3$
    b. xy^2z^3
    c. 3^2c^2d

5. *a.* $2 \cdot 3xyy$
    b. $aaabb$
    c. $3 \cdot 3 \cdot 3cdd$

6. *a.* 13
    b. 8
    c. 5

7. *a.* 3
    b. 8
    c. 2

8. 50.24 square inches

9. *a.* $6xy + 2y$
    b. $5a^2 - 3a$
    c. $2r + 4s$

10. *a.* x^3y^3
    b. $12ab^4$
    c. r^4s^3

11. *a.* $4x^2 - 2x^3$
    b. $ab^3 - b^2$
    c. r^2s^2

12. *a.* $2ab$
    b. 1
    c. $3xy$

13. *a.* 1
    b. $7y$
    c. $13a$

14. *a.* $x + y$
    b. xy
    c. $\dfrac{x}{y}$

15. Terms   **16.** Binomials   **17.** Numerical coefficient
18. 1   **19.** 0   **20.** 3

EXERCISES 2.1 (PAGE 27)

1.

3. 2   **5.** 0   **7.** -2 **9.** -80
11. -7 **13.** -5 **15.** -15 **17.** -4

19.

21.

23.

25. Yes   **27.** Yes   **29.** No   **31.** Yes
33. 3   **35.** 8   **37.** 8   **39.** 4

EXERCISES 2.2 (PAGE 29)

1. 6   **3.** -4 **5.** 3   **7.** -8
9. 5   **11.** -6 **13.** 6   **15.** -7
17. 1   **19.** -10 **21.** -3 **23.** -5
25. 7   **27.** -2 **29.** 3   **31.** 2
33. 11   **35.** 2   **37.** -7 **39.** 5
41. 10   **43.** -1 **45.** 4   **47.** 1
49. $-x$ **51.** $-2y$ **53.** 0   **55.** $-hk$
57. $-5cd$ **59.** xy **61.** $5x$ **63.** $-8a$
65. $5b$ **67.** $5x^2 - x$ **69.** $3a^2 - 5a$ **71.** $-x^2 + 5x$
73. $-x^3 + 3x^2 + 2x$ **75.** $-2a^3 + 5a^2 + 1$ **77.** $6x - y - z$
79. $4xy^2$ **81.** $6x^2y - 7z + 3$ **83.** t
85. $9m^2 - 5m + 3$ **87.** $3a^2 - 3b^2$ **89.** $-x^2 - 4x$
91. $ab^2 - 4a^2bt + abt^2$ **93.** $-5g^2 - 6ag$ **95.** $-3a^2bc + 4ab^2c$
97. $7ab + 4c - 3d$

EXERCISES 2.3 (PAGE 32)

1. 0   **3.** -1 **5.** -9
7. -5 **9.** 8   **11.** 6
13. 5   **15.** 7   **17.** -4
19. $-x$ **21.** $-3x$ **23.** $6y$
25. xy **27.** $-5x^2y$ **29.** $4r^2$
31. -13 **33.** -7 **35.** $6x$
37. $-2g$ **39.** 0   **41.** $5a + b$
43. $-x^2 - x - 1$ **45.** $-2x - 8y + 2z$ **47.** $-x^2 + 4x - 4$
49. $-y^2 - 3y$ **51.** $-z^2 - 4z$ **53.** 0
55. $-x^2y - 4xy + xy^2$ **57.** $-3xy + 1 + x^2y^2$ **59.** $2xy^2 + xy - 2x$

61. $4x + 2z$ **63.** $2a$ **65.** $-x + 2y + 6z$
67. $3x$ **69.** $x + 7$ **71.** $2a + 10b$

EXERCISES 2.4 (PAGE 36)

1. -6	**3.** -12	**5.** -16	**7.** 0
9. 0	**11.** 8	**13.** -12	**15.** 8
17. 15	**19.** 24	**21.** 8	**23.** 24
25. $6x^2y$	**27.** $-2x^3y$	**29.** x^3y^2	**31.** $6a^4$
33. $-a^2b^4c^2$	**35.** $6b^6$	**37.** 4	**39.** -1
41. 25	**43.** $-x^3$	**45.** $-a^3$	**47.** $-x^3y^4$
49. $9x^2y^2$	**51.** $-2x^3y^2$	**53.** $6xyz^2$	

EXERCISES 2.5 (PAGE 37)

1. 4	**3.** -4	**5.** 0	**7.** Meaningless
9. -8	**11.** 9	**13.** -3	**15.** xy^2
17. -1	**19.** $-4x^2$	**21.** $6xy^2$	**23.** $-2x$
25. x	**27.** $-3y$	**29.** $-3x^2$	**31.** 1
33. $4xy$	**35.** $2hy^2$	**37.** -3	**39.** $-18y^2$
41. $x - 3$	**43.** $2x$	**45.** 0	**47.** 0
49. $-3x$	**51.** 0	**53.** 0	**55.** $5y$
57. $4ab$			

EXERCISES 2.6 (PAGE 39)

1. 4	**3.** 4	**5.** -1	**7.** 16
9. 16	**11.** 7	**13.** -4	**15.** -1
17. 0	**19.** 3	**21.** -2	**23.** -1
25. 0	**27.** -4	**29.** -8	**31.** 0
33. 3	**35.** -3	**37.** 5	**39.** 7
41. 0	**43.** -6	**45.** 0	**47.** -18
49. 5	**51.** 4	**53.** -16	**55.** 1
57. -18			

CHAPTER 2 REVIEW

1.
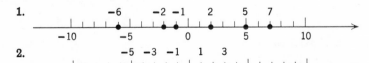

2.
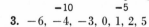

3. $-6, -4, -3, 0, 1, 2, 5$ **4.** 3
5. *a.* -2 **6.** *a.* -3
     b. -6 *b.* -3
     c. 1 *c.* -3

7. *a.* $12x$

   b. $7x^2 + 2x$

   c. $4ab^2$

8. *a.* -2

   b. -4

   c. 2

9. *a.* -7

   b. x

   c. x

10. *a.* $2x$

   b. $8x^2 - xy - 3y^2$

   c. $x^2y + 3xy + 3xy^2$

11. *a.* $x^2 - x - 1$

   b. $x^2 - 5x + 13$

   c. $-x^2 + 3y^2 - 2z^2$

12. *a.* $3y + z$

   b. $a + 2b - 5c$

   c. $-x$

13. *a.* $12x$

   b. $6x$

   c. 8

14. *a.* 5

   b. -4

   c. 8

15. *a.* $-y$

   b. -1

   c. x

16. *a.* 5

   b. 0

   c. $-2x$

17. *a.* $4x$

   b. $-5x$

   c. 1

18. *a.* 4

   b. -3

   c. 0

19. *a.* -2

   b. 0

   c. 3

20. *a.* -2

   b. -7

   c. 7

CHAPTER 2 CUMULATIVE REVIEW

1.

2. -6 -5 -4 -3 -2 -1 0 1 2 3 4 5 6

3. $2y^3$

4. $2 \cdot 2 \cdot 3 \cdot 3 \cdot xyyy$

5. 16

6. $3x^3 - 2y^3$

7. $-3x^4$

8. $-3n$

9. $2a - 4b + c$

10. $3b$

11. 0

12. 520 feet

13. $A = 36$ square inches

   $P = 24$ inches

14. $A = 113.04$ square inches

   $C = 37.68$ inches

15. 4

16. -5

17. $-(a - b + c)$

18. $-(a + b - c)$

19. 0

20. -2

EXERCISES 3.1 (PAGE 43)

1. $x + 2 = 8$

3. $2x + 5x = 21$

5. $3x - x = 10$

7. $x + 3 = 2x$

9. $2x - 5 = x + 3$

11. $3x = x + 12$

13. $A = lw$

15. $V = lwh$

17. $A = \pi r^2$

EXERCISES 3.2 (PAGE 44)

1. No   **3.** Yes   **5.** No   **7.** No   **9.** No

11. Yes   **13.** No   **15.** Yes   **17.** Yes   **19.** Yes

EXERCISES 3.3 (PAGE 47)

1. $x = 1$ **3.** $3 = y$ **5.** $x = 3$ **7.** $x = 3$

9. $x = 7$ **11.** $x = 9$ **13.** 3 **15.** 7

17. 5   19. 7   21. 7   23. 7
25. -3 27. -3 29. 4   31. -3
33. 1   35. -4 37. 2   39. 7
41. 10   43. 3   45. 2   47. 0
49. 4

EXERCISES 3.4 (PAGE 49)

1. $x = 2$ 3. $-3 = x$ 5. $x = -2$ 7. $x = 3$
9. $2 = x$ 11. $x = 2$ 13. 5   15. -8
17. -6 19. 2   21. 1   23. 1
25. 2   27. 2   29. 1   31. 0
33. 4   35. -4 37. 7   39. -4
41. 2   43. 4   45. 2   47. 3
49. 4

EXERCISES 3.5 (PAGE 52)

1. $x = 8$ 3. $-5 = x$ 5. $x = 12$ 7. 8
9. 30   11. -6 13. -21 15. -6
17. 0   19. 10   21. 8   23. -12
25. -12 27. -42 29. 15   31. -12
33. -32 35. -3 37. 25   39. 10
41. 6   43. 15

EXERCISES 3.6 (PAGE 54)

1. -4 3. 2   5. -4 7. 3
9. 18   11. 2   13. -3 15. -4
17. -2 19. 3   21. 4   23. 3
25. 8   27. 3   29. 3   31. 2
33. 2   35. 6   37. 9   39. 0
41. 8   43. 24   45. -2

EXERCISES 3.7 (PAGE 55)

1. $x = a$ 3. $x = a$ 5. $x = 3a$ 7. $y = \dfrac{b}{a}$

9. $y = \dfrac{-2a}{b}$ 11. $y = \dfrac{5}{3a}$ 13. $x = \dfrac{-a^2}{c}$ 15. $x = 2$

17. $x = \dfrac{bc}{a}$ 19. $t = \dfrac{d}{r}$ 21. $l = \dfrac{v}{wh}$ 23. $d = \dfrac{c}{\pi}$

25. $r = \dfrac{d}{t}$ 27. $h = \dfrac{v}{lw}$ 29. $r = \dfrac{I}{pt}$ 31. $\pi = \dfrac{A}{r^2}$

33. $b = \dfrac{s}{2\pi r}$ 35. $g = \dfrac{v - k}{t}$ 37. $m = \dfrac{Fd^2}{kM}$ 39. $x = -a$

41. $x = \dfrac{2}{5} c^2$ 43. $x = 2c$

EXERCISES 3.8 (PAGE 57)

1. Let x = the number; $x + 28 = 63$
3. Let x = the number; $x + 23 = 47$
5. Let x = the number; $x + 4x = x + 20$
7. Let x = smaller integer, $x + 1$ = second integer, $x + 2$ = largest integer; $x + x + 1 + x + 2 = 24$
9. Let x = smallest integer, $x + 2$ = second integer, $x + 4$ = largest integer; $x + x + 2 + x + 4 = 4x$
11. Let x = the shorter piece, $3x$ = the other; $x + 3x = 24$
13. Let x = the width, $3x$ = the length; $x + x + 3x + 3x = 56$
15. Let x = side of square; $4x = 24$
17. Let x = the third angle; $x + 40 + 70 = 180$
19. Let x = the smallest angle, $x + 10$ = second angle, $x + 20$ = largest angle; $x + x + 10 + x + 20 = 180$

EXERCISES 3.9 (PAGE 59)

(Answers to Exercises 3.8, 1–9)
1. 35   **3.** 24   **5.** 5   **7.** 7, 8, 9   **9.** 6, 8, 10
(Answers to Exercises 3.9, 1–9)
1. 7   **3.** 42, 44   **5.** $-10, -11, -12$ **7.** 18, 36   **9.** Loser: 2163, winner: 2213
(Answers to Exercises 3.8, 11–19)
11. 6 feet, 18 feet   **13.** Width: 7 feet, length: 21 feet   **15.** 6 feet
17. 70°   **19.** 50°, 60°, 70°
(Answers to Exercises 3.9, 11–19)
11. 17 inches from one end   **13.** 18 feet.   **15.** Width: 36 feet, length: 46 feet
17. 16 inches, 20 inches, 20 inches   **19.** 50°, 60°, 70°

CHAPTER 3 REVIEW

1. a. $3 + x = 2x - 2$
   b. $V = \frac{4}{3}\pi r^3$
   c. $\frac{3}{4}x = 21 - 6$
2. a. 6
   b. 2
   c. -1
3. a. 5
   b. 0
   c. -1
4. a. -18
   b. 9
   c. -3
5. a. -2
   b. 6
   c. 3
8. a. $a = \dfrac{f}{m}$
   b. $g = \dfrac{v - k}{t}$
   c. $b = 2M - a$
9. $x + 2$
10. $x + 2$
11. $x + 1, x + 2, x + 3, x + 4$
12. $3x$
13. $x + 7, x - 7$
14. $x + 18, x - 12$
15. 12, 13, 14, 15
16. 3, 5, 7

17. 38 feet   **18.** 8 feet, 11 feet, 13 feet
19. 5   **20.** 45°, 60°, 75°

CHAPTER 3 CUMULATIVE REVIEW

1. 9   **2.** $3^2, \dfrac{4^2}{2}, \dfrac{4 + 2^3}{12}, 5^2 - 3^2$

3. Numerical coefficient or coefficient   **4.** Exponent
5. Positive   **6.** $|-5|$ **7.** Less than
8. *a.* x^5 **9.** *a.* 81   **10.** 192 feet/second
   b. x^6 *b.* -81
11. 4 seconds   **12.** 6 hours   **13.** $-4y^2$
14. Before   **15.** Coefficients   **16.** Equivalent

17. 1   **19.** $\dfrac{b + 2}{2}$ **20.** $-14, -16, -18$

EXERCISES 4.1 (PAGE 64)

1. $3x + 3$ **3.** $6x + 15$ **5.** $-2x - 6$
7. $2ax + 2a^2$ **9.** $2\pi R - 2\pi r$ **11.** $6x - 6y$
13. $a^2b - ab^2$ **15.** $-x^2 + xy$ **17.** $2x^3 + 2x^2 - 4x$
19. $-x^5 - 2x^4 + 3x^3$ **21.** $2ax - ax^2 - a^2x^2$ **23.** $6y^3 + 9xy^2 - 3y^2$
25. $-a$ **27.** $2ax + x + a$ **29.** $-ax + ay - 2y$
31. $-3ax$ **33.** $2x$ **35.** 6
37. $ax^2 - bx^2 + cx^2$ **39.** $-4abx - aby + 2ab + b$ **41.** $-a - c$
43. $a - 2b + c$ **45.** $-3x - 2y + z$ **47.** $-1 + 3x - x^2$
49. 0   **51.** $-2x$

EXERCISES 4.2 (PAGE 67)

1. $2(x + 2)$ **3.** $3(2x + y)$ **5.** $4x(x - 1)$
7. $a(x^2 + 1)$ **9.** $3x(2ax + 1)$ **11.** $3y(3by + 2)$
13. $a(b + c - d)$ **15.** $a(a - 1 + b)$ **17.** $3x(x - 2y + 3)$
19. $12axy(x + 2y - 1)$ **21.** $-a(a + b)$ **23.** $-x(1 + x)$
25. $-b(ac + a + c)$ **27.** $-3y(2y^2 + y + 1)$ **29.** $-x(1 - x + x^2)$

31. $-xy^2(y^3 + y^2 - 1)$ **33.** $d = k(1 + at)$ **35.** $S = \pi r^2 \left(\dfrac{h}{3} + 1 \right)$

37. $V = 2ga^2(D - d)$ **39.** $A = r^2(a + b + 6 - \pi)$

EXERCISES 4.3 (PAGE 68)

1. $x^2 + 5x + 6$ **3.** $a^2 - 3a - 10$ **5.** $x^2 - 2x - 8$
7. $a^2 + 4a + 4$ **9.** $x^2 - 2x - 3$ **11.** $x^2 - 2x - 48$
13. $x^2 - 4$ **15.** $x^2 + 4x + 4$ **17.** $x^2 - 2x - 15$
19. $x^2 - 100$ **21.** $9 - x^2$ **23.** $64 - 16x + x^2$
25. $x^2 + 8x + 16$ **27.** $x^2 - 14x + 49$ **29.** $x^2 - 2x + 1$
31. $x^2 + 4x + 4$ **33.** $x^2 - 4bx + 3b^2$ **35.** $x^2 + xy - 2y^2$

37. $x^2 + 4ax + 4a^2$ **39.** $a^2 - 2ab + b^2$ **41.** $y^2 - 36a^2$
43. $x^2 - t^2$ **45.** $2x^2 + 6x + 4$ **47.** $6y^2 + 60y + 150$
49. $6x^2 - 12x + 6$ **51.** $a^3 + 4a^2 - 5a$ **53.** $a^3 - 4a$
55. $xy^2 - 6xy + 9x$

EXERCISES 4.4 (PAGE 71)

1. $(x + 3)(x + 4)$ **3.** $(x + 5)(x + 2)$ **5.** $(y - 2)(y - 3)$
7. $(x + 7)(x - 5)$ **9.** $(b + 10)(b - 2)$ **11.** $(a + 12)(a - 2)$
13. $(x - 7)(x + 5)$ **15.** $(z + 10)(z + 10)$ **17.** $(y - 10)(y + 5)$
19. $(x - 9)(x + 8)$ **21.** $(x - 15)(x + 3)$ **23.** $(x + 9)(x + 5)$
25. $(7 + x)(3 - x)$ **27.** $(5 + c)(2 + c)$ **29.** $(9 + x)(7 - x)$
31. $(8 - z)(4 - z)$ **33.** $(8 - x)(1 - x)$ **35.** $(x + 2a)(x + 2a)$
37. $(a - 2b)(a - b)$ **39.** $(s + 3a)(s - 2a)$ **41.** $(ab - 2)(ab + 1)$
43. $(x - 3)(x + 3)$ **45.** $(x - 1)(x + 1)$ **47.** $(z - y)(z + y)$
49. $(xy - 4)(xy + 4)$ **51.** $(ax - 7b)(ax + 7b)$ **53.** $(6 - x)(6 + x)$

EXERCISES 4.5 (PAGE 74)

1. $10a^2 + 17a + 3$ **3.** $6y^2 + y - 1$ **5.** $4b^2 - 4b + 1$
7. $2x^2 + 7x + 6$ **9.** $4y^2 + 12y + 9$ **11.** $16y^2 + 48y + 36$
13. $3x^2 - 11x - 4$ **15.** $12x^2 - 25x - 7$ **17.** $35y^2 + 74y + 35$
19. $2x^2 + 3ax - 2a^2$ **21.** $3x^2 + 4ax + a^2$ **23.** $6x^2 + ax - a^2$
25. $9x^2 - 4y^2$ **27.** $4x^2 - 1$ **29.** $x^2 - 4xy + 4y^2$
31. $9x^2 - 6xy + y^2$ **33.** $64x^2 + 48xy + 9y^2$ **35.** $4x^2 + 12xy + 9y^2$
37. $6x^2 - 16x - 6$ **39.** $12y^2 - 3$ **41.** $12x^2 - 60x + 75$
43. $2x^3 + x^2 - 10x$ **45.** $4x^3 - 4x^2 + x$ **47.** $9r^3 - r$

EXERCISES 4.6 (PAGE 76)

1. $(3a + 1)(a + 1)$ **3.** $(2x - 1)(x - 1)$ **5.** $(3b - 1)(3b - 1)$
7. $(2x + 3)(x - 1)$ **9.** $(2x - 3)(x + 1)$ **11.** $(3a + 1)(2a - 1)$
13. $(2y - 1)(2y - 1)$ **15.** $(4y + 1)(y - 1)$ **17.** $(4a - 3)(a - 2)$
19. $(4a + 5)(a - 1)$ **21.** $(8x - 5)(2x + 1)$ **23.** $(16x + 5)(x - 1)$
25. $(3x + 1)(3x - 8)$ **27.** $(2y + 3)(2y + 5)$ **29.** $(2t + s)(t - 3s)$
31. $(3x - a)(x - 2a)$ **33.** $(4y + b)(y + b)$ **35.** $(2a + 5b)(2a + 3b)$
37. $(2b - 3)(2b + 3)$ **39.** $(5x - 4)(5x + 4)$ **41.** $(3 - 2x)(3 + 2x)$
43. $(9 - 2x)(9 + 2x)$ **45.** $(2a - 11b)(2a + 11b)$ **47.** $(5y - 7x)(5y + 7x)$
49. $(7ax - 12by)(7ax + 12by)$ **51.** $(2xy - 9)(2xy + 9)$ **53.** $(6ab - 1)(6ab + 1)$

EXERCISES 4.7 (PAGE 77)

1. $2(x + 2)(x + 3)$ **3.** $y(y - 3)(y + 1)$
5. $5(c - 3)(c - 2)$ **7.** $2(3x + 1)(x + 1)$
9. $2a(4y + 1)(y - 1)$ **11.** $3y(3y + 1)(3y - 2)$
13. $9(2x - 3)(x + 1)$ **15.** $3a(4b + a)(b + a)$
17. $2xy(5y - 2x)(5y + 4x)$ **19.** $3axy(2x + 3y)(x - 2y)$
21. $3x(x - 1)(x + 1)$ **23.** $2(x - 2y)(x + 2y)$

25. $x^3(1 - x)(1 + x)$ **27.** $3(ab - 2cd)(ab + 2cd)$
29. $\pi(R - r)(R + r)$

EXERCISES 4.8 (PAGE 78)

1. -8	**3.** 3	**5.** -28	**7.** 306
9. 510	**11.** 462	**13.** 28	**15.** 66
17. 240	**19.** 594		

EXERCISES 4.9 (PAGE 79)

1. 3	**3.** 6	**5.** 2	**7.** -3
9. 3	**11.** 5	**13.** -5	**15.** 4
17. -5	**19.** 0	**21.** 2	**23.** -4
25. 3	**27.** 1	**29.** 4	**31.** 5
33. 1	**35.** 4		

EXERCISES 4.10 (PAGE 80)

1. *a.* $x + 4$
   b. $5x$
   c. $5(x + 4)$
7. $3(w + 6)$

3. $3(n + 6)$

5. *a.* $w + 3$
   b. $3w$
   c. $2(w + 3)$

9. *a.* $27 - n$
   b. $3n$
   c. $3(27 - n)$

11. *a.* $n + 16$
   b. $5n$
   c. $2(n + 16)$

13. *a.* $10 - x$
   b. $2x$
   c. $5(10 - x)$
19. $5n + 10(n + 3)$ or
   $15n + 30$

15. *a.* $x + 4$
   b. $25x$
   c. $10(x + 4)$
21. *a.* $x - 4$
   b. $7x$
   c. $6(x - 4)$

17. *a.* $n - 3$ *d.* $10(n - 3)$
   b. $n + 2$ *e.* $n + 2$
   c. $25n$
23. 5, 3

25. $-6, -2, 0$
31. 6, 17

27. 8 feet, 14 feet
33. 10 nickels,
   13 dimes

29. 8 feet from one end
35. 9 pennies,
   15 nickels,
   3 dimes

37. 2 nickels,
   2 dimes,
   9 quarters
43. 7 tons, 11 tons

39. 400 adult,
   600 children

41. 40 pounds

CHAPTER 4 REVIEW

1. *a.* $3x^3 + 3x^2$
   b. $2xy^2 - 2x^2y$
   c. $-x^2 + y - 1$
4. *a.* $a^2(1 + b)$
   b. $4(b - 1)$
   c. $b(1 - b - b^2)$

2. *a.* $2a - a^2$
   b. $-ab + b^2$
   c. $3ab + 3b^2 + 3bc$
5. *a.* $x^2 + x - 6$
   b. $6a^2 - 17a + 12$
   c. $4a^2 - 12a + 9$

3. *a.* $3a^2(1 - 2b)$
   b. $2x(x^2 + 2x + 3)$
   c. $-y^2(1 + y)$
6. *a.* $x^2 - ax - 2a^2$
   b. $2x^2 + bx - b^2$
   c. $4b^2 + 4b + 1$

7. a. $(x - 7)(x + 3)$ 8. a. $(a - 7)(a - 3)$ 9. a. $2(x + 3)(x + 4)$
   b. $(5a + 1)(2a + 3)$ b. $(3b + 1)(b + 1)$ b. $3(y + 10)(y - 2)$
   c. $(2x - 3)(2x + 3)$ c. $(2b - 1)(b + 2)$ c. $4x(x - 1)(x + 1)$

10. a. $(x - 2a)(x - a)$ 11. a. 20   12. 748
    b. $(x - a)(x + a)$ b. 2
    c. $2(2b - c)(b + 2c)$ c. -6

13. $24 - x$ 14. $10x$ 15. $25(x + 3)$

16. $5(y - 2)$ 17. $30(x + 4)$ 18. 5, 11

19. Width: 8 feet,   20. 15 dimes,
    length: 18 feet   23 nickels

CHAPTER 4 CUMULATIVE REVIEW

1.

2. $3 \cdot 3 \cdot 3 \cdot 3xxxyyy$ 3. 112   4. $-x^2 - 6x + 5$

5. $-x^2 - x - 3$ 6. $2x^2 - 11x$ 7. 20 sq. in.

8. $-4b$ 10. nc 11. $(80 - y)°$

12. $(y - 6)°$ 13. $(x - y)°$ 14. $47 - x$

15. $4x - 1$ 16. 36, 37, 38   17. Width: 8 feet,
                                                      length: 18 feet

18. 5 inches, 9 inches,   19. 7 feet, 21 feet,   20. 6, 16
    12 inches   7 feet

EXERCISES 5.1 (PAGE 90)

1. $\dfrac{3}{7}$ 3. $\dfrac{3}{a}$ 5. $\dfrac{5}{x + y}$ 7. $\dfrac{2x}{2 + x}$

9.

11.

13.

15.

17.

19.

21. $\dfrac{3}{4}$ **23.** $\dfrac{2}{3}$ **25.** $\dfrac{-3}{5}$ **27.** $\dfrac{-a}{b}$

29. $\dfrac{-a}{b}$ **31.** $\dfrac{-x}{y}$ **33.** $\dfrac{7x}{8y}$ **35.** $-c$

37. $\dfrac{-(x+2)}{4}$ **39.** $\dfrac{5}{x+2}$

EXERCISES 5.2 (PAGE 92)

1. $\dfrac{3}{4}$ **3.** $\dfrac{-3}{5}$ **5.** $\dfrac{8}{5}$ **7.** $\dfrac{1}{3a^2}$

9. $\dfrac{-2}{15y^3}$ **11.** $\dfrac{-7}{5x^2}$ **13.** xy^2 **15.** $\dfrac{-1}{a^2b}$

17. x **19.** $\dfrac{-2xy}{z}$ **21.** $\dfrac{2b^2c}{3a}$ **23.** 1

25. $\dfrac{3}{4}$ **27.** $-4(x-y)$ **29.** 1 **31.** -2

33. $\dfrac{2}{x-a}$ **35.** $\dfrac{-1}{x-4}$ **37.** $\dfrac{1}{x+1}$ **39.** $\dfrac{1}{a-b}$

41. $\dfrac{a-b}{a+b}$ **43.** $\dfrac{a}{a+1}$ **45.** $\dfrac{x-2}{x-3}$ **47.** $\dfrac{a+3}{a-1}$

49. No   **51.** No   **53.** No   **55.** No

57. Yes   **59.** No

EXERCISES 5.3 (PAGE 96)

1. $2x-3$ **3.** $x+3$ **5.** $4y-1$

7. $2x^2+x+3$ **9.** $2xy-y+x$ **11.** $-3xy^2+y-1$

13. $2y^2+y-\dfrac{2}{3}$ **15.** $x+1+\dfrac{3}{x}$ **17.** $2y^2-1+\dfrac{2}{3y^2}$

19. $x^2+2x-1-\dfrac{1}{x}$ **21.** $-x+1-\dfrac{1}{x}$ **23.** $x^2+xy+\dfrac{x}{y}$

25. $x+6$ **27.** $x+1$ **29.** $x+7$

31. $2x+1$ **33.** $x+3$ **35.** $2x+3$

37. $x+1+\dfrac{-1}{x+2}$ **39.** $x-2+\dfrac{1}{x+5}$ **41.** $x-1+\dfrac{-1}{x+6}$

43. $2x-1+\dfrac{-1}{x+1}$ **45.** $2x-3+\dfrac{-2}{2x+1}$

EXERCISES 5.4 (PAGE 99)

1. 6 **3.** 36 **5.** 84 **7.** 132

9. 385 **11.** x^2y **13.** xyz **15.** m^2n^3

17. $24x^2y$ **19.** $(x+y)(x-y)$ **21.** $x^2(x+2)$ **23.** $(x+4)(x-1)^2$

EXERCISES 5.5 (PAGE 101)

1. $\dfrac{4}{6}$ 3. $\dfrac{6}{21}$ 5. $\dfrac{20}{48}$

7. $\dfrac{63}{15}$ 9. $\dfrac{10}{6x}$ 11. $\dfrac{-12ab^2}{12b^3}$

13. $\dfrac{-3x^2y}{3y^3}$ 15. $\dfrac{72}{36}$ 17. $\dfrac{xy^2}{xy}$

19. $\dfrac{3x^4y}{3x^2y}$ 21. $\dfrac{x+y}{2(x+y)}$ 23. $\dfrac{-2a(a+4)}{5(a+4)}$

25. $\dfrac{2a(a+3)}{a+3}$ 27. $\dfrac{3(x+y)}{(x-y)(x+y)}$ 29. $\dfrac{-3(x+1)}{(2x-1)(x+1)}$

31. $\dfrac{7a(b-3)}{(b+2)(b-3)}$ 33. $\dfrac{a^2}{a(a-3)}$ 35. $\dfrac{-3(x-y)}{(x+y)(x-y)}$

37. $\dfrac{y(y+2)}{(y-1)(y+2)}$ 39. $\dfrac{(x+y)(x+y)}{(x-y)(x+y)}$ 41. $\dfrac{3}{6}, \dfrac{2}{6}$

43. $\dfrac{5}{35}, \dfrac{21}{35}$ 45. $\dfrac{-10}{24}, \dfrac{9}{24}$ 47. $\dfrac{-3b}{3ab}, \dfrac{a}{3ab}$

49. $\dfrac{5a^2}{4ab^2}, \dfrac{-8b}{4ab^2}$ 51. $\dfrac{-a^3}{a^2b^2}, \dfrac{2b}{a^2b^2}$ 53. $\dfrac{-9}{3(x-a)}, \dfrac{2(x-a)}{3(x-a)}$

55. $\dfrac{3(a+b)}{ab(a+b)}, \dfrac{a^2b}{ab(a+b)}$

57. $\dfrac{-x(x+4)}{(x+1)(x+2)(x+4)}, \dfrac{2x(x+2)}{(x+2)(x+1)(x+4)}$

59. $\dfrac{3(x+3)}{(x-1)(x+1)(x+3)}, \dfrac{(x-2)(x-1)}{(x-1)(x+1)(x+3)}$

EXERCISES 5.6 (PAGE 106)

1. $\dfrac{3}{5}$ 3. $\dfrac{5}{11}$ 5. $\dfrac{2x+1}{3}$ 7. $\dfrac{3}{x}$

9. $\dfrac{a}{b}$ 11. $\dfrac{3}{y}$ 13. $\dfrac{9a}{7b}$ 15. $\dfrac{x+4}{2}$

17. $\dfrac{2x+y}{3x}$ 19. $\dfrac{x}{a}$ 21. $\dfrac{x^2+x}{2}$ 23. $\dfrac{4x}{y}$

25. $\dfrac{x+6}{2}$ 27. $\dfrac{a+3b}{a-b}$ 29. $\dfrac{-a}{a+b}$ 31. $\dfrac{3x+2y}{x+y}$

33. $\dfrac{1}{x+2y}$ 35. $\dfrac{6a-b}{3}$ 37. $3x+y$ 39. $\dfrac{u}{2u-v}$

41. $\dfrac{x-1}{x+2}$ 43. $\dfrac{4}{x-1}$ 45. $\dfrac{1}{x-y}$ 47. $\dfrac{x+5}{x}$

EXERCISES 5.7 (PAGE 110)

1. $\dfrac{3}{4}$

3. $\dfrac{-x}{2}$

5. $\dfrac{1}{2a}$

7. $\dfrac{1 - 2a}{ax}$

9. $\dfrac{2a - 4}{3a}$

11. $\dfrac{2x^2 - 3x + 1}{x^3}$

13. $\dfrac{5}{6}$

15. $\dfrac{4x}{15}$

17. $\dfrac{13a}{12}$

19. $\dfrac{1}{6x}$

21. $\dfrac{2x + 9y}{3xy}$

23. $\dfrac{bc + ac + ab}{abc}$

25. $\dfrac{-x - 4}{6}$

27. $\dfrac{8y - 5}{6}$

29. $\dfrac{11 + 2x}{6}$

31. $\dfrac{14x - 5}{6x}$

33. $\dfrac{x - 5y}{6x}$

35. $\dfrac{6a^2 - 5ab + 6b^2}{12ab}$

37. $\dfrac{3}{2(x + y)}$

39. $\dfrac{-2}{3(x + 1)}$

41. $\dfrac{9}{4(2a + b)}$

43. $\dfrac{2x^2}{(x - 3)(x + 3)}$

45. $\dfrac{38}{(3x - 4)(5x + 6)}$

47. $\dfrac{-3a - 9}{(2a + 1)(a - 2)}$

49. $\dfrac{-8x}{(x + 2)(x - 2)}$

51. $\dfrac{-1}{(x + 2)(x + 3)}$

53. $\dfrac{3x^2 - 3xy + 4y^2}{(x + y)(x - y)}$

55. $\dfrac{3}{(x + 1)(x + 1)(x - 2)}$

57. $\dfrac{x^2 - x}{(x - 2)(x + 3)(x + 5)}$

59. $\dfrac{2x^2 + 13x + 6}{(x + 1)(x + 2)(x + 2)}$

EXERCISES 5.8 (PAGE 115)

1. $\dfrac{3x}{4}$

3. $\dfrac{-3r}{5}$

5. $\dfrac{5(x - y)}{7}$

7. $\dfrac{-7(b - a)}{4}$

9. $\dfrac{2}{3}a$

11. $-\dfrac{1}{3}y$

13. $\dfrac{2}{5}(x + 3)$

15. $\dfrac{-5}{7}(a - b)$

17. $\dfrac{3}{8}$

19. $\dfrac{81}{110}$

21. $\dfrac{1}{3}$

23. y

25. $\dfrac{4x^2}{5}$

27. $4y$

29. $\dfrac{-x}{y}$

31. $\dfrac{49rt}{4}$

33. $\dfrac{-b}{az}$

35. $\dfrac{3}{4}$

37. 5

39. 1

41. $\dfrac{x - 3}{x + 7}$

43. $\dfrac{3x - 2}{3x + 2}$

45. $\dfrac{x + y}{x + 3y}$

47. $\dfrac{x - 2}{2x(x + 1)}$

49. 1

51. $\dfrac{y - 3}{y - 6}$

EXERCISES 5.9 (PAGE 119)

1. 3   **3.** $\dfrac{1}{8}$ **5.** $\dfrac{1}{2}$ **7.** 1

9. $\dfrac{5}{16b^2}$ **11.** $\dfrac{-x}{v}$ **13.** $12y$ **15.** $\dfrac{-x}{16y}$

17. $\dfrac{3bx}{ay}$ **19.** $\dfrac{a}{2}$ **21.** $\dfrac{5}{2}$ **23.** $\dfrac{5}{6x}$

25. $\dfrac{2x + y}{x + 2y}$ **27.** $\dfrac{y - 1}{y + 7}$ **29.** $\dfrac{(x - 4)(x + 3)}{(x - 1)(2x + 1)}$ **31.** $\dfrac{1}{y - 1}$

33. $\dfrac{2x - 1}{x + 3}$ **35.** $\dfrac{(a + 9)(a - 7)(a - 3)}{(a - 1)(a + 6)(a - 8)}$

EXERCISES 5.10 (PAGE 122)

1. $\dfrac{3}{20}$ **3.** $\dfrac{1}{4}$ **5.** $\dfrac{6}{11}$ **7.** $\dfrac{1}{s}$

9. 1   **11.** $\dfrac{x}{6}$ **13.** $\dfrac{1}{4}$ **15.** $\dfrac{1}{4}$

17. $\dfrac{1}{14}$ **19.** 5   **21.** $\dfrac{5}{3y^2}$ **23.** $\dfrac{y^2 - 1}{y^2 + 1}$

25. $\dfrac{2x^2 - 3xy}{8x - 12y}$ **27.** $\dfrac{a}{11b}$

EXERCISES 5.11 (PAGE 125)

1. 1   **3.** 6   **5.** 12   **7.** 2

9. 3   **11.** $\dfrac{1}{2}$ **13.** 15   **15.** 5

17. 6   **19.** 5   **21.** 4   **23.** 3

25. 3   **27.** 2   **29.** 15   **31.** $\dfrac{a + b}{2}$

33. -4 **35.** $\dfrac{4a - 3b}{a}$ **37.** No solution   **39.** $\dfrac{-ab - 3b}{3}$

41. No solution

EXERCISES 5.12 (PAGE 128)

1. 5   **3.** 14, 15   **5.** 10   **7.** 6

9. 18   **11.** 6 inches, 6 inches, 4 inches   **13.** 20°, 70°

15. Slower driver: 40 mph, faster driver: 60 mph   **17.** $1\frac{3}{4}$ mph   **19.** Slower man: 30 mph, faster man: 60 mph

EXERCISES 5.13 (PAGE 131)

1. $\dfrac{1}{5}$ **3.** $\dfrac{1}{4}$ **5.** $\dfrac{3}{1}$ **7.** $\dfrac{2}{5}$

9. $\dfrac{3}{10}$ **11.** $\dfrac{8}{5}$ **13.** $\dfrac{8}{3} = \dfrac{24}{9}$ **15.** $\dfrac{21}{24} = \dfrac{7}{8}$

17. $\dfrac{15}{x} = \dfrac{10}{4}$ **19.** $\dfrac{6}{2} = \dfrac{x}{x+1}$ **21.** 15   **23.** 15

25. $\dfrac{3}{2}$ **27.** 4   **29.** -2 **31.** 4

33. 40 pounds   **35.** $36\frac{4}{11}$ gallons   **37.** 135 quarts   **39.** 825 bricks
41. \$2.24   **43.** 9 parts

CHAPTER 5 REVIEW

1.

2. *a.* $\dfrac{-3}{x+y}$

   b. $\dfrac{a}{x}$

   c. $\dfrac{-(b-2)}{4}$

3. *a.* $\dfrac{2(x-3)}{3}$

   b. $\dfrac{-(x^2+1)}{3}$

   c. $\dfrac{-3(2x+y)}{4}$

4. *a.* $\dfrac{xz^2}{y}$

   b. $\dfrac{1}{b+1}$

   c. $\dfrac{1}{a-1}$

5. *a.* $\dfrac{6}{2(x-y)}$

   b. $\dfrac{3(a+2)}{a^2+5a+6}$

   c. $\dfrac{x(x-1)}{x^2-3x+2}$

6. *a.* $\dfrac{10}{15}, \dfrac{9}{15}$

   b. $\dfrac{3y}{x^2y^2}, \dfrac{-2x}{x^2y^2}$

   c. $\dfrac{a}{a^2-1}, \dfrac{3(a-1)}{a^2-1}$

7. *a.* $\dfrac{4}{5}$

   b. $\dfrac{x}{y}$

   c. $\dfrac{-5}{3}$

8. *a.* $\dfrac{7}{3x}$

   b. $\dfrac{3s+2r}{rs}$

   c. $\dfrac{2a-3b}{a^2b^2}$

9. *a.* $\dfrac{4a+2b}{(a-b)(a+b)}$

   b. $\dfrac{a^2-a+1}{a(a-1)(a+1)}$

   c. $\dfrac{6x+26}{(x+1)(x+5)(x-5)}$

10. *a.* $\dfrac{x^2}{6}$

   b. $\dfrac{5(x-2)}{x}$

   c. 1

11. *a.* $\dfrac{7s}{r}$

   b. $\dfrac{(a-b)(a-1)}{a}$

   c. x^3

12. *a.* $\dfrac{9}{4}$

   b. $\dfrac{5}{7}$

   c. $\dfrac{6}{11}$

13. *a.* $\dfrac{b-a}{b+2}$

   b. $\dfrac{x^2(y-1)}{y^2(x-1)}$

   c. $\dfrac{1+3y}{2y-3}$

14. *a.* 6

   b. $\dfrac{-4}{3}$

   c. 7

15. *a.* 3

   b. 4

   c. $\dfrac{-1}{2}$

16. *a.* 1

   b. -1

   c. 3

17. *a.* $\dfrac{2b}{3a}$

   b. $\dfrac{-b}{9}$

   c. 2

18. 2

19. Width: 3 feet,
length: 8 feet

20. Faster car: 30 mph,
slower car: 20 mph

CHAPTER 5 CUMULATIVE REVIEW

1. $C = \dfrac{5F - 160}{9}$

3. Commutative

4. 13

5. 0

6. 375

7. $\dfrac{42}{13}$

8. -28

9. $x + 4$

10. $(x - 2)(x + 2)(x^2 + 4)$

11. $5b(b + 1)(b + 1)$

12. $x - 4$

13. $\dfrac{9}{5}$

14. 5

15. 6

16. $\dfrac{ab}{c}$

17. 10 inches

18. 30 nickels,
20 dimes

19. 8, 10, 12

20. $24

EXERCISES 6.1 (PAGE 138)

2. *a.* 2, π
  b. C, *r*
  c. Increases
  d. *r*
  e. C
  f. 18.84

3. *a.* (1, 3)
  b. (3, 5)
  c. (0, 2)
  d. (−2, 0)
  e. (−1, 1)
  f. (−6, −4)

5. *a.* (10, 32)
  b. (5, 17)
  c. (0, 2)
  d. (−5, −13)
  e. (−1, −1)
  f. (−15, −43)

7. *a.* (2, 8)

  b. (1, 4)

  c. (0, 0)

  d. (−1, −4)

  e. (−2, −8)

  f. (−3, −12)

9. *a.* (4, 13)

  b. (1, 7)

  c. (0, 5)

  d. (−1, 3)

  e. (−2, 1)

  f. (−3, −1)

11. *a.* $\left(10, \dfrac{14}{3}\right)$

  b. $\left(5, \dfrac{4}{3}\right)$

  c. (0, −2)

  d. $\left(-5, \dfrac{-16}{3}\right)$

  e. $\left(-10, \dfrac{-26}{3}\right)$

  f. (−15, −12)

EXERCISES 6.2 (PAGE 141)

1.

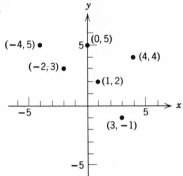

3.

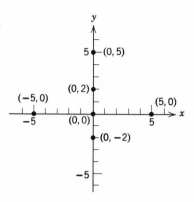

5.

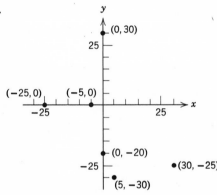

7.

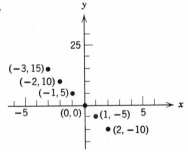

9. Result is a straight line

11. *a.* Ordinate
   b. Abscissa

13. Origin

15. On a straight line bisecting the angles at the origin in the first and third quadrants

17.

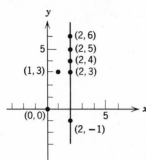

a. Yes c. Yes
b. No d. No

19. 2

EXERCISES 6.3 (PAGE 143)

1.

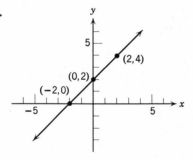

a. (0, 0) d. On the line through these points
b. (2, 8) e. (1, 4), (3, 12)
c. (4, 16) f. Two
g. Yes

3.

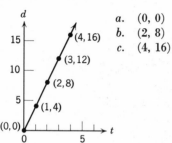

5.

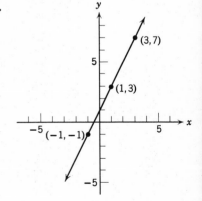

7.

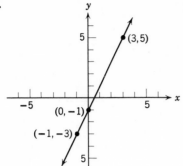

9.

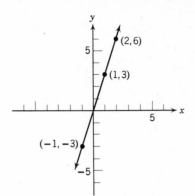

11.

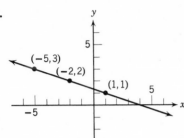

13.

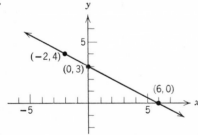

15.

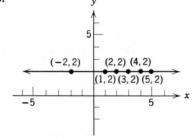

b. Yes   *e.* Yes
c. Yes   *f.* Yes
d. No

17.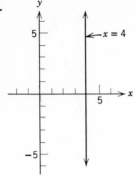

19.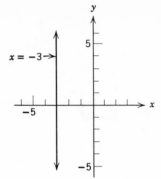

21.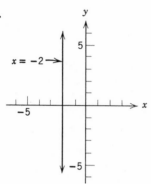

23.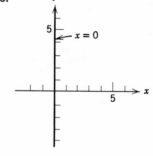

EXERCISES 6.4 (PAGE 146)

1.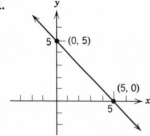

3.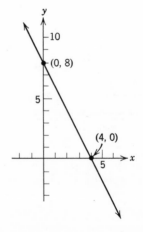

5.

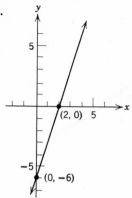

7.

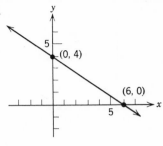

9.

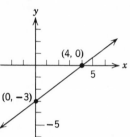

11.

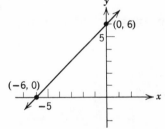

13.

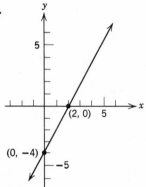

15.

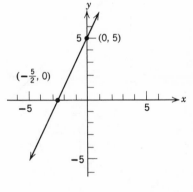

17.

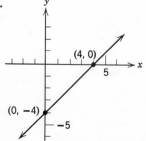

19.

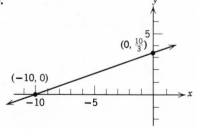

21.

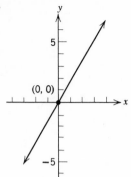

23.

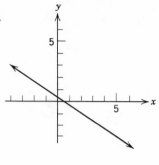

EXERCISES 6.5 (PAGE 149)

1.   (2, 6)

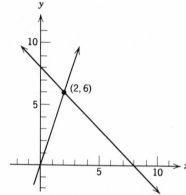

3.   (1, 2)

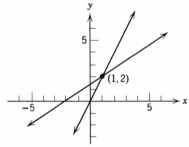

5. 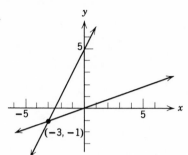 $(-3, -1)$

7. 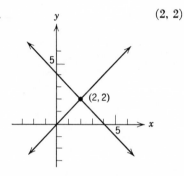 $(2, 2)$ **9.** 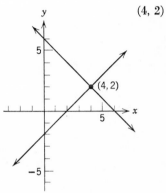 $(4, 2)$

11. 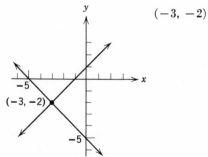 $(-3, -2)$

13. 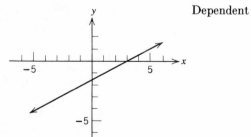   Dependent

15.

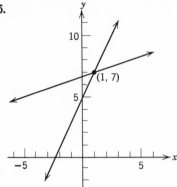

(1, 7)

17.

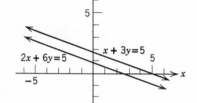

Inconsistent

19.   (−2, −1)

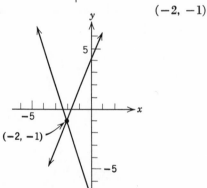

EXERCISES 6.6 (PAGE 150)

1. (3, 2)	**3.** (−1, 4)	**5.** (6, 2)	**7.** (1, 1)
9. (7, −2)	**11.** (−1, 1)	**13.** (1, 1)	**15.** (5, 2)
17. (1, −1)	**19.** (−4, 10)	**21.** (5, −1)	**23.** (4, 3)

25. $(-4, 3)$ **27.** $(-2, -1)$ **29.** $(0, 2)$ **31.** $(-1, -2)$
33. $(-4, 2)$ **35.** $(3, 1)$ **37.** $(4, 3)$ **39.** $(3, 5)$

EXERCISES 6.7 (PAGE 153)

1. $(1, 2)$ **3.** $(2, 2)$ **5.** $(-2, -1)$ **7.** $(-3, -2)$
9. $(5, -2)$ **11.** $(8, 5)$ **13.** $(1, 2)$ **15.** $(10, -2)$
17. $(1, 1)$ **19.** $(-1, -3)$ **21.** $(-1, 1)$ **23.** $(1, 0)$
25. $(1, -1)$ **27.** $(4, 3)$ **29.** $(4, 3)$ **31.** $(-3, 2)$
33. $(2, 3)$ **35.** $(-4, 10)$ **37.** $(6, 2)$ **39.** Dependent

EXERCISES 6.8 (PAGE 156)

1. 8, 17   **3.** 9 feet, 11 feet   **5.** Width: 2 inches,
                                                 length: 12 inches

7. 16 pounds,   **9.** Lot: $3500,   **11.** Walls: 9 hours,
12 pounds   house: $8500   trim: 15 hours

13. 60 flat cars   **15.** Corn: $0.31,   **17.** $14 for doll,
                          bread: $0.41 $41 for train

19. 6, 18   **21.** Dimes: 20,   **23.** $2160 at 4%,
                      quarters: 14 $1440 at 6%

CHAPTER 6 REVIEW

1. *a.* π **2.** $y = 2x - 4$ **3.** $y = \dfrac{3x + 6}{2}$

b. C, d
c. Increases

4. *a.* $(3, 7)$ **5.** *a.* $(4, -1)$
b. $(-2, -3)$ *b.* $(-2, -7)$
c. $(0, 1)$ *c.* $(0, -5)$
d. $(-\frac{1}{2}, 0)$ *d.* $(-6, -11)$

6. 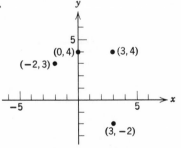   **7.**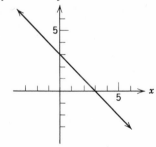

8.

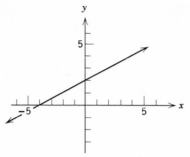

9.

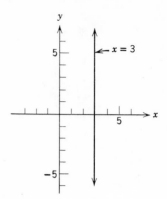

10.

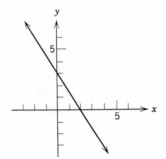

11.   At $x = 8$

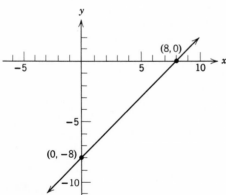

12. At $y = -8$ **13.** $(-1, 4)$

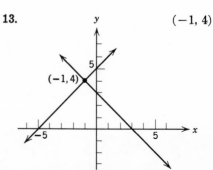

14.

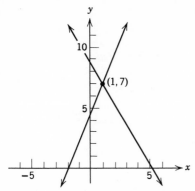

(1, 7)

15.

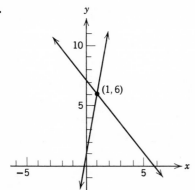

(1, 6)

16.

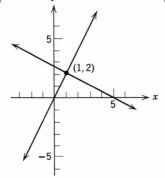

(1, 2) **17.** 32 pounds, 52 pounds

18. Width: 27 inches, length: 48 inches

19. −16, −24

20. 0, −2

CHAPTER 6 CUMULATIVE REVIEW

1.

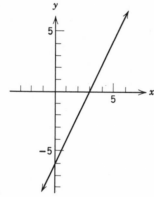

$-1 \quad 0 \quad 1 \quad 2 \quad 3$

$-5 \qquad\qquad 0 \qquad\qquad 5$

2. $\dfrac{1}{2}$ **3.** 88 inches   **4.** 2064

5. $\dfrac{3}{2}$ **6.** $\dfrac{a+b}{a-b}$ **7.** $\dfrac{24a-5}{24}$

8. $\dfrac{-x+8}{(x+1)(x-2)}$ **9.** $\dfrac{3}{5}$ **10.** $\dfrac{3}{4}$

11. x **12.** $x-4$ **13.** 12

14. 1   **15.** 2   **16.** $ab-a$

17.

$$y$$

18. $(4,-1)$ **19.** 2, 26   **20.** 7, 8

REVIEW OF FACTORING (PAGE 161)

1. $5(x+2y)$ **2.** $3(x^2+2x-1)$ **3.** $-2(x^2+2)$
4. $a(b-c)$ **5.** $a(bc+b-c)$ **6.** $xy(x-y+1)$
7. $(x+3)(x+2)$ **8.** $(y-3)^2$ **9.** $(y-8)(y+1)$
10. $(y+7)(y-5)$ **11.** $(x-4)(x+4)$ **12.** $(y-b)(y+b)$
13. $(2y-3)(y+1)$ **14.** $(3y-1)(2y+1)$ **15.** $(3x-2)(2x-3)$
16. $(3x+7)(x-5)$ **17.** $(2x-5)(2x+5)$ **18.** $(3y-2c)(3y+2c)$
19. $2(2y+1)(y+1)$ **20.** $3(2x+1)(x+3)$ **21.** $2(3x+1)(3x-8)$
22. $5(8x-5)(2x+1)$ **23.** $12(y-2)(y+2)$ **24.** $2(5x-4)(5x+4)$
25. $(x+a)^2$ **26.** $(x-a)^2$ **27.** $(y+3b)^2$
28. $(y-2b)^2$ **29.** $(x+4a)^2$ **30.** $(y-5b)^2$

EXERCISES 7.1 (PAGE 163)

1. Yes   **3.** No   **5.** Yes
7. No   **9.** No   **11.** Yes

13. 3

19. $\frac{1}{4}$

25. 0, 5

31. 1, $-\frac{3}{2}$, 7

37. 0, -3

43. $-2, 3$

49. $\frac{3}{2}$, $-\frac{3}{4}$

55. 3, 2, 1

61. 0, $-\frac{1}{2}$, $\frac{1}{2}$

67. 0, $\dfrac{b}{4}$

15. 5

21. 4

27. $-\frac{3}{2}$, 2

33. 2, 3

39. 2, -3

45. 0, 4

51. $\frac{2}{3}$, $-\frac{2}{3}$

57. 0, -2, 1

63. $a, -a$

69. $0, \dfrac{-3b}{2}, \dfrac{2b}{3}$

17. $\frac{1}{2}$

23. 2, 3

29. 0, 1, -1

35. 0, 4

41. 1, -8

47. $-4, 3$

53. 0, $-\frac{3}{2}$

59. 0, -4, 3

65. $-\dfrac{a}{2}, a$

71. $0, b, -\dfrac{b}{8}$

EXERCISES 7.2 (PAGE 166)

1. 0, -2

7. 0, 1

13. 4, -4

19. 3, -3

25. 4, -4

31. 0, 5

37. 0, 1

43. $2a, -2a$

3. 0, $\frac{5}{2}$

9. 1, -1

15. 8, -8

21. $\frac{1}{3}$, $-\frac{1}{3}$

27. 0, -2

33. $a, -a$

39. $0, \dfrac{c}{3}$

45. $\dfrac{3b}{a}, -\dfrac{3b}{a}$

5. 0, $\frac{9}{2}$

11. 2, -2

17. 3, -3

23. $\frac{3}{2}$, $-\frac{3}{2}$

29. 0, -2

35. $c, -c$

41. $0, \dfrac{1}{b}$

EXERCISES 7.3 (PAGE 168)

1. 1, 1

7. $-1, -6$

13. 2, -7

19. $-1, 6$

25. $-1, \frac{4}{3}$

31. $-1, 7$

37. $-1, 2$

43. $\frac{3}{2}$, -2

49. $-5, 3$

55. $\frac{1}{2}$, 1

61. $-a, -a$

67. $-2, 3$

73. $-\frac{1}{2}$, 2

79. 1, 1

85. 2, -3

91. 10, 20

97. $-\frac{1}{2}$, 2

3. 4, -1

9. 4, -3

15. $-6, -6$

21. $-1, 4$

27. $\frac{1}{3}$, $\frac{3}{2}$

33. $\frac{3}{2}$, $\frac{3}{2}$

39. 1, $-\frac{7}{2}$

45. $-\frac{3}{2}$, $-\frac{3}{2}$

51. $-1, -2$

57. $-\frac{1}{2}$, 2

63. $-b, 4b$

69. 1, 2

75. $\frac{1}{3}$, $-\frac{3}{2}$

81. $-3, 5$

87. 2, 2

93. 2, 13

5. $-2, -6$

11. 6, 4

17. 1, 15

23. 5, -6

29. $\frac{1}{2}$, $\frac{1}{2}$

35. $\frac{1}{3}$, $\frac{1}{3}$

41. $-4, 5$

47. $-\frac{3}{4}$, $-\frac{5}{2}$

53. 1, -3

59. $-1, 2$

65. $-4c, 5c$

71. 1, 1

77. $-1, 2$

83. $-\frac{1}{2}$, 2

89. $-2, 5$

95. 5, -6

EXERCISES 7.4 (PAGE 173)

1. 0, 5   **3.** 8, 9   **5.** 12, 14
7. 5, 6   **9.** 4   **11.** $\frac{3}{4}, \frac{4}{3}$
13. 5, 7   **15.** 8, 9   **17.** Width: 2 feet,
                                        length: 6 feet

19. Width: 6 inches,   **21.** Width: 8 inches,   **23.** Side of smaller square:
length: 7 inches   length: 12 inches   5 inches, side of larger
                                                     square: 9 inches

25. 10 mph   **27.** Rate going: 45 mph,
                        rate returning: 60 mph

CHAPTER 7 REVIEW

1. 0, 2, -5 **2.** 0, 2   **3.** 7, -7
4. 3, -3 **5.** 0, 4   **6.** 6, -6
7. $\frac{b^2}{a}, \frac{-b^2}{a}$ **8.** 0, ca^2 **9.** $-1, 5$
10. $-2, 9$ **11.** 3, -4 **12.** 4, 4
13. $-2, 8$ **14.** $-\frac{1}{2}, 3$ **15.** $-1, 4$
16. 4, -6 **17.** 4, 26   **18.** 5, 6
19. Width: 2 inches,   **20.** 5, 6
length: 6 inches

CHAPTER 7 CUMULATIVE REVIEW

1. -1 **2.** 0   **3.** $-3, -\frac{5}{2}, -\frac{5}{3}, 0, \frac{3}{8}, \frac{3}{7}, 3$

4. $x(x-1)(x-2)$ **5.** $2x^2 + 5x - 12$ **6.** $\frac{x+2}{3}$

7. $2x - 6$ **8.** $\frac{3 - 2x}{x(x+1)}$ **9.** $\frac{3(x+3)}{x^2 + 2x - 3}$

10. $\frac{3x+2}{2x+3}$ **11.** $(3, 3)$

12.

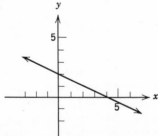

13. 44   **14.** $\frac{1}{3}$ **15.** $\frac{20}{15}$
16. Lighter package: 55 pounds,
heavier package: 85 pounds

17. 0, 1   **18.** $\frac{3}{5}$, $-\frac{3}{5}$ **19.** $-1, 3$
20. 4, 6

EXERCISES 8.1 (PAGE 180)

1. 4   **3.** -9 **5.** ± 12

7. 3   **9.** $\frac{1}{6}$ **11.** $\pm\frac{2}{3}$

13. $\sqrt{9}$ **15.** $-\sqrt{49}$ **17.** $\sqrt{169}$

19. $-\sqrt{25}$ **21.** $\sqrt{\frac{1}{4}}$ **23.** $-\sqrt{\frac{49}{64}}$

25. x **27.** $2x$ **29.** $-ac^2$
31. $\pm 6a^3$ **33.** $11ab$ **35.** $-(a + b)$

37. $\frac{a}{b}$ **39.** $\pm\frac{3}{xy}$ **41.** $\sqrt{x^2}$

43. $\sqrt{x^2y^4}$ **45.** $\sqrt{16y^4}$ **47.** $-\sqrt{64x^4y^4}$

49. $-\sqrt{100x^{20}y^{20}}$ **51.** $\pm\sqrt{(2x + y)^2}$ **53.** $\sqrt{\frac{1}{4}}$

55. $\sqrt{\frac{9}{16}}$ **57.** $\pm\sqrt{\frac{16b^4}{25}}$ **59.** $\sqrt{\frac{1}{a^2}}$

61. $-\sqrt{\frac{9x^2}{y^2}}$ **63.** $\sqrt{\frac{(a + b)^2}{a^2}}$

EXERCISES 8.2 (PAGE 182)

1. Rational   **3.** Irrational   **5.** Irrational
7. Rational   **9.** Rational   **11.** Irrational
13. Rational   **15.** Irrational   **17.** Rational
19. Irrational   **21.** 7.55   **23.** 1.73
25. 2.24   **27.** -5.10 **29.** 3.46
31. -8.66 **33.** 1.41   **35.** -1.73
37. 2.73   **39.** 1.59   **41.** 12.94
43. -22.88 **45.** 2.91   **47.** 0.51
49. 0.32   **51.** 0.72

53.

55.

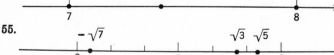

57.

59.

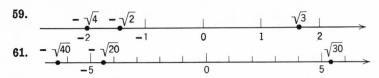

61.

63.

EXERCISES 8.3 (PAGE 185)

1. $2\sqrt{2}$	**3.** $3\sqrt{2}$	**5.** $-2\sqrt{5}$	**7.** $-6\sqrt{2}$
9. 8	**11.** $12\sqrt{2}$	**13.** $5\sqrt{5}$	**15.** $-6\sqrt{30}$
17. $\pm12\sqrt{5}$	**19.** $\pm18\sqrt{6}$	**21.** $x\sqrt{x}$	**23.** $y^3\sqrt{y}$
25. $-x^5\sqrt{x}$	**27.** x^3	**29.** $\pm x^4$	**31.** x^6
33. $2x$	**35.** $3x\sqrt{x}$	**37.** $-2y^2\sqrt{6y}$	**39.** $8y^2$
41. $7x^3\sqrt{x}$	**43.** $\pm4x\sqrt{2x}$	**45.** $4x\sqrt{5}$	**47.** $-8\sqrt{x}$
49. $\pm y\sqrt{5y}$	**51.** $4x\sqrt{3y}$	**53.** $5xy\sqrt{x}$	**55.** $-3a^2\sqrt{5b}$
57. $3x$	**59.** $8xy$	**61.** $-3\sqrt{cd}$	**63.** $yz\sqrt{7}$
65. $\frac{3}{4}xy$	**67.** $\pm\frac{5}{6}y$	**69.** $2x$	**71.** $6\sqrt{x}$
73. $49y\sqrt{y}$	**75.** $2x^2\sqrt{y}$	**77.** $-a\sqrt{a}$	**79.** $\pm2x^3$
81. $\sqrt{x}$	**83.** $b^2c\sqrt{ac}$	**85.** 10.39	**87.** 16.59
89. 14.18	**91.** -12.32	**93.** -31.18	**95.** 36.59

EXERCISES 8.4 (PAGE 188)

1. $3\sqrt{3}$	**3.** $\sqrt{5}$	**5.** 0	**7.** $5\sqrt{3}$
9. $-3\sqrt{2}$	**11.** $-4\sqrt{3}$		**13.** $4\sqrt{2}-4\sqrt{3}$
15. $5\sqrt{3}+3\sqrt{2}$	**17.** $8+6\sqrt{6}$		**19.** $3\sqrt{2}-2$
21. $2\sqrt{3}$	**23.** $5\sqrt{a}$		**25.** $12\sqrt{x}$
27. $2b\sqrt{b}$	**29.** $-5y\sqrt{xy}$		**31.** $4\sqrt{3}+4$
33. $-30-5\sqrt{7}$	**35.** $4\sqrt{2}-4\sqrt{3}$		**37.** $3+9\sqrt{a}$
39. $-4\sqrt{a}+4\sqrt{b}$		**41.** $2\sqrt{2}-6\sqrt{3}-10$	
43. $-\sqrt{a}-\sqrt{b}+\sqrt{c}$		**45.** $x\sqrt{x}+3x$	
47. $x\sqrt{x}+2x\sqrt{y}$		**49.** $xy^2\sqrt{x}+2xy$	
51. $2(1+\sqrt{3})$	**53.** $4(\sqrt{2}-3)$		**55.** $4(\sqrt{5}+2)$
57. $8(1-4\sqrt{5})$	**59.** $6(1+4\sqrt{2})$		**61.** $3(1+\sqrt{2})$
63. $4(1-\sqrt{2})$	**65.** $3(7+\sqrt{2})$		**67.** $4(1+\sqrt{y})$
69. $2y(3-\sqrt{2})$	**71.** $2+3\sqrt{3}$		**73.** $3-\sqrt{5}$
75. $-1+\sqrt{2}$	**77.** $2+3\sqrt{3}$		**79.** $\dfrac{1+\sqrt{2}}{2}$

81. $\dfrac{1 - \sqrt{3}}{2}$ **83.** $\dfrac{2 + \sqrt{2}}{3}$ **85.** $\dfrac{\sqrt{3} - 1}{5}$

87. $\dfrac{2\sqrt{10} - \sqrt{3}}{3}$ **89.** $\dfrac{\sqrt{11} + 1}{a}$ **91.** $\dfrac{5 + 3\sqrt{2}}{b}$

93. $\dfrac{3 + \sqrt{3}}{6}$ **95.** $\dfrac{4\sqrt{5} - 1}{10}$ **97.** $\dfrac{6 + 5\sqrt{3}}{15}$

99. $\dfrac{3\sqrt{3} - 4}{12}$ **101.** $\dfrac{4\sqrt{3} - 3\sqrt{2}}{6}$ **103.** $\dfrac{8 + 3\sqrt{2}}{2}$

105. $\dfrac{\sqrt{3} + 5}{5}$ **107.** $\dfrac{3\sqrt{3} + 6}{2}$

EXERCISES 8.5 (PAGE 192)

1. $\sqrt{15}$ **3.** $\sqrt{30}$ **5.** $3\sqrt{2}$ **7.** 4

9. $x\sqrt{6}$ **11.** $2xy\sqrt{3y}$ **13.** $12a$ **15.** $5x\sqrt{6y}$

17. $\sqrt{30}$ **19.** 10 **21.** $6\sqrt{6}$

23. $6x\sqrt{x}$ **25.** $abc\sqrt{abc}$ **27.** x^4

29. $3\sqrt{2} + \sqrt{6}$ **31.** $3\sqrt{2} + 2\sqrt{3}$ **33.** $4\sqrt{5} + 5\sqrt{2}$

35. $\sqrt{6} + 3\sqrt{2}$ **37.** $3 + \sqrt{6}$ **39.** $2\sqrt{5} - 2$

41. $1 - 2\sqrt{2}$ **43.** $2 + 2\sqrt{5}$ **45.** 1

47. -11 **49.** $-24 - \sqrt{15}$ **51.** $12 + 5\sqrt{35}$

EXERCISES 8.6 (PAGE 195)

1. 3 **3.** 5 **5.** 3 **7.** $2\sqrt{a}$

9. $\sqrt{3b}$ **11.** $\sqrt{b}$ **13.** $2\sqrt{7b}$ **15.** 1

17. a **19.** $b\sqrt{3}$ **21.** $\dfrac{5\sqrt{2}}{2}$ **23.** $\dfrac{2\sqrt{x}}{x}$

25. $\dfrac{a\sqrt{b}}{b}$ **27.** $\dfrac{\sqrt{3}}{3}$ **29.** $\dfrac{\sqrt{2a}}{a}$ **31.** $\dfrac{\sqrt{3ab}}{b}$

33. $\dfrac{3\sqrt{x}}{x}$ **35.** $\dfrac{5\sqrt{y}}{y}$ **37.** $\sqrt{2a}$ **39.** $\sqrt{6x}$

41. $4\sqrt{a}$ **43.** $2\sqrt{3xy}$ **45.** $\dfrac{2\sqrt{6}}{3}$ **47.** $\dfrac{3\sqrt{2}}{2}$

49. $\dfrac{6\sqrt{10}}{5}$ **51.** $\dfrac{5\sqrt{x}}{x}$ **53.** $\dfrac{2\sqrt{2x}}{x}$ **55.** $\dfrac{x\sqrt{y}}{y}$

57. 0.38 **59.** 2.12 **61.** 1.34 **63.** 1.73

65. 3.27

CHAPTER 8 REVIEW

1. $\sqrt{6}, -\sqrt{\dfrac{2}{3}}$

2. *a.* 9.644

    b. 13.712

    c. 1.414

3.

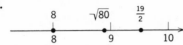

4. *a.* $6\sqrt{2}$

    b. $-3\sqrt{10}$

    c. $5\sqrt{7}$

5. *a.* y^2

    b. $x^7\sqrt{x}$

    c. $xy^3\sqrt{xy}$

6. *a.* $3x\sqrt{3}$

    b. $3x\sqrt{3}$

    c. $x\sqrt{3}$

7. *a.* $4\sqrt{7}$

    b. $\sqrt{6}$

    c. $5\sqrt{11}$

8. *a.* $-8\sqrt{3}$

    b. $\sqrt{x}$

    c. $x\sqrt{y}$

9. *a.* $3\sqrt{y} - 18$

    b. $y\sqrt{xy} - 2y^2$

    c. $\sqrt{6} - 3\sqrt{2}$

10. *a.* $2(1 - \sqrt{2})$

    b. $3(\sqrt{3} - \sqrt{5})$

    c. $x^2(3 - \sqrt{5})$

11. *a.* $1 - 2\sqrt{3}$

    b. $3 - 3\sqrt{3}$

    c. $1 - \sqrt{2}$

12. *a.* $\dfrac{3 - \sqrt{3}}{2}$

    b. $\dfrac{3\sqrt{15}}{5}$

    c. $\dfrac{4 - \sqrt{3}}{6}$

13. *a.* $\dfrac{2\sqrt{5} - 9}{6}$

    b. $\dfrac{2\sqrt{3} - 5}{5}$

    c. $\dfrac{3\sqrt{6} + 8}{4}$

14. *a.* $\sqrt{15}$

    b. $16\sqrt{2}$

    c. $3x\sqrt{2x}$

15. *a.* $5\sqrt{6}$

    b. 12

    c. $2x\sqrt{3x}$

16. *a.* $2\sqrt{3} - \sqrt{6}$

    b. $\sqrt{14} - 7\sqrt{2}$

    c. $4 - 2\sqrt{6}$

17. *a.* 1

    b. -2

    c. $12 - 7\sqrt{3}$

18. *a.* 3

    b. $\sqrt{6a}$

    c. $a\sqrt{3}$

19. *a.* $\dfrac{\sqrt{15}}{5}$

    b. $\dfrac{2\sqrt{15}}{5}$

    c. $\dfrac{\sqrt{6x}}{2x}$

20. *a.* $\dfrac{\sqrt{17x}}{x}$

    b. $\dfrac{\sqrt{6y}}{2x}$

    c. $2\sqrt{14}$

CHAPTER 8 CUMULATIVE REVIEW

1. Two
2. -4
3. $-6ab^3c$
4. $\dfrac{5a - 9b}{6}$
5. $\dfrac{a - 1}{4x(2a + 5)}$
6. $x^2 + 3x - 1$
7. $(2x - 3)(2x - 3)$
8. -5
9. 6
10. $146 - n$
11. $25x$
12. Dependent
13. $\dfrac{9d}{7b}$
14. $-\frac{1}{2}, 3$
15. $54,100$
16. $-\sqrt{16}$
17. $3x^3\sqrt{7x}$
18. 14 inches
19. $8\sqrt{2} - 4\sqrt{5}$
20. $-1, 0$ and $4, 5$

EXERCISES 9.1 (PAGE 202)

1. $2, -2$
3. $4, -4$
5. $7, -7$
7. $\sqrt{3}, -\sqrt{3}$
9. $\sqrt{10}, -\sqrt{10}$
11. $\sqrt{6}, -\sqrt{6}$
13. $2\sqrt{3}, -2\sqrt{3}$
15. $3\sqrt{2}, -3\sqrt{2}$
17. $3\sqrt{2}, -3\sqrt{2}$
19. $2, -2$
21. $\sqrt{5}, -\sqrt{5}$
23. $0, 0$
25. $2\sqrt{5}, -2\sqrt{5}$
27. $3, -3$
29. $2\sqrt{2}, -2\sqrt{2}$
31. $\sqrt{a}, -\sqrt{a}$
33. $ab\sqrt{3a}, -ab\sqrt{3a}$
35. $\dfrac{\sqrt{30b}}{6}, -\dfrac{\sqrt{30b}}{6}$
37. $t = \dfrac{\sqrt{2gs}}{g}, t = -\dfrac{\sqrt{2gs}}{g}$
39. $r = \dfrac{\sqrt{\pi A}}{2\pi}, r = -\dfrac{\sqrt{\pi A}}{2\pi}$
41. $d = \dfrac{\sqrt{3Ik}}{I}, d = -\dfrac{\sqrt{3Ik}}{I}$
43. $25, -25$
45. $8, -8$
47. $5\sqrt{2}, -5\sqrt{2}$
49. $3, -1$
51. $7, -3$
53. $6, 4$
55. $a + 5, a - 5$
57. $a + 3, -a + 3$
59. $a + b, a - b$
61. $-3 + \sqrt{2}, -3 - \sqrt{2}$
63. $-5 + \sqrt{5}, -5 - \sqrt{5}$
65. $-10 + 2\sqrt{2}, -10 - 2\sqrt{2}$
67. $5 + \sqrt{a}, 5 - \sqrt{a}$
69. $-1 + \sqrt{b}, -1 - \sqrt{b}$
71. $b + \sqrt{a}, b - \sqrt{a}$

EXERCISES 9.2 (PAGE 207)

1. $2, -6$
3. $1, 1$
5. $4, -5$
7. $-1, -2$
9. $-1, 4$
11. $-2, 5$
13. $1 + \sqrt{2}, 1 - \sqrt{2}$
15. $\dfrac{3 + \sqrt{21}}{2}, \dfrac{3 - \sqrt{21}}{2}$
17. $\dfrac{-1 + \sqrt{13}}{2}, \dfrac{-1 - \sqrt{13}}{2}$
19. $\frac{1}{2}, -\frac{3}{2}$
21. $\frac{1}{2}, -2$
23. $-\frac{5}{2}, 3$

EXERCISES 9.3 (PAGE 210)

1. $a = 1, b = -3, c = 2$

3. $a = 1, b = -1, c = -30$

5. $a = 1, b = -2, c = 0$

7. $a = 4, b = 0, c = -3$

9. $a = 2, b = -7, c = 6$

11. $a = 6, b = -5, c = 1$

13. $a = 1, b = -8, c = 4$

15. $a = 2, b = -2, c = -1$

17. $a = 6, b = 7, c = -3$

19. $a = 9, b = 6, c = -8$

21. $1, 2$

23. $-2, 6$

25. $3, -5$

27. $\dfrac{-3 + \sqrt{13}}{2}, \dfrac{-3 - \sqrt{13}}{2}$

29. $\dfrac{3 + \sqrt{17}}{2}, \dfrac{3 - \sqrt{17}}{2}$

31. $0, 2$

33. $0, 5$

35. $0, 7$

37. $0, 3$

39. $\dfrac{\sqrt{3}}{2}, -\dfrac{\sqrt{3}}{2}$

41. $2, \frac{3}{2}$

43. $\frac{1}{3}, -\frac{1}{2}$

45. $\frac{5}{2}, -\frac{1}{3}$

47. $1 + \sqrt{2}, 1 - \sqrt{2}$

49. $2 + \sqrt{6}, 2 - \sqrt{6}$

51. $1, -\frac{1}{2}$

53. $\frac{3}{2}, -\frac{5}{2}$

55. $\frac{3}{2}, \frac{2}{3}$

57. $3, -\frac{3}{2}$

EXERCISES 9.4 (PAGE 214)

1. $(0, -3)$

3. $(-1, 0)$

5. $(-2, 5)$

7. $(0, -2)$

9. $(1, 0)$

11. $(-2, 0)$

13. $(0, 12)$

15. $(2, 2)$

17. $(4, 0)$

19.

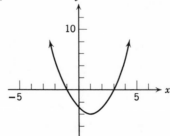

21.

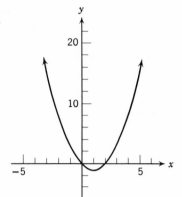

23.

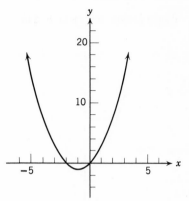

25.

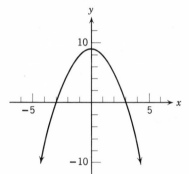

27.

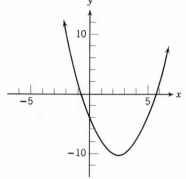

29. 0, 2; −2, 2; −2, 0; none

31.

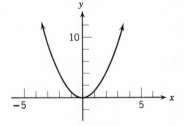

33.

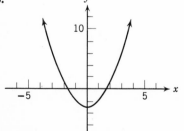

35.

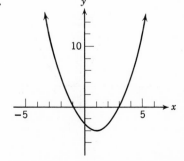

EXERCISES 9.5 (PAGE 217)

1. 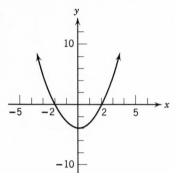 $-2, 2$

3. 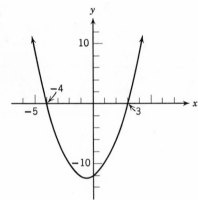 $3, -4$

5. 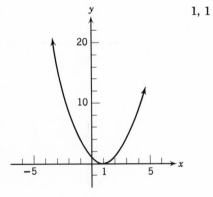 $1, 1$

7.

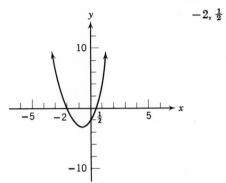

$-2, \frac{1}{2}$

9.

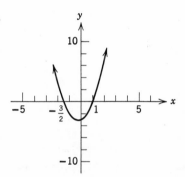

$-\frac{3}{2}, 1$

11.

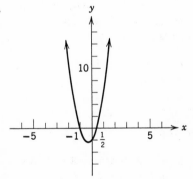

$-1, \frac{1}{2}$

13.

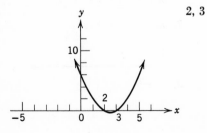

$2, 3$

15   0, 3

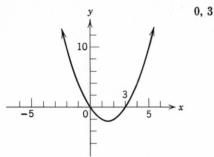

17. $-\frac{1}{2}, -\frac{1}{2}$

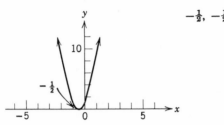

EXERCISES 9.6 (PAGE 218)

1. 5 feet   **3.** $3\sqrt{2}$ feet   **5.** 127 feet

7. 12 inches   **9.** $2\sqrt{10}$ inches   **11.** Width: 9 inches,
                                                         length: 12 inches

13. Width: 2 inches,   **15.** Width: 3 inches,   **17.** 50 feet
length: 5 inches   length: 6 inches

19. $30\sqrt{2}$ feet

CHAPTER 9 REVIEW

1. *a.* $-5, 5$ **2.** *a.* $-\sqrt{7}, \sqrt{7}$ **3.** *a.* $-1, 5$
    b. $-3, 3$ *b.* $-\sqrt{6}, \sqrt{6}$ *b.* $-4, -2$

4. *a.* $3, 11$ **5.** *a.* $-3 + \sqrt{a}, -3 - \sqrt{a}$
    b. $a + c, a - c$ *b.* $2 - a, -2 - a$

6. *a.* $1, -4$ **7.** *a.* $-1, -1$
    b. $\dfrac{3 + \sqrt{21}}{2}, \dfrac{3 - \sqrt{21}}{2}$ *b.* $-1, 2$

8. $-1, 5$ **9.** $3, -5$

10. $\dfrac{3 + \sqrt{5}}{2}, \dfrac{3 - \sqrt{5}}{2}$ **11.** $\frac{4}{3}, 3$

12.

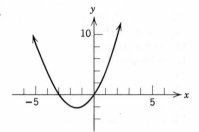

13.

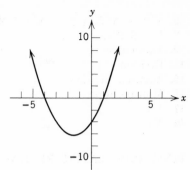

14.

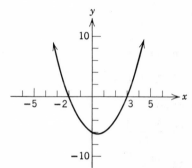

$-2, 3$

15. ± 16 **16.** $\pm 6 \sqrt{2}$ **17.** $\sqrt{130}$ inches

18. $8 \sqrt{2}$ inches   **19.** 30 feet   **20.** 14 mph

CHAPTER 9 CUMULATIVE REVIEW

1. $2 \cdot 2 \cdot 2 \cdot 3xxxyy$ **2.** 1   **3.** 1

4. $2a^2$ **5.** 0   **6.** (1, 2)

7. $\dfrac{3x + 4}{x(x + y)}$ **9.** $5x^2 \sqrt{y}$ **10.** $a - x$

11. Two   **12.** Either $a = 0$, $b = 0$ or both a and $b = 0$ **13.** 27

14. 8, 32   **15.** 12 inches, 8 inches, 10 inches   **16.** 30°, 60°, 90°

17. Altitude: 3 inches, base: 12 inches   **18.** 7, 9   **19.** Width: 11 inches, length: 22 inches

20. Altitude: 4 inches, base: 12 inches

EXERCISES CHAPTER 10 (PAGE 227)

1. 3, 7, 1, 4   **2.** $-1, 3, 6, \sqrt{9}, -2, -\sqrt{4}$

3. $\sqrt{1}, -\sqrt{\frac{4}{9}}, \frac{1}{100}, -\frac{3}{5}, \frac{1}{2}, \sqrt{100}$ **4.** $-\sqrt{3}, \sqrt{\frac{3}{4}}, \sqrt{10}, \sqrt{7}$

5. $\sqrt{2}, -\sqrt{2}, \sqrt{\frac{2}{3}}, -\sqrt{\frac{2}{3}}, 2\sqrt{3},$ 6. $n+1, n^2, 3n, n+3n$

7. Distributive   8. Commutative

9. Associative   10. Symmetric

11. Division   12. Addition

13. Addition, division   14. No

15. Multiplication   16. No

17. Yes   18. Yes

19. No   20. One-to-one correspondence

FINAL CUMULATIVE REVIEW I (PAGE 229)

1. 71, 73, 79, 83, 89, 97

2. $a + b = b + a$; $ab = ba$

3. $-4, -2, -1, 3, 5, 6$

4. $V = \pi\, dh$ 5. $30 - x$

6. $2a^2$ 7. $2x + 1 + \dfrac{-1}{3x}$

8. $a = 8$ inches, $b = 10$ inches, $c = 16$ inches

9. $\dfrac{2b}{a + 2b}$ 10. $\dfrac{3a + 3}{4a}$

11. $\dfrac{3ax^2y}{10}$ 12. $\dfrac{4a - 3b}{a}$

13. 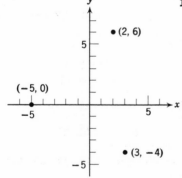   14. $(1, 1)$

15. 4   16. $\dfrac{\sqrt{y}}{4}$

17. 2   18. 3.46

19. -3 20. 13 and 15

FINAL CUMULATIVE REVIEW II (PAGE 230)

1. 2   2. Zero   3. Yes   4. $\dfrac{24}{b}$

5. $5b$ **6.** -5 **7.** 7 and 12   **8.** $\dfrac{a^2 + b^2}{ab}$

9. $\dfrac{3(x - 3)}{x^2 - 9}$ **10.** $\dfrac{2}{3x}$ **11.** Proportion

12.

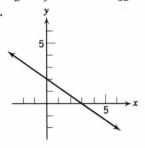

13. $x + y = 1$ **14.** $(-1, 3)$ **15.** $8, -2$ **16.** $\sqrt{5}, \sqrt{6}, \sqrt{7}, \sqrt{8}, \sqrt{10}$

17. $4xy\sqrt{10xyz}$ **18.** $\dfrac{2 - \sqrt{2}}{2}$ **19.** $\dfrac{-5 \pm \sqrt{17}}{2}$ **20.** $-1, 2$

FINAL CUMULATIVE REVIEW III (PAGE 231)

1. $2 \cdot 2 \cdot 2 \cdot 3 \cdot 3 \cdot 5$ **2.** 30

3. $-a^2 - 2a$ **4.** No

5. 625 square inches   **6.** $ab(c - 1)$

7. $3(2x - 3)(x + 1)$ **8.** $5n + 10(n + 6)$ or $15n + 60$

9. $\dfrac{-6b}{5}$ **10.** $\dfrac{5}{6x}$

11. $x - 8$ **12.** $\dfrac{2}{a + b}$

13. Numerator: 20   **14.** 342 bricks

15. Linear   **16.** $y = \dfrac{4x + 2}{3}$

17. 1   **18.** $6a^3b^2c^2\sqrt{c}$

19. $3\sqrt{a}$ **20.** $4\sqrt{10}$ feet

FINAL CUMULATIVE REVIEW IV (PAGE 231)

1.

2. $r + s$; rs **3.** -3

4. 5   **5.** $-28, -26, -24$

6. $-3bx$ **7.** $2(x - 2)(x + 2)$

8. 96 children's tickets, 164 adult tickets

9. $x - 1$

10. $\dfrac{3x + 5}{(x + 2)^2}$

11. $16x$

12. 9

13. 192 miles

14. Two

15. $\dfrac{4}{3}$

16. $(0, -6)$; $(2, 0)$; $(-3, -15)$

17. $\dfrac{a}{4}$

18. $0, \dfrac{1}{4}$

19.

-6 and 5

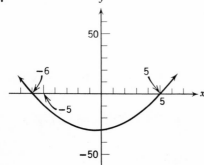

20. Width: 12 inches, length: 16 inches

FINAL CUMULATIVE REVIEW V (PAGE 232)

1. 1

2. Integers

3. 10

4. $(y - 1)(y - 11)$

5. $-8b^2$

6. $\dfrac{2(w + 8)}{3}$

7. $\dfrac{-(1 - a)}{3}$ or $\dfrac{-1 + a}{3}$

8. $x^2 - 2x + 1$

9. $\dfrac{h^2}{6 + h}$

10. $\dfrac{875}{t}$

11. 15

12. Means; extremes

13.

14. $(1, 7)$

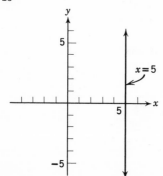

15. -3 and 7

16.

17. 9

18. $\dfrac{-5 \pm \sqrt{17}}{2}$

19. $\dfrac{2}{3}$ and -3

20. 9

FINAL CUMULATIVE REVIEW VI (PAGE 233)

1. -20

2. 11

3. x

4. $-17°$

5. $\dfrac{a + 2}{a - 1}$

6. Winner: 1844, loser: 1782

7. $3y^2$

8. $(a - 5b)(a + 5b)$

9. $4(n - 8)$

10. 60

11. $\dfrac{11}{2}$

12. $\dfrac{-3x - 11}{6}$

13. 22

14. 2

15. $\dfrac{b(a + c)}{2}$

16. 8.46

17.

$(1, 2)$

18. 0 and $\dfrac{-3}{2}$

19. $-1 \pm \sqrt{5}$

20. ± 12

FINAL CUMULATIVE REVIEW VII (PAGE 234)

1. -1

2. $1 \pm \sqrt{6}$

3. $4b - 5c$

4. $x^3 \cdot x^2 = x^5$

5. $(2y + 3)(2y + 5)$

6. $6(22 - y)$

7. $\dfrac{3}{y}$

8. $\dfrac{2ac}{b}$

9. $\dfrac{b - a}{b + a}$

10. 20 mph
    30 mph

11. $(3, 13)$; $(-2, -2)$; $(0, 4)$; $(6, 22)$

12. 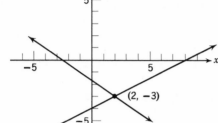 $(2, -3)$

13. $(3, -2)$

14. $0, 2$

15. $\dfrac{1}{2}, -18$

16. 16

17. $1 + \sqrt{2}$

18. $2\sqrt{3b}$

19. $\dfrac{\pm \sqrt{c}}{b}$

20. 4 mph

FINAL CUMULATIVE REVIEW VIII (PAGE 235)

1. Commutative

2. 5

3. $n + 2, n + 4, n + 6$

4. $(a - 4b)(a - 2b)$

5. $-4xy$

6. $18\dfrac{2}{7}$ feet or $45\dfrac{5}{7}$ feet from one end

7. $\dfrac{x + 6}{x - 2}$

8. $\dfrac{2}{a + b}$

9. $b - a$

10. $x + 8 + \dfrac{33}{x - 5}$

11. $(-1, 0)$

12. 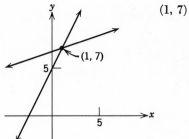 $(1, 7)$

13. 67 pounds and 79 pounds

14. $-2, 7$

15. $10xy \sqrt{2x}$

16. $7 \sqrt{5}$

17.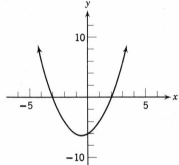

18. $\sqrt{10}$

19. $\dfrac{1 \pm \sqrt{15}}{2}$

20. Width: 12 inches, length: 20 inches

FINAL CUMULATIVE REVIEW IX (PAGE 236)

1. 4

2. -4

3. $a^2 - 3ab$

4. 24, 26, 28

5. $2(x - 11)(x - 1)$

6. $n + 28$

7. 5

8. $\dfrac{2y - 3x}{xy}$

9. $\dfrac{1}{16b}$

10. $2x - 1 + \dfrac{1}{x + 2}$

11. $\dfrac{b - a}{c}$

12.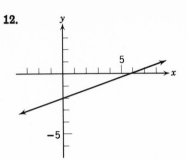

13.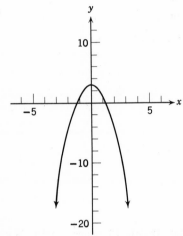

14. (1, 2)

15. 4 nickels
7 dimes
9 quarters

16. $3x \sqrt{10}$

17. $1 + 3 \sqrt{3}$

18. 4.23

19. 20 miles

20.

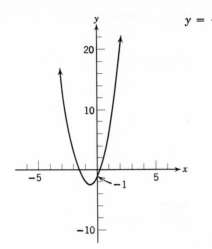

$y = -1$

FINAL CUMULATIVE REVIEW X (PAGE 237)

1.

23   29 31   37
20   25   30   35   40

2. $2 \cdot 2 \cdot 2 \cdot 2 \cdot 3 \cdot 5 \cdot x \cdot x \cdot y$

3. $-5, -2, -1, 1, 3, 5, 7$

4. $-2a - 5b$

5. $2ab - 2b^2$

6. $3(x - 4y)(x - 2y)$

7. $\dfrac{1}{3a + 4}$

8. $\dfrac{b}{7}$

9. $\dfrac{a - 5}{(a - 3)^2}$

10. 2

11.

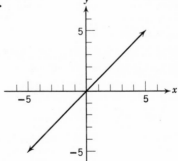

12. $(2, -1)$

13. $6\sqrt{3}$

14. $\sqrt{2} - \sqrt{3}$

15.

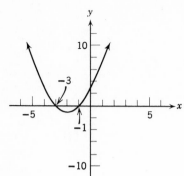

At $x = -1$ and $x = -3$

16. 8 and 9

17. 30°; 60°

18. $600

19. Chair: $120, desk: $520

20. 12 inches

INDEX